The

BOOK OF BIRD LIFE

Midnight in the Orchard and a Screech Owl Family

The
BOOK OF BIRD LIFE

A Study of Birds in Their Native Haunts

ARTHUR A. ALLEN, Ph.D.

*Professor of Ornithology Emeritus
and Honorary Director
Laboratory of Ornithology
Cornell University*

SECOND EDITION

Photographs by the Author
Paintings by Dr. W. C. Dilger

D. VAN NOSTRAND COMPANY, INC.

PRINCETON, NEW JERSEY

TORONTO   LONDON

NEW YORK

D. VAN NOSTRAND COMPANY, INC.
120 Alexander St., Princeton, New Jersey (*Principal office*)
24 West 40 Street, New York 18, New York

D. VAN NOSTRAND COMPANY, LTD.
358, Kensington High Street, London, W.14, England

D. VAN NOSTRAND COMPANY (Canada), LTD.
25 Hollinger Road, Toronto 16, Canada

First Edition, September 1930
Eleven Reprintings
Second Edition, April 1961

61- 3177

PRINTED IN THE UNITED STATES OF AMERICA

To
E.G.A.
Companion in field and study

Contents

List of Illustrations

COLOR

Screech Owl Family — *frontispiece*

Ruffed Grouse Displaying
Cowbird Display
Wild Turkey Displays
Sharp-tailed Grouse Challenge
Sharp-tailed Grouse Dance

BLACK AND WHITE

Introduction to First Edition

The study of birds has always been a popular pastime. There is something so engaging about the flight of birds, their bright colors, their cheerful songs, and their mysterious comings and goings that a great literature has grown up about them. Ever since the days of Aristotle, and perhaps before, bird-lovers have felt constrained to put their observations and experiences on permanent record. It seems as though everything of interest concerning birds must already be in the pages of some book and one hesitates to offer yet another volume for ornithological shelves already crowded.

It is now a pleasant task to familiarize oneself with the names of all the birds that visit one's home territory. The excellent colored pictures of North American birds by such artists as Fuertes, Brooks, Sutton, Weber, Peterson, and Eckleberry have received such wide distribution through books and periodicals that anyone with the slightest desire to know the birds about him can do so with comparatively little effort. Some may wish to go no further in their studies of birds than the learning of their names. Others may wish to increase their pleasure by observing the habits of those which they have identified, by keeping records of their migrations, by watching their courtship performances, by finding their nests and observing their home-life, by studying how they change their plumage and how they appear at different ages or at different times of the year.

For this class of observers it seemed that another book on birds might still be welcome; one that should be a guide to bird habits rather than bird identification; one that might help to direct one's observations into productive channels and enable him to interpret what he sees birds do.

The present volume can scarcely be called a manual; it does not attempt to discuss the detailed habits of a single species completely. Rather, it aims to outline the underlying principles that govern the actions of any bird and to suggest methods of study.

Nearly everyone has enjoyed some unusual experience with birds which he may have been at a loss to explain. The Robin that pecks the cellar window; the Killdeer that trails a broken wing; the small bird chasing the larger one; the disappearance of birds in late summer before the fall migration; the night singing of Catbirds; the drumming of the Ruffed Grouse; the hammering of the Woodpeckers all demand a rational explanation. It is the purpose of this book, not only to explain such behavior, but so to equip the reader that all his past experiences with birds naturally arrange themselves in an orderly way and every new experience demands and receives a satisfactory explanation.

Part I deals with the laws that govern the occurrence of birds in any locality; their relation to the environment and to each other; the principles underlying song, courtship, nesting, and other habits; the nature of the many nice adaptations of structure, and the explanation of the varied colors of birds together with the relations of birds to man.

Part II deals with those methods of bird study used primarily in the field with living birds. The collecting of specimens, the study of their anatomical relationships, the principles of museum preparation and exhibition, though equally important, have been purposely omitted as they form quite a different phase of ornithology apart from the study of the living bird.

In selecting the illustrations for each chapter the author has attempted to use such as portray the point under discussion better than would the same space given to printed words. Most of them are from photographs of wild free birds taken from observation blinds; a few of them are from photographs of captive specimens, and a very few from museum specimens. If the photographs are not otherwise marked, it may be assumed that they are photographs of wild birds taken by the author.

Most of the chapters presented and many of the illustrations appeared originally in the School Department of *Bird-Lore*. The author feels particularly indebted to Dr. Frank M. Chapman, who was at that time the Editor of *Bird-Lore*, not only for permission to republish this material in book form, but for the many courtesies and the great assistance he always gave.

Should he attempt to express his appreciation to all those from whom he has received help or inspiration, the author would begin with a wise mother who fostered his childhood's interest in birds and encouraged his more mature studies; he would mention many teachers and later students of his own at Cornell University from whom he still continues to derive great inspiration. He would include many friends among sportsmen and bird-lovers who have attended his lectures and by their responsiveness have encouraged him to assemble those observations and reflections with which he has attempted to interest them. Nor could he fail to include his wife, Elsa Guerdrum Allen, whose helpful criticism in the preparation of the manuscript is responsible for any merit it may have, and whose constant cooperation has made possible the numerous photographs which illustrate the pages and such observations as never could have been made without the long hours spent in the photographic blinds. The acknowledgment would not be complete without mention of that great benefactor of science, August Heckscher. Through grants from a fund established by him at Cornell University for the promotion of research, the author was enabled to make studies of the birds of Florida and of Labrador, and some of the observations and some of the photographs secured on these trips have been included in this volume. In later years similar grants from the National Geographic Society enabled the author to extend greatly his observations and activities.

It is obviously impossible to include in a book of the size and scope of this one a complete presentation of all the facts bearing upon the various topics discussed. The author has attempted, therefore, rather so to present the subject that the reader will be tempted to investigate the references at the close of the book and secure for himself a greater knowledge of the subjects that interest him than could possibly be presented in one small volume.

A.A.A.

Ithaca, N. Y.
February, 1930.

Introduction to Second Edition

When the publisher of the original edition of this book suggested that after thirty years and 12 printings it might be desirable to revise the original manuscript and add some new illustrations, the author at first thought it might be better to write an entirely new book. In re-reading the old one, however, he discovered that the basic facts had not substantially changed during the intervening years and that in spite of the remarkable increase in the number of ornithologists and bird watchers, reader interest seemed about the same.

Of course, there has been a considerable increase in the number of bird books on all phases of ornithology as well as in the number of bird observers, and the accumulated reports in our bird periodicals are quite impossible to summarize in one small text. Modern advances in bird photography, cameras, films, lenses and methods of lighting, likewise tax the ingenuity of an author interested in modernizing. Whether I have succeeded in adding the salient advances of the new while still retaining the virtues of the old the reader must judge, but in the meantime the author offers this new edition of a volume which generous readers have commended for thirty years.

The book never was intended as an all-inclusive text and the omissions will be quite conspicuous to the technically-trained ornithologist. On the other hand, those who are interested chiefly in extending and interpreting their own observations and who need a readable introduction to general ornithology may find this new edition helpful.

It is hoped that the addition of Dr. William C. Dilger's paintings of the distinguishing characteristics of the families of North American birds will simplify their recognition and give the reader a clearer understanding of how birds are classified. The author trusts, likewise, that the color plates in this edition will not only prove attractive in themselves but that they will illustrate some of the biological principles involved in the behavior of birds and in their plumage variations.

The reading references at the end are by no means complete but they should suffice for the general student wishing to extend his ornithological horizon in any direction.

In offering this second edition of the *Book of Bird Life* the author is reminded of thirty pleasant years of association with colleagues and students from whom he has received many helpful suggestions. I appreciate particularly the assistance of my wife, Elsa Guerdrum Allen, in her thoughtful editing of the original as well as the revised versions of the book, and I wish especially to thank Dr. Sally Foresman Hoyt for her valuable help without which this revised edition might never have been undertaken.

A.A.A.

Ithaca, N. Y.
February, 1961

Part I—The Living Bird

1

The History of Birds

About one hundred and thirty million years ago, in what is now Central Europe but what was then a tropical sea with many coral islands, there lived a strange bird. It was somewhat smaller than a Crow but what its colors were we shall probably never know, for all there is left of it is the print of its bones and feathers in the silt where it finally came to rest. As the years rolled by, this silt was overlaid with other silt, and this with sand and silt again hundreds of feet deep until under the great pressure it changed to stone. And the unfortunate bird, or what was left of it, changed to stone also, and there it lay for over a hundred million years.

In the meantime, great changes took place over its head. The great sea disappeared; mountains pushed up and their tops were worn off by the slow action of the weather; they subsided and other mountains pushed upward and settled again. Tropical forests flourished for ages and were succeeded by arctic snows with sheets of ice, mountain high, and these also disappeared.

This strange bird traveled in even stranger company, for, while he doubtless had many fellows about which we know nothing because they escaped his slimy grave, and numerous relatives who climbed about the great cycad trees or sailed from one tree fern to another, he lived in an age of reptiles. Overhead flapped the leather-winged Pterosaurs, 'dragons of the air,' like huge bats. Crocodiles swarmed in the rivers; turtles basked in the sun; lizards skittered over the arid sands; and in the sea were dolphin-like creatures covered with scales, and curious long-necked alligators, with their legs developed as flippers. Could he have lived a few million years longer he would have seen the reptiles at their height, with giant dinosaurs 80 feet in length, many of them ferocious. But had he lived in this age he would have been a different bird and more like our modern birds.

And so this strange bird lay in his stony bed until modern Europe

3

arose with its host of humanity and myriads of migrating birds as we know them today. Intelligent man dug into the hills and took from their depths the stones for his buildings and the metals for his machines, and in the evolution of his arts he discovered a method of reproducing colored pictures by using a very smooth-grained slab of stone to hold the colors. This art was called lithography, and many

FIG. 1. Restoration of the Archæopteryx, the earliest known bird. This is a feathered model by Dr. George M. Sutton and Morris Pell based on accurate measurements of the fossil imprint in the British Museum found in the Solenhofen shales of Bavaria in 1861. It was a bird about the size of a pigeon with teeth on its jaws and a long lizard-like tail with 20 pairs of feathers. The bird had numerous other reptilian characteristics.

beautiful reproductions of famous paintings were distributed by its means. It became very popular about the middle of the nineteenth century, and lithographic stones were in great demand and quarries were sunk deep into the ground wherever the ancient limestone gave promise of having the proper texture. And so it came to pass that, in 1861, a certain geologist named Andreas Wagner, working near Solenhofen, Bavaria, unearthed the fossilized remains of this strange bird about which we have been talking. A single fossil feather had been discovered a few years earlier, and in 1877 the remains of another bird were unearthed, which supplements that of Wagner, so that together they give us a very concrete idea of what this ancient bird was like. It was given the name Archæopteryx.

That it was a bird there can be little doubt, although in many respects it was like the numerous reptiles which lived all about it. Its body was covered with feathers, at least posteriorly; it had well-developed wings with strong flight-feathers, and its legs and feet were very similar to those of modern birds, except that strong quills were borne upon the legs. Were it not for the strange lizard-like tail, with a row of twenty large feathers down each side, one might almost pass by this fossil without a thought of its being different from our present-day birds. But when one's attention has been caught by the curious tail, and he examines the rest of the fossil critically, he discovers a number of ways in which this ancient bird differed from our birds and resembled some of the strange reptiles of its time. In the first place, its bill was very broad and blunt, reminding one more of the snout of a lizard, and, moreover, its jaws were armed with teeth set in sockets like those of the reptiles. Its upper jaw was rather fully equipped with thirteen teeth on each side, but the lower jaw had but six altogether. "As scarce as hens' teeth" would, therefore, have meant but little one hundred and thirty million years ago, even if there had been someone living to say it. Another way in which this bird was similar to its reptilian congeners was in the presence of three free fingers with which it could grasp the branches and climb about like an iguana. No bird today has more than the thumb free, and this is of but little service except possibly, in young Hoactzins of northern South America, which have both the thumb and index finger armed with claws.

All of the hand-bones (metacarpals) of modern birds are fused into one bone, as are, likewise, the foot-bones (metatarsals). This ancient bird had legs and toes similar to our modern birds, with three toes in front and one behind, and a long 'tarsus' (the fused metatarsals and tarsal bones). This type of tarsus is not characteristic of modern reptiles, but some of the dinosaurs which lived at the same time with the Archæopteryx possessed it. It is probable, therefore, that this type of leg was developed for a terrestrial or running habit with birds, before the appearance of wings and feathers, and it is believed that the ancestors of both the birds and the dinosaurs will be found in a group of primitive reptiles, the so-called pseudo-suchians, or false crocodiles.

FIG. 2. Rarest bird in North America—a pair of Ivory-billed Woodpeckers, now nearly extinct. Photographed in Florida by the author in 1924.

If the characteristics which I have mentioned were the only ones which ancient and modern birds have in common with reptiles, we probably would not be justified in claiming that they had a common ancestor that lived only a few million years before the Archæopteryx. But there are many other ways in which even modern birds are similar to reptiles. It is rather difficult to describe these similarities without getting into technical language or without assuming a greater knowledge of anatomy than the ordinary reader possesses. Quite naturally, the external parts of the bird, which are brought in direct contact with the environment, change more rapidly than the internal structure, and, if we are to search for fundamental characters, we must go beneath the surface. Thus, if we examine the backbone of the Archæopteryx, we find that the vertebræ, in being concave at both ends, are more like those of the early reptiles than they are like those of modern birds. The fact that there were only ten in its neck, less than in any modern bird, is likewise a reptilian character. As in reptiles, the shoulder girdle of a bird is reinforced by a strong coracoid bone, and the skull articulates with the first vertebra by a single occipital condyle. Modern birds have scales on their legs which are similar to those of reptiles, and it is believed that the feathers themselves are but glorified scales, although we have still to unearth a fossil bird which will show the transition from one to the other. Nor is it any wonder that such a bird or reptile has not yet been found when we stop to think how few dead birds are transformed into fossils. Thousands of birds are dying every day in this world, but not once in a lifetime does one perish under conditions suitable for preserving its bones or its feathers in the silt or the mud that will make the future rock. Perhaps some ornithologist a million years from now may unearth some fossil Ducks when the bed of the Great Salt Lake has turned to stone, for a few of the thousands that are being killed by botulism may get covered with silt before they are devoured by maggots and scattered by the wind and waves. But it will be only the purest luck, if we unearth any of the so-called 'Pro-Aves' that lived before the Archæopteryx and complete the chain from the primitive reptiles to the bird. And even should such a fossil bird-reptile or reptile-bird be found, we would still have a few gaps to fill before we could build a complete bridge from the Archæopteryx to the modern bird.

From twenty-five to fifty million years probably elapsed after the Archæopteryx before the next birds of which we know anything evolved, and by that time they had become so specialized and so diverse that they were much more like our modern birds than like the Archæopteryx. Of the two that are best known, one, the Hesperornis, looked a good deal like a modern Loon or a Comorant and the other, the Icthyornis, probably resembled a Tern or a Gull. The former had become so specialized as a diver that it had probably lost the power of flight, for its wings give every evidence of being degenerate. Both were alike, however, and similar to the Archæopteryx, in that they possessed true teeth. They were discovered in the cretaceous shales of Kansas, and, so far as is known, represent the last appearance of teeth in avian history. From this time on, all of the fossil birds that have been discovered appear more or less similar to present-day birds, and there is every reason to believe that some of our present birds have existed unchanged for over a million years. Some, like the Sparrows and Thrushes, that are found over a large part of the globe, undoubtedly had their small beginnings, and others, like the Ostriches, that are today rather restricted in their distribution, at one time wandered over much of the earth if we can judge from their fossil remains which have been unearthed in many parts of Europe and Asia where they have long since become extinct. The 1931 Checklist of North American birds included 167 species that have long since ceased to exist and are known only as fossils and also 136 fossil birds that still exist in our modern fauna. And, in the world at large, according to Wetmore, 787 species had been described by the end of 1949.

It is interesting to contemplate whence each of our birds has come and whither it is heading—whether to conquer the earth with its progeny or to sink before long into oblivion. The processes which are going on today are the same as those that have been transpiring for millions of years. So incomplete are the records and so small our vision that it is exceedingly difficult to interpret even what is going on before our eyes. The Great Auk, the Labrador Duck, the Passenger Pigeon, the Heath Hen, the Eskimo Curlew have joined the great army of the Archæopteryx and Hesperornis. The Whooping Crane, the California Condor and the Ivory-billed Woodpecker may

FIG. 3. Second rarest bird in North America—the Whooping Crane. A pair with their single young on the Aransas Refuge in Texas, photographed by the author in 1957. In 1960 there were only 31 of this species left alive, wintering on the Aransas Refuge and nesting somewhere south of the Great Slave Lake in northern Canada.

soon follow them into extinction in spite of all we can do to protect them.

The most we can hope for is that an intensive study of each of these vanishing species will be made before it is too late, perhaps such studies as will give us some inkling of the natural laws that have made and destroyed thousands of species of birds during the last two hundred million years.

2

The Classification of Birds

A number of years ago it was my privilege to spend the greater part of a year in the Andes of northern South America collecting birds for the American Museum of Natural History. Dr. F. M. Chapman was at that time working out the distribution of bird life in Colombia, just as Audubon and Wilson and Baird and the earlier ornithologists worked out the distribution of birds in this country. It was a fertile field for discovery, for although thousands of specimens of birds had been sent to European museums in years past, they had been taken largely by native collectors in well-known localities and little or no information about the birds accompanied the skins. Doctor Chapman made a couple of exploratory expeditions and then directed his various collectors into all of the little known parts of the country, with the result that he amassed in the American Museum not only a vast body of facts about the distribution of the birds of Colombia but a very large collection of specimens, some of which were obviously different from any that had ever come out of the country before.

Picture yourself with specimens before you representing the various plumages of some thirteen hundred different kinds of birds. It is your job to put like with like, to find out what has been written about each kind, to give a name to any kind for which you can find no published description, to write a description of it so that anyone coming after you will recognize the same kind of bird from your description, and finally to assemble all the records of the bird's occurrence and determine its range and the factors controlling its distribution together with its probable origin. If this were your job, the first thing that you would demand would be that each kind of bird should have a definite name—a name that would be used by every ornithologist, be he French or German or Russian or Chinese; and secondly, that some scheme of orderly arrangement be adopted and followed by everyone. Otherwise it would be a hopeless undertaking either to recognize whether your birds have ever before been described, or to bring together all the known facts about each kind. And before you had studied far you would bless the man who invented the present relatively simple system of classification.

Today our North American birds are so well known and their common names in such general use that some of the younger ornithologists are inclined to become impatient with proposed changes

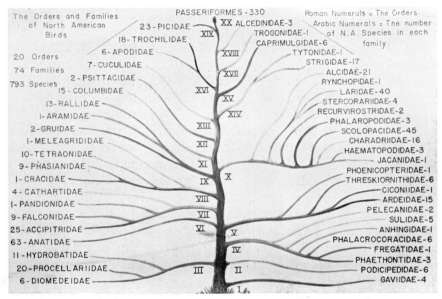

The Orders and Families of North American Birds

20 Orders
74 Families
793 Species

PASSERIFORMES - 330

Roman Numerals = The Orders. Arabic Numerals = The number of N.A. Species in each family.

23 - PICIDAE — XIX
18 - TROCHILIDAE
6 - APODIDAE
7 - CUCULIDAE
2 - PSITTACIDAE
15 - COLUMBIDAE — XVI
13 - RALLIDAE
1 - ARAMIDAE
2 - GRUIDAE — XIII
1 - MELEAGRIDIDAE
10 - TETRAONIDAE
9 - PHASIANIDAE — XI
1 - CRACIDAE — IX
4 - CATHARTIDAE
1 - PANDIONIDAE — VIII
9 - FALCONIDAE — VII
25 - ACCIPITRIDAE — VI
63 - ANATIDAE
11 - HYDROBATIDAE — IV
20 - PROCELLARIIDAE — III
6 - DIOMEDEIDAE

XX ALCEDINIDAE - 3
TROGONIDAE - 1
CAPRIMULGIDAE - 6
TYTONIDAE - 1
STRIGIDAE - 17
ALCIDAE - 21
RYNCHOPIDAE - 1
LARIDAE - 40
STERCORARIIDAE - 4
RECURVIROSTRIDAE - 2
PHALAROPODIDAE - 3
SCOLOPACIDAE - 45
CHARADRIIDAE - 16
HAEMATOPODIDAE - 3
JACANIDAE - 1
PHOENICOPTERIDAE - 1
THRESKIORNITHIDAE - 6
CICONIIDAE - 1
ARDEIDAE - 15
PELECANIDAE - 2
SULIDAE - 5
ANHINGIDAE - 1
PHALACROCORACIDAE - 6
FREGATIDAE - 1
PHAETHONTIDAE - 3
PODICIPEDIDAE - 6
GAVIIDAE - 4

Fig. 4. The Orders and Families of the Birds of North America arranged as an evolutionary tree from the oldest, Loons (Gaviiformes) at the base to the most modern, Perching Birds (Passeriformes) at the top. The numbers indicate the number of species in each family. The main branches represent the Orders I-XX, the smaller branches the Families.

in their classification and the ever-increasing refinement in distinctions between local races. They content themselves with a knowledge of the relatively stable common names of the birds, excluding from their consideration all matters pertaining to the scientific name, generic distinctions, and even the broader concepts of Families and Orders. Facts and terms in common usage among the older ornithologists are coming to have little meaning to the younger generation, so it may be worth while to review briefly in this chapter some of the main features of the classification of birds.

Let us begin with the Animal Kingdom, with its great multiplicity of forms, including everything in the living world not included in the Plant Kingdom. One has little difficulty in distinguishing between plants and any of the higher animals, but many of the lowest forms of life, such as the yeasts and bacteria and diatoms are not so easily separated. It is not easy to find a constant difference between the two. That which comes nearest to separating them is their means of nutrition. No true animal has the power of manufacturing starch from the elements. Even man, with all his creative ability, is dependent upon the chlorophyll of plants which, alone, in

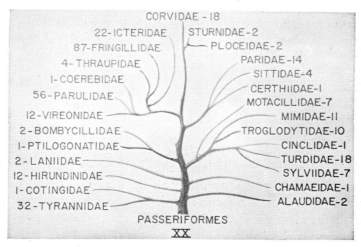

Fig. 5. The Families of Perching Birds of North America, arranged as an evolutionary tree with the oldest family, the Flycatchers (Tyrannidae) at the bottom and the most recent, Crows (Corvidae) at the top.

the presence of sunlight, have the ability to transform the elements of the air and the soil into this one universal food. There are some parasitic or saprophytic plants which cannot manufacture starch because they do not contain chlorophyll and there are a few of the Protozoa, among the animals, which apparently contain chorophyll. But, in general, the plants are the great food manufacturers for all animals, whether they get it directly in the form of potatoes and wheat, or indirectly in the form of meat and eggs. So birds belong to the Animal Kingdom.

Each Kingdom is divided into a number of divisions or branches called Phyla (singular Phylum), the more familiar of those belonging to the Animal Kingdom being the Protozoa or one-celled animals, the sponges, the corals, the flat worms, the round worms, the starfishes, the earthworms, the molluscs, the insects and their allies, and the vertebrates or back-boned animals. Birds, of course, belong to the last-named, technically known as the Phylum Chordata. This Phylum is divided into a number of Subphyla because, in addition to containing the typical vertebrates, it has to include certain marine wormlike animals which, though externally resembling some of the worms much more than they do the typical vertebrates, still have the characteristic vertebrate structure with an internal skeleton or backbone, with a hollow 'spinal cord' dorsal to it, a body cavity below it, and with paired slits connecting the mouth cavity with the exterior.

This brings up a point which it will be well to have clear from the beginning in any consideration of the classification of birds, and that is, the basis for classification. What is the fundamental principle underlying all classification? Is it merely a grouping for convenience, such as putting black with black and white with white, or does it indicate actual 'blood relationship'? Modern classification is based entirely on the latter principle. The Protozoa are put together into one Phylum because it is believed that, no matter how diverse they may be in general appearance, they all have a common ancestor not too remote and are therefore related. The sponges are grouped together for the same reason, and so on. The common ancestors of each Phylum are much closer to all the members of that Phylum than they are to the members of any other Phylum, just as your great grandfather is more closely related to you and all of your cousins than he is to me.

It is not always easy to tell what constitutes 'blood relationship' and what constitutes superficial resemblance. Indeed it is sometimes so difficult that even the best authorities differ, and some birds, as well as other animals, have been juggled from one group to another as more detailed studies of their anatomy have thrown more light upon their kinship. The difficulties arise in what have been called 'convergent and divergent evolution.' Certain of birds' structures, such as their bills and feet, are most nicely adapted to specialized methods of securing their food and it is believed that these adjustments have come about through long ages by the weeding out of those individuals that varied in the wrong direction, and the preservation of those that varied in the right direction through what Darwin called "the struggle for existence and the survival of the fittest." Troubles appear when two birds of very different ancestry have the same food habits and develop the same types of bills or feet. For example, the Terns, the Herons, and the Kingfishers are not at all closely related, but all secure their fish by spearing and all have javelin-like bills. This is a case of 'convergent evolution.' On the other hand some birds that are really closely related have developed very different methods of feeding and their bills have become quite diverse, such, for example, as the bills of the Terns, Gulls, and Skimmers or the Sparrows, Grosbeaks, and Crossbills. These are cases of 'divergent evolution.' If we really want to know the actual blood relationships of birds, therefore, we must go deeper and study those structures that are less easily modified, such as the shape and arrangement of the bones or the muscles or the tendons. It is not always possible to assign a definite value to different structures or variations in these structures in subdividing a Phylum of the Animal Kingdom into its various Classes and lesser groups, but the effort is always made to indicate the age or relative remoteness from the common ancestor and an attempt is usually made to arrange the groups in their correct sequence.

Thus the Phylum Chordata is divided into four Subphyla, the one of major importance being the Subphylum Vertebrata, and this in turn is divided into seven classes: the lampreys, the sharks, the fishes, the amphibians, the reptiles, the birds, and the mammals. The birds, Class Aves, are all alike in possessing feathers, and inasmuch as no other animals possess such structures the birds are most easily defined. Confining ourselves to the birds, we find that the Class Aves is divisible into twenty-seven major groups* or what are called 'Orders,' twenty of which are found in North America. All of the birds of each Order resemble each other in points of fundamental structure, such as the shape and arrangement of the bones of the head, the shape of the breast bone, etc., and they have some external characters in common also, such as the arrangement of the toes, the number of tail feathers, etc., but their size, color, shape of wing and bill vary widely. All of the members of each Order are

* Some recent ornithologists, notably Erwin Streseman, raise many of the commonly recognized suborders to the higher rank and recognize as many as 51 Orders, but American Ornithologists in their 1957 Check list limit the number in North America to twenty.

much more like each other than they are like the members of any
other Order. If the Orders are to be arranged in proper sequence,
those which retain structures nearest to those of reptiles will be
considered the most primitive and come first, and those whose
structures have become most modified will be considered highest
and come last.

These Orders are thought to have equal rank or value as representative stages in the development of birds but they are by no
means equal in size, the Order of Perching Birds, for example, containing over half of the known species of birds. Nor do they represent exactly successive stages in the evolution from the most primitive to the highest Orders and a linear arrangement is somewhat
misleading. Were it feasible they should be arranged like the
branches of a tree emanating from Reptilian roots; but the exact
manner of branching is entirely hypothetical and no two authorities
entirely agree. See Figure 4.

Each Order is divided into a number of Families based upon such
characters as the general shape of the bill, relative lengths of the
wing feathers, the scales of the tarsus and other details of structure
largely external. Variations in color or color pattern are not of
sufficient importance to be considered in defining Families of birds,
for there is a great range of color in most Families. An effort is
always made to make the Families of the different Orders of equal
value but this has not always been possible, particularly in the
Order of Perching Birds, where, because of the great number of
species and the relatively small range of variation, the different
Families are less distinct and based upon minor variations. If several
Families of an Order are more like each other than they are like the
rest of the Order, they are often grouped together in a Super-family,
or the Order may be subdivided into several Suborders to show this
relationship. For general usage, however, these divisions need not be
considered and, unless one is specially interested in the taxonomy
of birds, a knowledge of the Orders and Families will suffice his
purposes. We will next list the Orders and Families of North
American birds as now recognized and published in the Check list
of North American Birds.*

The accompanying plates (Figs. 6–79) will show a typical member
of each family with enlarged views of the important structural char-

* Prepared by a Committee of the American Ornithologists' Union, Fifth edition 1957.

acteristics upon which the family is based. These are listed below each figure. Familiarity with the families makes identification of the species much easier.

I. The Order of Loons, Gaviiformes, has but one Family, Gaviidæ

II. The Order of Grebes, Podicipediformes has but one Family, Colymbidæ

III. The Order of Albatrosses and Petrels, Procellariiformes, has three Families, Diomedeidæ or Albatrosses, Procellariidæ or Fulmars, and Shearwaters, and Hydrobatidæ or Storm Petrels.

IV. The Order of Pelicans and Cormorants, Pelecaniformes, contains six Families as follows:
1. The Tropic-birds, Family Phaëthontidæ
2. The Pelicans, Family Pelecanidæ
3. The Gannets and Boobies, Family Sulidæ
4. The Cormorants, Family Phalacrocoracidæ
5. The Darters, Family Anhingidæ
6. The Man-o'-war-birds, Family Fregatidæ

V. The Order of Storks, Herons and Ibises, Ciconiiformes, contains four Families:
1. The Herons and Bitterns, Family Ardeidæ
2. The Storks and Wood Ibises, Family Ciconiidæ
3. The true Ibises and Spoonbills, Family Threskiornithidæ
4. The Flamingos, Family Phœnicopteridæ

VI. The Order of Ducks, Geese and Swans, Anseriformes, contains but one Family, Anatidæ, but the seven Subfamilies are so distinct that they are usually considered as families:
1. The Swans, Subfamily Cygninæ
2. The Geese, Subfamily Anserinæ
3. The Tree Ducks, Subfamily Dendrocygninæ
4. The Dabbling Ducks, Subfamily Anatinæ
5. The Diving Ducks, Subfamily Fuligulinæ
6. The Ruddy Ducks, Subfamily Erismaturinæ
7. The Mergansers, Subfamily Merginæ

VII. The Order of Vultures, Hawks and Eagles, Falconiformes, contains four Families as follows:
1. The American Vultures, Family Cathartidæ
2. The Hawks and Eagles, Family Accipitridæ with seven Subfamilies
3. The Ospreys-Pandionidæ
4. The Falcons and Caracaras, Family Falconidæ

VIII. The Order of Gallinaceous birds, Galliformes, contains four Families in North America:

       1. The Chachalacas, Curassows and Guans, Family Cracidæ
       2. The Grouse, Family Tetraonidæ
       3. The Pheasants (Natives of Asia) and Quails Family Phasianidæ
       4. The Turkeys, Family Meleagrididæ

IX. The Order of Cranes and Rails, Gruiformes, contains but three Families of North American birds, though there are six Suborders that are not represented in our fauna:
       1. The Cranes, Family Gruidæ
       2. The Limpkins, Family Aramidæ
       3. The Rails, Gallinules and Coots, Family Rallidæ

X. The Order of Shore-birds, Gulls, Auks, etc., Charadriiformes, contains a varied assemblage of ten very dissimilar Families of North American birds:
       1. The Jacanas, Family Jacanidæ
       2. The Oystercatchers, Family Hæmatopodidæ
       3. The Plovers, Surfbirds and Turnstones, Family Charadriidæ
       4. The Woodcock, Snipe and Sandpipers, Family Scolopacidæ
       5. The Avocets and Stilts, Family Recurvirostridæ
       6. The Phalaropes, Family Phalaropodidæ
       7. The Skuas and Jaegers, Family Stercorariidæ
       8. The Gulls and Terns, Family Laridæ
       9. The Skimmers, Family Rynchopidæ
      10. The Auks, Murres and Puffins, Family Alcidæ

XI. The Order of Pigeons and Doves, Columbiformes, contains but one Family of North American birds, the Columbidæ

XII. The Order of Parrots, Macaws, etc., Psittaciformes, contains but one Family that is represented in North America, the Family of Parrots, Psittacidæ

XIII. The Order of Cuckoos, Cuculiformes, is likewise poorly represented in North America, containing but the one Family of Cuckoos, Cuculidæ

XIV. The Order of Owls, Strigiformes, contains two Families, the Barn Owls, Family Tytonidæ, and Typical Owls, Family Strigidæ

XV. The Order of Whip-poor-wills and Nighthawks, Caprimulgiformes, contains but one Family of North American birds, the Caprimulgidæ

XVI. The Order of Hummingbirds and Swifts, Apodiformes contains two Families, that of the Swifts, Apodidæ and the Hummingbirds, Trochilidæ

XVII. The Order of Trogons, Trogoniformes, contains only the Trogons. Family Trogonidæ

XVIII. The Order of Kingfishers, Coraciiformes rather extensive in other parts of the world, contains only the one Family, Alcedinidæ or Kingfishers, in North America

XIX. The Order of Woodpeckers, Piciformes, likewise contains but one North American Family, the Picidæ or Woodpeckers

XX. The Order of Perching Birds, Passeriformes, is by far the largest of all the Orders and contains twenty-six Families in North America:

1. The Cotingas, Family Cotingidæ
2. The Tyrant Flycatchers, Family Tyrannidæ
3. The true Larks, Family Alaudidæ
4. The Swallows, Family Hirundinidæ
5. The Crows, Magpies and Jays, Family Corvidæ
6. The Titmice, Verdins and Bushtits, Family Paridæ
7. The Nuthatches, Family Sittidæ
8. The Creepers, Family Certhiidæ
9. The Wren-tits, Family Chamaeidæ
10. The Dippers, Family Cinclidæ
11. The Wrens, Family Troglodytidæ
12. The Thrashers and Mockingbirds, Family Mimidæ
13. The Thrushes, Solitaires and Bluebirds, Family Turdidæ
14. The Kinglets, Gnatcatchers, and Old World Warblers, Family Sylviidæ
(14a. The Accentors, Family Prunellidæ—accidental in Alaska.)
15. The Pipits and Wagtails, Family Motacillidæ
16. The Waxwings, Family Bombycillidæ
17. The Silky Flycatchers, Family Ptilogonatidæ
18. The Shrikes, Family Laniidæ
19. The Starlings, Family Sturnidæ (introduced from Europe)
20. The Vireos, Family Vireonidæ
21. The Honey Creepers, Family Coerebidæ
22. The Wood Warblers, Family Parulidæ
23. The Weaver Finches, Family Ploceidæ (introduced from Europe)
24. The Blackbirds, Orioles and Meadowlarks, Family Icteridæ
25. The Tanagers, Family Thraupidæ
26. The Finches, Sparrows, Grosbeaks and Crossbills, Family Fringillidæ

FIGS. 6-79. The Families of North American Birds with their distinctive characteristics. Paintings* by Dr. William C. Dilger, Laboratory of Ornithology, Cornell University.

FIG. 6. *Gaviidæ*—the Loons. 1. Legs set far back; tail short but well formed. 2. Tarsi flattened. 3. Toes four—front ones fully webbed, with nails rather than claws. 4. Bill—higher than wide—sharply pointed—no fluting or serrations. 5. Wings pointed—primaries much longer than tertials.

FIG. 7. *Podicipedidæ*—the Grebes. 1. Like Loons, but smaller. 2. Tail rudimentary. 3. Toes lobed.

* Kodachrome slides, in full color, of these paintings are available from the author.

FIG. 8. *Diomedeidæ*—the Albatrosses. 1. Size larger; wings long and narrow. 2. Bill hooked—nostril tubes separate on sides of bill. 3. Front toes webbed— hind toe rudimentary.

FIG. 4. *Procellariidæ*—Shearwaters, Fulmars and large Petrels. 1. Wings long and narrow—size variable. 2. Nostril tubes together on top of bill, but separated by septum. 3. Front toes webbed; hind toe rudimentary.

FIG. 10. *Hydrobatidæ*—The Storm Petrels. 1. Birds small. 2. Nostril tube single on top of bill. 3. Front toes webbed; hind toe small or wanting.

FIG. 11. *Phaëthontidæ*—The Tropic Birds. 1. All four toes joined by webs. 2. Bill pointed. 3. Central tail feathers greatly lengthened.

FIG. 12. *Pelecanidæ*—Pelicans. 1. All four toes webbed. 2. Bill with large pouch.

FIG. 13. *Sulidæ*—Gannets and Boobies. 1. All four toes webbed. 2. Bill pointed and heavy—pouch rudimentary. 3. Tail relatively short.

Fig. 14. *Phalacrocoracidæ*—Cormorants. 1. All four toes webbed. 2. Bill hooked. 3. Gular sac bare. 4. Tail strong—not fluted.

Fig. 15. *Anhingidæ*—Snake Birds. 1. All four toes webbed. 2. Bill long, pointed. 3. Tail long, fluted.

FIG. 16. *Fregatidæ*—Frigate Birds. 1. All four toes partially webbed. 2. Bill long, hooked. 3. Tail deeply forked. 4. Gular sac bare.

FIG. 17. *Ardeidæ*—Herons (two subfamilies). 1. Bill long, straight, sharply pointed. 2. Lores bare, head feathered. 3. Toes 4, all on same level, not webbed, middle nail with comblike margin; hind toe well developed. 4. Neck curved in flight. 5. Legs long.

FIG. 18. *Ciconiidæ*—Wood Storks. 1. Legs long. 2. Toes 4 on same level, webs small or absent. 3. No comb on nail. 4. Neck held straight in flight. 5. Bill long, decurved without groove. 6. Head naked in adult.

FIG. 19. *Threskiornithidæ*—*Ibises* (two subfamilies). 1. Legs long. 2. Bill long, decurved or flattened at tip. Grooved. 3. Toes all on same level. 4. Lores bare, head feathered. 5. Neck straight in flight.

FIG. 20. *Phœnicopteridæ*—Flamingos. 1. Legs and neck long. 2. Bill bent in middle—fluted. 3. Hind toe elevated, front toes webbed. 4. Lores bare. 5. Neck extended in flight.

FIG. 21. *Anatidæ*—Waterfowl (seven subfamilies). 1. Legs short, front toes webbed. 2. Tarsi rounded. 3. Bill usually broad and flat—its sides fluted or guttered, or narrower with tooth-like projections. 4. Tip of maxilla with nail or hook. 5. Wings pointed—primaries stiff.

FIG. 22. *Cathartidæ*—American Vultures. 1. Hawk-like but with head and fore-neck naked. 2. Bill with blunt hook and large nostrils piercing its basal portion. 3. Claws blunt and with hind toe not half as long as the middle.

FIG. 23. *Accipitridæ*—Typical Hawks (five subfamilies). 1. Head feathered. 2. Bill strongly hooked but not notched, with nostrils opening through a fleshy cere at base. 3. Hind toe longer than shortest front toe and all with strong curved claws. 4. Wings more or less rounded. 5. Tarsal scales square transverse.

FIG. 24. *Pandionidæ*—Osprey. 1. Hawk-like but with toes capable of being held two front and two back. 2. Tarsal scales rounded. 3. Cutting edge of bill smooth.

FIG. 25. *Falconidæ*—Caracaras and Falcons (two subfamilies). 1. Hawk-like, with small circular nostrils with central bony tubercle. 2. Front of tarsus reticulate with rounded scales. 3. Cutting edge of bill with notch or tooth.

Fig. 26. *Cracidæ*—Curassows, Guans and Chachalacas. 1. Fowl-like with long tails. 2. Tarsus and toes not feathered, nor with spurs. 3. Toes on same level. 4. Throat more or less bare.

Fig. 27. *Tetraonidæ*—Grouse and Ptarmigan. 1. Fowl-like with the tarsus and sometimes the toes feathered. 2. Nostril openings likewise feathered.

FIG. 28. *Phasianidæ*—Quail, Pheasants and Peacocks (two subfamilies). 1. Fowl-like, with tarsus not feathered, but often spurred. 2. Head always feathered. 3. Hind toe slightly elevated. 4. Tarsus usually but not always spurred.

FIG. 29. *Meleagrididæ*—Turkeys. 1. Fowl-like, tarsus bare and spurred. 2. Head naked and with caruncles.

FIG. 30. *Gruidæ*—The Cranes. 1. Large marsh birds over 3 feet long. 2. Legs long, hind toe small, elevated, tail well developed. 3. Neck long, not folded like Herons in flight. 4. Crown more or less bare.

FIG. 31. *Aramidæ*—The Limpkins. 1. Medium-sized marsh birds, under 30 inches in length. 2. Head fully feathered. 3. Hind toe longer, on same level as front toes, no webbing. 4. Outer primary narrowed and incurved. 5. Tail well developed. 6. Wings rounded. 7. Neck extended in flight.

FIG. 32. *Rallidæ*—Rails, Gallinules and Coots (two subfamilies). 1. Smaller marsh birds, 5-15 inches long. 2. Outer primary normal. 3. Tail poorly developed. 4. Toes on same level, never webbed, but lobed in Coots. 5. Head fully feathered.

FIG. 33. *Jacanidæ*—Jacanas. 1. Small shore birds with exceedingly long toes and claws for distributing weight on floating vegetation. 2. Frontal shield above bill conspicuous.

FIG. 34. *Haematopodidæ*—Oystercatchers. 1. Large black and white plover-like birds with bills over 3 inches long. 2. Vertically compressed, with wedge-shaped tip.

FIG. 35. *Charadriidæ*—Plovers, Turnstones and Surf-birds (two subfamilies). 1. Long-legged shore birds with bills shorter and heavier than the Sandpipers. 2. Toes usually three, never webbed or lobed. 3. Tarsus usually with rounded scales. 4. Wings long and pointed.

FIG. 36. *Scolopacidæ*—Woodcock, Snipe and Sandpipers (three subfamilies). 1. Shore birds with bills longer and more slender. 2. Hind toe usually present, front toes often slightly webbed. 3. Wings long, pointed.

FIG. 37. *Recurvirostridæ*—Avocets and Stilts. 1. Shore birds with unusually long legs and long slender bills. 2. Rather fully webbed toes.

Fig. 38. *Phalaropidæ*—Phalaropes. 1. Small shore birds with dense plumage and lobed toes. 2. Females larger and brighter than males.

Fig. 39. *Stercorariidæ*—Jaegers and Skuas. 1. Long-winged gull-like water birds with nail-like hook on bill and a scaly shield or cere at base. 2. Central tail feathers elongated in Jaegers. 3. Front toes webbed. 4. Nostrils piercing bill behind nail.

FIG. 40. *Laridæ*—Gulls and Terns (two subfamilies). 1. Long-winged water birds usually light colored with hooked (Gulls) or pointed (Terns) bills and nostrils which perforate the bill. 2. Hind toe small, elevated. 3. Front toes webbed.

FIG. 41. *Rynchopidæ*—Skimmers. 1. Tern-like birds with blade-like bills, the lower mandible longer than the upper.

FIG. 42. *Alcidæ*—Auks, Murres and Puffins. 1. Marine birds with short pointed wings, dense plumage, ducklike bodies and short tails. 2. Bill varied but always pointed and never ducklike. 3. Hind toe lacking, front toes fully webbed.

FIG. 43. *Columbidæ*—Pigeons and Doves. 1. Land birds with relatively heavy bodies and small heads. 2. Bills slender, basal half grooved and nostrils opening through a soft fleshy cere. 3. Toes 4, all on same level, the hind toe as long as shortest front one.

Fig. 44. *Psittacidæ*—Parrots and Macaws. 1. Heavy bodied land birds with strong hooked bills with cere at base. 2. Toes (zygodactyl) two in front and two behind.

Fig. 45. *Cuculidæ*—Cuckoos, Roadrunners and Anis (three subfamilies). 1. Slender bodied land birds with long soft rounded tails. 2. Zygodactyl toes (two forward, two backward). 3. Bills slightly curved. No cere.

FIG. 46. *Tytonidæ*—Barn Owls. 1. Land birds with large eyes set in facial disk; bill strongly hooked with a cere largely concealed by feathers. 2. Tarsus and toes feathered, middle claw with a comblike edge. 3. Primaries not notched or emarginate. 4. Outer toe opposable so that foot can appear zygodactyl.

FIG. 47. *Strigidæ*—typical Owls. 1. Similar to Tytonidæ, but with no comb on middle nail. 2. One or more primaries notched or emarginate.

Fig. 48. *Caprimulgidæ*—Goatsuckers. 1. Land birds with large heads, small bills and very wide mouths. 2. Feet small, middle toe much the longest, its nail with a comb. 3. Plumage soft, mottled.

Fig. 49. *Apodidæ*—Swifts. 1. Superficially resembling Swallows with long narrow wings, small bills and wide gape. 2. Dull compact plumage, the tail feathers usually spine-tipped.

FIG. 50. *Trochilidæ*—Hummingbirds. 1. Size small, bill longer than the head, extremely slender, needlelike. Tongue tubular. 2. Feet very small, hind toe relatively short. 3. Plumage usually iridescent.

FIG. 51. *Trogonidæ*—Trogons. 1. Plumage soft, lax and usually brilliant. 2. Bill short, stout, hooked with cutting edge notched or toothed. 3. Wings short and rounded, tail long. 4. Inner toe reversed.

FIG. 52. *Alcedinidæ*—Kingfishers. 1. Sturdy compact birds with large crested heads and small feet. 2. Middle and outer toes joined for half their length. 3. Bill long, strong pointed.

FIG. 53. *Picidæ*—Woodpeckers. 1. Climbing birds with strong feet and claws, the toes normally arranged two forward and two backward. 2. Bill stout pointed or wedge-tipped, nostrils bristly. 3. Tail feathers normal with stiffened pointed tips.

Fig. 54. *Cotingidæ*—the Cotingas. 1. Typical Tanager-like birds with slightly hooked bills. 2. Extensive cohesion of the inner and middle toes. 3. Legs relatively short with the tarsus pycnaspidean—i.e. with large scales in front and tiny scales down the back.

Fig. 55. *Tyrannidæ*—Tyrant Flycatchers. 1. Stocky birds with large slightly crested heads. 2. Flat, triangular, slightly hooked bills with stiff rictal bristles. 3. Wings usually rounded but first primary not rudimentary. 4. Feet small, tarsus exaspidean—i.e. rounded with the line of union on the inside.

WARBLERS

Black and White Warbler

Worm-eating Warbler

Ovenbird

Wilson's Warbler

WARBLERS

Pine Warbler in Winter

Myrtle Warbler in Winter

WARBLERS

Magnolia Warblers (summer)

Chestnut-sided Warblers (summer)

WARBLERS

Golden-winged Warbler   Blue-winged Warbler

When these two (above) hybridize they produce Brewster's and Lawrence's Warblers.

Prothonatory (male) and Yellow (female) Warblers at Yellow Warbler's nest in "pseudohybridism."

Hooded Warbler

FIG. 56. *Alaudidæ*—the Larks. 1. Walking birds with long hind claw. 2. Legs relatively long, the tarsus scaled and holaspidean—i.e. rounded behind. 3. Bill relatively short and pointed, the nostrils with bristly tufts. 4. Wings pointed, rudimentary first primary absent in N.A. Larks

FIG. 57. *Hirundinidæ*—the Swallows. 1. Long-winged, weak-footed birds, the primaries twice as long as the secondaries. 2. Bill short and flattened, slightly hooked, gape wide. No rictal bristles.

FIG. 58. *Corvidæ*—Crows and Jays (two subfamilies). 1. Mostly large birds with stout pointed bills which have bristly feathers covering the nostrils. 2. Wings and tails rounded, the first primary short but not rudimentary. 3. Feet and claws heavy. Tarsus scutellate and bilaminate.

FIG. 59. *Paridæ*—Titmice, Verdins and Bushtits. 1. Small birds with comparatively short, stout rounded bills, neither notched nor hooked. Nostrils concealed by bristles. 2. Wings rounded with first primary rudimentary (less than $1/3$ the longest). 3. Feet strong, Passerine, scutellate. Structurally resemble small Jays.

Fig. 60. *Sittidæ*—Nuthatches. 1. Small blue-gray creeping birds. 2. Bill long, straight, slender without notch or hook. 3. Nostrils partially covered with bristles. 4. Wings pointed with rudimentary primary. 5. Tail short and square. 6. Feet and claws notably large.

Fig. 61. *Certhiidæ*—Creepers. 1. Small climbing birds with slender decurved bill and stiffened pointed tail feathers. 2. Toes Passerine but claws much curved and very sharp. 3. Tarsus scutellate. 4. Wing rounded with rudimentary primary.

Fɪɢ. 62. *Chamaeidæ*—Wren Tits. 1. Small brown titmouse-like birds with very soft lax plumage and rounded wings much shorter than the long, graduated tail. 2. Legs and feet strong, tarsus bilaminate.

Fɪɢ. 63. *Cinclidæ*—Dippers. 1. Small gray thrush-like birds with short tails, almost hidden by the long tail coverts. 2. Short, stiff, rounded wings, long strong legs and feet, with strongly curved claws. 3. Nostrils linear, opening beneath a large scale, partially covered with feathers.

FIG. 64. *Troglodytidæ*—Wrens. 1. Small brown birds with indistinctly barred wings and short rounded tails. 2. Bill slender, more or less decurved terminally. No rictal bristles. 3. Wings rounded.

FIG. 65. *Mimidæ*—Mockingbirds and Thrashers. 1. Bills rather long and slightly notched near the tip which is more or less decurved. Rictal bristles evident. 2. Wings rounded. 3. Tails long, rounded. 4. Tarsus long, scutellate.

FIG. 66. *Turdidæ*—Thrushes. 1. Medium-sized birds with strong bills notched near the tip, nostrils exposed and rictal bristles evident. 2. Wings strong, pointed, with rudimentary primary. 3. Tails square, feet strong, the tarsus smooth (booted), the scales indistinct. 4. Juvenal plumage spotted both above and below.

FIG. 67. *Sylviidæ*—Old World Warblers, Gnatcatchers and Kinglets (two sub-families). 1. Small slender birds with slender more or less booted or scutellate tarsus. 2. Slender bills which are nevertheless notched near the tip and with the nostrils more or less covered with bristly feathers. 3. Tails medium to long. 4. Juveniles never spotted like Thrushes.

FIG. 68. *Motacillidæ*—Wagtails and Pipits. 1. Lark size, walking birds with much lengthened claw on hind toe. 2. Bill slender with exposed nostril and subterminal notch. 3. Wings pointed with inner secondaries lengthened to equal primaries. 4. Tail long, feet long and slender, tarsus scutellate.

FIG. 69. *Bombycillidæ*—Waxwings. 1. Sleek, gray-brown, crested birds with yellow or pink-tipped tail feathers and usually waxy red tips to the secondaries. 2. Bill broad, flat, rather obtuse, notched near tip, nostrils fringed with bristly feathers, gape wide. 3. Wings pointed with rudimentary primary. 4. Feet rather weak— tarsus scutellate.

FIG. 70. *Ptilogonatidæ*—Silky Flycatchers. 1. Slender, long-tailed crested birds with bills and feet similar to Waxwings, but more slender. 2. Hind toe shorter. 3. Wings rounded.

FIG. 71. *Laniidæ*—Shrikes. 1. Robin-size grayish birds with strongly notched and hooked bills and nostrils fringed with bristly feathers. 2. Rictal bristles also present. 3. Tarsus scutellate. 4. Wings relatively short and rounded.

FIG. 72. *Sturnidæ*—Starlings. 1. An Old World family of walking birds similar to our Blackbirds and often highly iridescent. 2. Bills widened and flattened with wide gape, but straight and pointed. 3. Wings pointed with a rudimentary primary.

FIG. 73. *Vireonidæ*—Vireos. 1. Small, green-backed birds with rather stout bills, higher than broad at the base with the tip notched, slightly hooked. 2. Rictal bristles barely evident. 3. Some species with rudimentary primary. 4. Feet strong, toes short, somewhat joined at base. 5. Tarsus scutellate.

FIG. 74. *Coerebidæ*—Honey Creepers. 1. Small 9-primaried Warbler-like birds with usually slightly decurved bills and deeply bifid, penicillate tongues.

FIG. 75. *Parulidæ*—Wood Warblers. 1. Small, often brightly colored, 9-primaried insectivorous birds with pointed wings. 2. Slender legs, tarsus scutellate in front and sharp-edged behind. 3. Bill typically rounded, straight and pointed, without hook or notch and without rictal bristles, but there are exceptions to the rule.

FIG. 76. *Ploceidæ*—Weaverbirds. 1. An Old World family of sparrow-like birds, difficult to separate by external characters from the Fringillidae except by rudimentary primary. The introduced House Sparrow is the only N.A. representative of the family.

FIG. 77. *Icteridæ*—Meadowlarks, Blackbirds and Troupials. 1. Medium-sized birds, with blacks and yellows predominating, with strong scutellate legs. 2. Rather heavy straight sharply pointed bills that extend backward dividing the feathers on the forehead. 3. Wings pointed, without rudimentary primary.

FIG. 78. *Thraupidæ*—Tanagers. 1. Small to medium sized birds, males colorful, bills finch-like but with upper mandible less conical, somewhat swollen. 2. Cutting edge not angled at base but usually toothed or notched near middle.

FIG. 79. *Fringillidæ*—Grosbeaks, Finches, Sparrows and Buntings (three subfamilies). 1. Small to medium sized birds, with short stout conical bills, cutting edge angled at the base. 2. Obvious primaries 9, rudimentary primary lacking.

Each family is ordinarily divided into several Genera (singular Genus), in order to show relationships within the Family. Just as it would assist you in learning all of the children of the large Smith Family if you could group them into the John Smiths, the Paul Smiths, the George Smiths, etc., so it is an aid to have the Warblers grouped into the Chats, the Yellowthroats, the Waterthrushes, etc., with the several species in each Genus resembling each other more than they do any other members of the Family.

In large families it is natural to find that some of the genera are more like each other than they are like the other genera of the family so that it is helpful to recognize what are called 'sub-families.' Thus in the family of waterfowl (*Anatidae*) we find several genera of Swans more like each other than they are like any of the genera of geese. The genera of Geese, in similar manner, are more like each other than they are like any of the Swans or the Ducks, and so on. So we recognize six sub-families of waterfowl in the family Anatidae.

The characters used in defining Genera are usually details in the shapes of the bills, presence or absence of bristles, distinctive color patterns, etc. Members of the Family of Thrushes, for example, numbering some 600 species, and found all over the world, are all alike in being Perching Birds over five and a half inches in length with moderate bills bearing a small notch near the tip of the upper mandible, having square tails and having tarsi with indistinct scales or none, and with wings rather long and pointed, the third primary the longest, and the first always very short, less than an inch in length. Quite naturally some of these 600 species are more like each other than they are like the rest of the Family and so the Family is divided into about 70 Genera, some of which are recognizable by their color pattern alone. Thus we have the Genus of Robins (Turdus), all of which resemble our common American Robin. Then there is the Genus of Bluebirds (Sialia) all of which are much like our common Bluebird; the Genus Myadestes or Solitaires, and the Genus of Wood Thrushes (Hylocichla), all of which resemble our Wood Thrush, Veery, Olive-backed or Hermit Thrushes, and so on.

This brings us to the Species, formerly the ultimate division, and defined as the term to be applied collectively to all those individuals which resemble each other as closely as the offspring of the same parents. This admits of a certain amount of individual variation but

Fig. 80. Four Genera of Thrushes: *Top left:* the Robins (Turdus), *Top right:* the typical Thrushes (Hylocichla), *Lower left:* the Solitares (Myadestes), *Lower right:* the Bluebirds (Sialia); represented here by the American Robin, the Wood Thrush, Townsend's Solitaire, and the Bluebird.

recognizes the uniformity which runs through the thousands of individuals of the same kind and keeps them distinct from the individuals of another species. In recent years intensive studies of large numbers of individuals of many species, especially those that are wide-ranging, have shown that the individual variations of groups living in isolated or circumscribed environments often become general throughout all the individuals of the species living in that particular region and apparently become fixed and inherited. Perhaps the first individuals of the species that entered the region had this peculiarity and transmitted it to their offspring and thus finally to all of the individuals resulting from the original invasion. This peculiarity may occur occasionally in individuals in another part of the birds' range, but may be lost either by not being inherited or by cross-breeding. For example, red hair may not be a peculiarity of the Smith family, but the original Smiths that went to Greenland may have had red hair and their children and children's children may have inherited it until practically every Smith in Greenland comes to have red hair while only a few on the mainland have this particular adornment. Perhaps some other characters, such as freckles or slightly smaller stature, might become associated with the Greenland Smiths until, should there be a great family reunion, one interested in the Smiths could, with a degree of certainty, pick out the Greenland Smiths from all the others and perhaps also the Labrador Smiths by some other peculiarity, and the New York Smiths or the Brooklyn Smiths. These different groups of individuals would then be known as varieties or subspecies. Thus we have the common little Song Sparrow broken up into at least twenty different subspecies, each subspecies occurring only in a circumscribed portion of the enormous range of the species which extends between Alaska, North Carolina and Mexico. Some are larger and darker, some smaller and grayer, but all lie within the range of individual variation or at least show intergradations with the individuals of surrounding territory. Similarly the Canada Geese nest from Alaska to New Foundland and ten different subspecies are recognized, all with similar color pattern but some barely half the size of the largest. Different subspecies may migrate and winter together but each has a distinct breeding range. Should the variation of any subspecies be sufficiently distinct, or should the intergrades die out, the birds of that particular range would probably be considered species rather than subspecies.

Now that we have the 'parts' to the machinery of classification, how are we to assemble them so that anyone can run the machine? If it is a good machine, there will be use for it in other countries than our own, so we must first adopt a common language for it, and the language that has been adopted is Latin, either taken directly or from Greek with Latinized endings. The earliest ornithologists named their birds with long Latin sentences descriptive of the bird until the great Swedish naturalist, Linnæus, originated the binomial nomenclature and presented it to the world in revised form in the tenth edition of his *Systema Naturæ* in 1758. With a few very simple rules, he lifted a burden from the backs of all systematists which would have crushed them long before now.

Very briefly, his system of naming birds, and all other animals and plants as well, was to give each one a 'scientific name' consisting of two words, the name of the Genus to which it belongs, and the name of the species following it like a modifying adjective. He laid down the law that no generic name should be used twice in the Animal Kingdom, and that no specific name should be used twice in the same Genus, so that the combination of Genus plus species would always be diagnostic of the one group of individuals to which it was first given. The modern recognition of subspecies has modified the original binomial into a trinomial, but the law and the principle remain the same.

The generic name is always written with a capital letter, the species and subspecies with small letters, and there follows an abbreviation of the name of the ornithologist who originally described the species or subspecies. The word used for the species name can never be changed no matter how unhandy it may seem, but it is frequently necessary to change some of the original generic names if it is found, after more detailed studies, that the original describer (authority) did not classify his species correctly or if finer generic distinctions seem necessary. When such a change is made, the name of the original describer is enclosed in parentheses, to indicate that one will not find the original description in his works under the name given. Thus, the scientific name of the Eastern Bluebird is *Sialia sialis* (Linn.), indicating that the generic name that Linnæus gave to it has been changed. Linnæus in 1758 placed the Bluebird in the same genus (*Motacilla*) with the European Wagtails, but later studies have shown that the American Bluebirds are structurally quite different from the Wagtails, even belonging to a different family, so a new generic name *Sialia*, first used by Swainson in 1827, is now applied to all the New World Bluebirds and Linnæus' name is put in parentheses indicating that a change has been necessary in the generic name although his specific name remains the same. The scientific name of the Bluebird of southern Florida is *Sialia sialis grata* Bangs, indicating that Bangs discovered that the southern birds were different from the birds described by Linnæus, and that he has published a description of the Florida subspecies, which he did in 1898.

For the sake of uniformity, all family names end in *idæ* and all subfamily names in *inæ*, so that one can tell at a glance the value of such names when used.

There are now 74 families of North American birds accepted,* and each can be recognized by its combination of structural characters. The accompanying pages of drawings by Dr. W. C. Dilger show graphically how each of these families can be recognized, and the learning of these characteristics is part of the training of every serious orthithologist.

We will first arrange the 20 Orders of North American birds in the form of a tree (Fig. 4) with what are considered the most primitive birds (the Loons and the Grebes) emanating as branches from the base of the tree and the highest order (Perching Birds) as the topmost branch.

Each large branch (Orders, marked with Roman numerals) divides into its respective families and the number of North American species is indicated as Arabic numerals at the end of the branch: 74 families and 793 species.

Neither the Orders nor the Families are of equal numerical size. There is but one Family in the Order Gaviiformes, for example, and but four species, while the order of Perching Birds (Passeriformes, Fig. 5) has 26 families and 330 species in North America.

* Check list of North American Birds—Prepared by a Committee of the American Ornithologists' Union, and published in 1957.

3

The Distribution of Birds

Anyone interested in birds soon learns to recognize that each species has a particular type of environment which it prefers and outside of this habitat it is seldom found. Thus one finds the Bitterns and Rails in the marshes, the Bobolinks and Meadowlarks in the open fields, the Catbirds and Thrashers in the thickets, and so on. Of course some birds like Robins and Song Sparrows are very adaptable and are found throughout several types of environments but even these

FIG. 81. A pair of Ospreys, widely distributed throughout the world.

have their limitations. Before discussing the local distribution of birds, however, it may be well to take a bird's-eye view of the whole world and try to picture to ourselves how birds have come to their present homes.

Birds are restricted not only to certain types of habitats but most species are likewise restricted to certain parts of the world. Indeed there are more species that are confined to single valleys or single mountains than there are species that range over two continents, and only a very few like the Osprey range over almost the entire world.

The factors which control the distribution of bird life over the face of the globe are so many and so varied that we can mention only the major ones.

Did we have a complete history of all the birds that have ever lived, the problem of their distribution as well as the problem of their classification would be greatly simplified. Unfortunately our knowledge of fossil birds (see chapter I) is hopelessly incomplete. We find just enough remains to let us know that some groups of birds that are at present very restricted in their distribution were at one time wide ranging over the earth. The Trogons and Barbets, for example, which today are found only in Africa, Asia, and South

Fig. 82. Anna's Hummingbird of western U.S. Hummingbirds are found only in the New World.

America would puzzle us greatly were it not for a few fossil remains from Europe. These indicate that the families probably originated in Europe, or more likely Asia, and pushed across North America as well as across Europe when there was a wide land bridge between Siberia and Alaska. Thence they extended their range to South America as well as to Africa—only to have all of their kind killed off by some great cataclysm, such as the ice age, except at the extreme southern edges of their range. The Trogons and Barbets are ancient groups of birds and had ample time for thus extending their ranges before the various continents became separated.

Other families of birds have originated since the continents became separated and have never crossed. Thus the Wood Warblers,

Vireos, Tanagers and Hummingbirds are found only in the New World and probably had their origin in South or Central America while such families as the Hoopoes, Pittas, Rollers and Sunbirds of the Old World have never reached North or South America. The length of time that any large land mass has been cut off or isolated from the rest of the world, therefore, determines the character of its bird life.

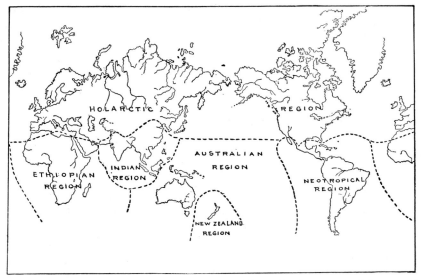

Fig. 83. The Zoological Regions of the World, each characterized by certain Families of birds restricted to it.

We can picture all of the land masses connected at one time when a land bridge existed between Siberia and Alaska, or even between Greenland and northern Europe. The groups of birds that then existed gradually permeated all the continents. Then as New Zealand and Australia and the New World were successively cut off from the rest of the world and new groups of birds arose, the distribution of each of these recent bird families was necessarily restricted by the degree of isolation of the land area where it had its start. The two main factors in controlling the distribution of bird life over the globe, therefore, have been the place of origin and the degree of isolation; and the distinctiveness of the fauna of any region depends upon the length of time that has elapsed since its isolation became complete. Thus New Zealand has been isolated from the rest of the world so long that not only is its bird fauna very limited but it has no native land mammals except the flying bats. In New Zealand alone are found the curious flightless Kiwis and, formerly, the giant Moas, now extinct. Australia, not far distant, remained connected to the rest of the world much longer and has a correspondingly richer fauna though it became isolated before modern mammals arose and all but three of its native mammals are marsupials. With the adjacent islands, it is the exclusive home of the Emus and Cassowaries, the Lyre Birds, the Lories, the Birds of Paradise, the Bowerbirds and other families, while such birds as the Pheasants, Bulbuls, true Finches and Woodpeckers which are abundant on the mainland of Asia never reached Australia before it was cut off and are not found there today.

Next in age of its isolation is probably South America and there is every zoological reason for believing that it was cut off from North America for long years after it had received its initial supply of birds from the North. Together with the West Indies and Central America it is now known as the Neotropical Region and contains more families of birds peculiar to it than any other Region. Among them may be mentioned the Rheas, Tinamous, Honey Creepers, Manakins, Cotingas, Plant Cutters, Wood Hewers, Ant-birds, Jacamars, Toucans, Motmots and others—some 27 families in all.

North America, and Europe and Asia north of the Himalayas have so many families of birds in common and so few distinct ones that they are ordinarily grouped together as one Zoological Region, the Holarctic. Europe boasts only one family of birds, the Bearded Tits, and North America likewise but one, the Wren-Tits, which are not found in other regions, and there is some question whether these birds should be given full family rank. The two large land areas have obviously not been disconnected long and quite a few of the species found on both sides of the Atlantic (such as the Ptarmigan, Snow Buntings, Lapland Longspurs, Brown Creepers and Kinglets) are, at best, only subspecifically distinct.

Africa below the Sahara Desert and including the island of Madagascar has apparently been isolated long enough to develop a few endemic families such as the Ostriches, Secretary Birds, Umbrettes and Honey-guides and is known as the Ethiopian Region; and Asia, south of the Himalayas, has developed at least one family, the

Broadbills, and many peculiar genera and species, and is generally spoken of as the Indian or Oriental Zoological Region.

Each of these six zoological regions is divisible into a number of Sub-regions and each Sub-region into a number of Provinces accordingly as it has developed *species* of birds peculiar to it. Thus the Holarctic Region is divisible into the Palearctic or Old World portion and the Nearctic or New World portion. The Nearctic Sub-region, including all of North America except southern Mexico and Central America, is ordinarily divided into six Provinces—an eastern Alleghanian extending from the Atlantic westward to the 100th meridian; a central or Missourian extending from the 100th meridian westward to and including the Rocky Mountains; a Californian including just the Pacific coast strip west of the Rockies; a Northeastern or Canadian Province; a Northwestern or Alaskan; and a Southern, Mexican or Sonoran. Each of these Provinces is characterized by a few birds not found in the others although many species are so widespread as to be identical throughout the Sub-region or at least to be represented only by subspecies in the different Provinces. Thus such species as the Mourning Dove, and the Barn, Tree and Cliff Swallows are found from coast to coast but the Sea-side, Pine-woods and Ipswich Sparrows are confined to the Eastern United States; the Wren-tits, Varied Thrush, Anna's Hummingbird and Plumed Quail are confined to the Pacific coast; and the Nutcrackers, Piñon Jays and Rosy Finches are typical of the Rocky Mountain or Missourian Province; while the Robins, Bluebirds and Song Sparrows, which are found in all Provinces, are represented in each by birds that are only sub-specifically distinct.

A much better division of the Nearctic Region, however, is that which divides it into transcontinental Life Zones—based upon the similarities of plants and animals rather than the differences. The Life Zone theory assumes that temperature is the main factor determining the distribution of plants and animals, but it is necessary to recognize arid and humid divisions of each Zone. According to Dr. C. Hart Merriam, who first promulgated the theory, a Life Zone is a transcontinental area bounded by definite isotherms and characterized by a definite assemblage of plants and animals. He adds the following laws of distribution:

1. "Animals and plants are restricted in northward distribution by the total quantity of heat during the season of growth and reproduction."

FIG. 84. Merriam's Life Zones of North America. Transcontinental areas bounded by definite isotherms and characterized by definite assemblages of plants and animals. Certain nesting birds are indicators of each zone.

That is, the season must be long enough to admit of the species completing its life cycle.

2. "Animals and plants are restricted in southward distribution by the mean temperature of a brief period covering the hottest part of the year." That is, northern species are prevented from extending their

ranges further southward by the extreme heat of the midsummer, though the more southern land might be satisfactory for them at other seasons of the year.

Inasmuch as so many different factors influence the temperature of a region such as latitude, altitude, prevailing winds, presence or absence of large bodies of water, oceanic currents, slope exposure, etc., these Life Zones are, of necessity, very irregular and the problem of mapping them, even for a limited region, is very complex. Certain breeding birds, like certain plants, are good indicators for each Life Zone and, if one knows what species of birds nest in his vicinity and where, he should have little difficulty in mapping the Life Zones of his region.

In brief, North America is divided into three Regions: the Tropical, Austral and Boreal, divisible again into several Life Zones, with Eastern Humid and Western Arid and Pacific Coast Humid divisions.

The Tropical Region reaches the United States only on the tip of Florida as far north as Lake Worth and the mouth of the Caloosahatchie River, and the lower Rio Grande Valley in Texas. It is characterized by such birds as the Noddy and Sooty Terns, Great White Heron, Reddish Egret, Caracara, Everglade Kite, White-crowned Pigeon, Mangrove Cuckoo and Black-Whiskered Vireo; also by such wanderers from Mexico as the Gray's Thrush, Rose-throated Becard, Derby Flycatcher, Chachalaca, the Groove-billed Ani and the Aplomado Falcon.

The Austral Region is divisible into the Lower Austral, Upper Austral and Transition Life Zones; the Eastern Humid divisions of which (east of the 100th meridian) are usually spoken of as the Austroriparian, Carolinian and Alleghanian Faunas or Life Zones, while the western arid divisions are known as Lower Sonoran, Upper Sonoran, and Transition. The Austroriparian Life Zone extends northward from the Tropical to a line extending approximately from Cape Charles, Virginia, to southern Kansas and it is characterized by such birds as the Water-Turkey, Snowy and Louisiana Herons, White Ibis, Black Vulture, Ground Dove, Ivory-billed Woodpecker, Chuck-Will's Widow, Painted Bunting, Bachman's Sparrow, Boat-tailed Grackle, Yellow-throated Warbler and Brown-headed Nuthatch.

The Carolinian Life Zone extends from the Austroriparian northward to a line approximately from southern New York and New England to northern South Dakota but in the Alleghany Mountains, owing to the altitude, naturally swings far to the south, even into northern Georgia. This Life Zone is characterized by such birds as the Tufted Titmouse, Carolina Wren, Yellow-breasted Chat, Hooded, Kentucky, Blue-winged, Worm-eating and Prothonotary Warblers, Louisiana Waterthrush, Cardinal, Fish Crow and Acadian Flycatcher.

The Alleghanian Life Zone extends northward from the Carolinian to the St. Lawrence Valley in the east and central Saskatchewan in the west wherever the altitude is not too great. It is characterized by such nesting birds as the Bobolink, Chestnut-sided Warbler, Veery and Rose-breasted Grosbeak, and the following species reach their greatest abundance in this zone: the Virginia and Sora Rails, Mourning Dove, Black-billed and Yellow-billed Cuckoos, Kingbird, Cowbird, Meadowlark, Baltimore Oriole, Chipping and Field Sparrows, Towhee, Indigo Bunting, Yellow-throated Vireo, Catbird, Brown Thrasher, House Wren, Long-billed Marsh Wren, White-breasted Nuthatch and Wood Thrush.

The Boreal Region is divisible into the Canadian, Hudsonian and Arctic Life Zones. The Canadian Life Zone includes most of Nova Scotia and New Brunswick, Maine, south and central Quebec, most of Ontario except the southernmost strip, most of Manitoba and Saskatchewan, and most of Alberta and south and central British Columbia, extending northward along the Mackenzie River to lat. 65° and southward in the Rocky Mountains. It extends even to the Mexican table-land at altitudes of from 8-13,000 feet and is characterized by its high development of coniferous forests and by such nesting birds as the Crossbills, Evening Grosbeak, Junco, Siskin, Brown Creeper, Spruce Partridge, Hawk Owl, Goshawk, Three-toed Woodpeckers, Yellow-bellied Flycatcher, Canada Jay, White-throated Sparrow, Tennessee, Myrtle, Blackpoll, Bay-breasted, Blackburnian, Magnolia and Canada Warblers, Winter Wren, Red-breasted Nuthatch, Ruby and Golden crowned Kinglets, Bicknell's, Swainson's and Hermit Thrushes.

The Hudsonian Life Zone extends from the Canadian to the upper limit of tree growth. It is characterized by such nesting birds as the Rough-legged Hawk, Great Gray Owl, Pine Grosbeak, Gray-cheeked Thrush, White-crowned Tree, Harris and Fox Sparrows, Greater Yellowlegs and Northern Shrike.

The Arctic Life Zone includes the areas beyond tree growth along the north coast of N. A., the Hudson Bay area, northern Labrador and along the Atlantic Coast of Labrador. Owing to the Labrador current, it extends even as far south as the islands along the north shore of the Gulf of St. Lawrence almost to Anticosta Island.

Characteristic birds of the Arctic Life Zone are the Ptarmigan, Gyrfalcons, Snowy Owls, Snow Buntings, Lapland Longspurs, Pipits, and numerous shore birds such as the Hudsonian Curlew, Stilt Sandpiper, Sanderling, Pectoral Sandpiper and Black-bellied and Golden Plovers.

The Life Zones of the arid western and the humid Pacific coast strip are usually spoken of as the Transition, Upper Sonoran and Lower Sonoran, corresponding to the Alleghanian, Carolinian and Austroriparian Life Zones of the East and, owing to the great differences in altitude and slope exposure, their extent is very irregular and presents many intricate problems.

Of course there is never a sharp line separating one zone from another and one living in a typically Transition Life Zone, may find a few Canadian species living on the higher hills of the vicinity or typically Austral species living in some of the more sheltered spots, but it is always interesting to determine to just which fauna one's particular home environment belongs, and then to go ahead and divide it into its several ecological groups according to the various preferences of the different species for woodlands, fields, marshes or shores.

Another method of arranging the facts of bird distribution in North America is according to the biome and ecotone concepts of the ecologists. According to Shelford, biomes are "the largest plant and animal communities in dynamic equilibrium in the final climax state." In other words the name 'biome' is applied to the major plant associations such as the tundra, the coniferous forest, the grasslands and the deciduous forest. Between the biomes are intermediate or transition areas where the biomes blend and these are called ecotones. The two most northern biomes, the tundra and coniferous forest with the intermediate sub-arctic forest ecotone correspond quite closely with the Arctic, Hudsonian and Canadian Life

Zones, and the distribution of nesting birds corresponds quite satisfactorily with that of the vegetation types. To the southward, however, the life zone theory seems to meet with fewer exceptions than the biome concept and explains more logically, for example, the admixture of northern and southern species along the Pacific Coast. Here the cool Japanese current, with attendant fogs, moderates the heat of summer so as to permit a southward extension of northern species, while the long growing season and moderate winters permits the northward extension of southern species so that one finds, side by side, such Hudsonian birds as the Swainson's Thrush (var. Russet-backed) and White-crowned Sparrow (var. Nuttall's Sparrow) nesting with Sonoran Mockingbirds, Brown Towhees and Bush-tits. On the other hand, the grassland biome which reaches from southern Texas to Alberta extends through three life zones and while a few species like Meadowlarks and Horned Larks are found throughout the area in only sub-specific differentiation, other species are quite distinct as one travels northward from one life zone to the next. There are, for example, the Botteri, Cassin's, Black-throated and Rufous-winged Sparrows and the White-tailed Hawk of the Lower Sonoran Zone; the Lark Bunting, the Canyon Towhee, the Chestnut-collared Longspur and the Lark Sparrow of the Upper Sonoran Zone and the McCowan's Longspur, Marbled Godwit, Baird's and LeConte's Sparrows of the Transition Zone all in the one 'Biome.'

Some birds are much more adaptable than others to temperature and humidity and enjoy a breeding range extending through several life zones such as the Yellow Warbler and Song Sparrow but even with these species, they are not found throughout any one zone. Like most birds they show a preference for certain habitats, avoiding extensive areas of climax forest or grassland but accepting almost any type of intermediate brushland that is not too arid. On the other hand, few birds show as decided habitat preferences as the Kirtland's Warbler that confines its nesting not only to the jack-pines of a few counties in northern Michigan but actually to only a few parts of those counties where the jack-pines are of a certain age group—from say, 10 to 20 years old.

The bird life of extensive climax biomes is relatively limited as compared with the birds of some of the ecotones or developmental stages where different types of vegetation are found in juxtaposition.

This has given rise to the so-called 'theory of edges' which emphasizes the fact that more birds are found along the edge of any particular habitat than are found in its center. This holds for the major concepts as well as for local habitats. In the far north, for example, one finds a much greater concentration of birds where the spruce forest merges with the tundra than he does either on the wide open tundra or in the pure spruce forest.

Similarly, on a small scale, one can greatly increase the number of birds in an acre of deciduous woodland by breaking it up into clumps of trees with grassland or paths between and one can also increase the birds of a meadow by planting a hedgerow around it or across it.

When we come to study any particular habitat in detail, we find that the characteristic birds are not evenly distributed through it but each finds the particular niche which best suits its complicated needs. We will, therefore, in the next three chapters, consider a few of the various bird communities, particularly those of northeastern United States.

4

Bird Communities

BIRDS OF THE WOODLANDS AND WOODLAND BORDERS

When one begins the study of birds, he is very soon impressed with the fact that each species, in addition to having its characteristic plumage and song, has its favorite resorts for feeding and for nesting. One soon learns to associate each type of environment with certain birds and he is as surprised to find a bird out of its accustomed place as he would be to hear it giving an exceptional song or wearing an unusual plumage. With most birds the nesting and the feeding areas are not far removed, although some birds like the Hawks, Herons, and Kingfishers do range far from their homes in search of food. On their migrations birds sometimes frequent very different environments from those in which they nest, and a study of the migratory birds alone might be very misleading to one endeavoring to classify birds ecologically. In general, however, the field birds will be found in the fields, the marsh birds in the marshes, the woodland birds in the woods, and so on. Thus the discovery of an Ovenbird or a Ruffed Grouse in one's garden, or of a Bobolink in the woods is quite exceptional and worthy of note. The majority of birds build their nests where they spend most of their time searching for food: the Woodpeckers in dead trees, the Orioles and Vireos at the tips of branches, the native Sparrows on or near the ground, though in this case there are many exceptions such as the Herons that nest in the tree-tops and the Black and White Warbler that nests on the ground. Making allowances for these exceptions and basing our classification upon the nesting habits of the birds, it is possible to arrange the summer birds of any region into major associations, and many of these can be subdivided into smaller groups of birds that choose similar habitats for nesting.

We will first discuss *The Birds of the Woodlands*. Of course, there are many types of woodlands in this great country of ours and each type attracts certain birds more than others. One would not expect the live oaks and cabbage palms of Florida to shelter the same birds as the hemlocks and chestnuts of New York or the spruces of Canada. Some of the woodland birds, like the Ovenbird and Redstart, live, during the summer, from Virginia to Newfoundland; others, like the Yellow-throated and Kentucky Warblers, seldom reach New York State, while still others like Wilson's Warbler and the Gray-cheeked Thrush, seldom stop for the summer within the boundaries of the United States. In our discussion, therefore, we will have to pursue a middle course or limit ourselves to the birds of wide distribution. Wherever the woodland is located, the birds inhabiting it will divide themselves naturally into those which frequent the forest floor and those which live among the branches of the trees, with an inter- mediate group nesting and spending most of their lives in the stratum of bushes and herbaceous plants that are found in most types of forests. Of the arboreal birds, some make their homes in holes in dead trees or cavities in live trees; some prefer the lower branches, and others go clear to the tree-tops to build their nests.

Birds and trees are so intimately associated in the minds of every- one that it seems almost heresy to claim that a forest of trees is a poor place for birds, but such is almost invariably the case. It is the edges of the forests and the clearings that attract birds in num- bers, and even the typical forest species are more abundant in such places. The farther one penetrates the woodlands, ordinarily the scarcer become the birds, both in number and variety, and one re- marks on the great silence, the hush that seems to fall on all nature. The plaintive note of a Pewee, the wiry notes of a Red-eyed Vireo, or the solemn cadences of a Hermit Thrush seem only to accentuate the silence. If one tramps the woods in winter searching for old bird's nests, likewise he will be struck with the increasing scarcity of nests as he makes his way towards the center of the forest area. In the bird sanctuary known as Sapsucker Woods in central New York, only 36 of the 84 species that nest within its borders are typical wood- land species.

Birds of the Forest Floor:

There are not many birds that nest on the ground in our eastern woodlands, and a number of those that regularly do so occasionally lift their nests into the ferns or low bushes. The Ruffed Grouse and the Ovenbird, of all the species, seem the most terrestrial, but even they occasionally mount into the trees to feed or to sing and seem to prefer to nest not far from a woodland road or a clearing if not at the edge of the woods. The Veery, and further north, the Hermit Thrush are birds of the forest floor although both venture into the open, and the Veery, at least, sometimes raises its nest into the low bushes. Of the woodland Warblers, the Canada and Nashville both elect the forest floor for their nests, and the Black-and-White breaks the rules by descending from his ceaseless search on trunk and branch to build a nest of bark and rootlets at the base of some small

FIG. 85. Ruffed Grouse on its nest, a bird of the forest floor.

tree or on the side of some wooded bank. The Towhee is another bird that may well be included in this group of forest birds, although more often he is found about clearings or pasture lots and occasionally, like the Veery, builds his nest in a thick bush. Farther north his place is taken by the Juncos and the White-throated Sparrows which, while occasionally found in the heart of the forest, seem to prefer the forest borders and the clearings. In the open pine woods of the Southern States, the Bob-white replaces the Grouse, the Pine-woods Sparrow replaces the Thrushes, the White-throats and the Juncos, and the White-eyed Towhee its northern cousin. The Grouse and the Ovenbird are perhaps the most widespread of all these terrestrial forest birds.

Birds of the Undergrowth:

The nature of the undergrowth in our forests varies from the dense impenetrable palmetto scrub of our southern forests to the barren carpet of needles in our northern pine and spruce forests, and the bird life varies accordingly. The two extremes shelter but few birds, but the intervening woodlands have their characteristic species that seem to find conditions most desirable for the building of their homes in this vegetation growing in the shade of the trees. The undergrowth reaches its best development in the clearings and woodland borders, so that perhaps the majority of species should not be considered true woodland birds. A few there are, however, that enjoy the densest shade. In our Canadian woods the Winter Wren delights in fallen logs and upturned roots and builds its spherical nest of moss wherever it can find a suitable cranny, even in the deepest part of the forest. By his side the Black-throated Blue Warbler builds its woody nest in the sprouts that spring up from the base of some old beech or in the carpet of yew that covers the ground. Its place is taken in more southern woodlands by the Hooded-Warbler, while the Mourning and Chestnut-sided Warblers and the Indigo Bunting seem more partial to clearings or open woods where the undergrowth is more dense.

Birds of the Lower Branches:

It is impossible to draw a sharp line between the lower and the higher branches of a tree and in some cases it is difficult to say where the undergrowth leaves off and the lower branches of the trees begin. In this transitional stratum, however, we find some of our most typical and most abundant woodland birds nesting. In woodlands where there is an undergrowth of spicebush and elderberry or other tall bushes, these birds frequently nest in them, but otherwise they select the saplings or the lower branches of the forest trees. Among their number are some like the Robin, the Wood Thrush, the Blue Jay, and the Red-eyed Vireo, which have learned to accommodate their lives to the conditions offered by our shade trees and gardens. Others, like the Scarlet Tanager, the Rose-breasted Grosbeak, and the Redstart, occasionally follow their lead into the open, but others are never known to leave the protection of the forest when it comes time for nesting. Such are the Ruby and the Golden-crowned Kinglets, the Blue-headed Vireo, and the Magnolia Warbler of the northern woods, and the Acadian Flycatcher of the more southern bottomlands.

FIG. 86. Hooded Warbler at its nest, a bird of the forest undergrowth.

Birds of the Tree Trunks and Hollow Branches:

With a few exceptions this group of birds consists of the various Woodpeckers and the birds that have learned to use holes in trees as a safe place for their nests. The Red-cockaded Woodpecker of the South digs his hole in a living pine and the Hairy Woodpecker often uses a living tree in the north, but the others, for the most part, used dead trees or branches for their carpenter work. In the northern woods the Pileated and Three-toed Woodpeckers and the Yellow-bellied Sapsucker are strictly woodland species, and the Hairy and Downy are found there more often than not. The Flicker and Red-headed Woodpecker are more adaptable and often nest in trees far removed from the woodlands. The Southern Pileated and the Red-bellied Woodpeckers are likewise woodland species, though the nature of the pine woods frequented by the Red-bellied often brings him quite into the open. Of the birds that utilize the Woodpecker holes or natural cavities in woodland trees, the majority, like the Wood Duck, the Sparrow Hawk, and the Crested Flycatcher are found rather indiscriminately in the forest or in the open wherever suitable cavities invite. The Screech Owl belongs to the same class, but the Great Horned and Barred Owls ordinarily confine themselves to the forest trees. Of the Nuthatches. the northern Redbreasted Nuthatch is the most forest-loving, while the White-breasted and the southern Brown-headed are more partial to open groves and clearings. The Chickadees and the Tufted Titmice are normally woodland species, but both can be lured into gardens and will even accept nesting-boxes. The Brown Creeper is strictly a woodland species and hides its nest behind a loose piece of bark, a habit doubtless acquired from its method of feeding.

Birds of the Higher Branches and Tree-Tops:

Just what makes a Blackburnian Warbler decide to settle in the top of a hemlock or a Black-throated Green Warbler to select the top of a sapling, or a Cerulean Warbler to pick a branch fifty feet from the ground for its nest, while their relatives are satisfied with the lower branches or the undergrowth will probably never be known. Likewise with the Vireos, the Warbling goes to the tree-tops, the Yellow-throated to the middle of the tree, while the Red-eyed always nests on the lowest branches, and yet all three sing and hunt their crawling food together in the tree-tops. The Pine Warbler does not like the lower branches, nor do the Wood Pewee, the Olive-sided Flycatcher, the Purple Finch, and the Pine Siskin, and the Orioles are well known for their intricately woven cradles hung to the tips of the higher branches. Crows, Hawks, Eagles, and Herons likewise place their nests ordinarily as high as they can find sufficient support for them, and it is the exception to find one with higher branches near by that will support a photographer or even a camera.

It is interesting to contemplate how the various birds have come by their present nesting-sites. In the first place, it is interesting to know that each species has rather rigid requirements for the site that are adhered to by practically all members of the species. Some species and some individuals are much more adaptable than others and are capable of changing their nesting-sites with changing natural conditions, while others perish, or at least disappear, when the exact requirements of their nesting-sites are not found. The process of evolution is still evident with some of the birds that now regularly nest in the tree-tops to escape their enemies. On Gardiner's Island, where terrestrial enemies are few, the Ospreys nest on the ground, while elsewhere on the mainland they nest in the tops of tall trees, especially on the tops of inaccessible stubs. The Night Herons may have originally nested like the Bitterns on the ground in the marshes, as they still do in some of the western swamps, or in the button-bushes as they do in some of the Florida rookeries, but today in our Northern States they are usually forced to build in the tops of the tallest trees in the swamps.

In addition to the birds mentioned as typical woodland species, one sometimes finds birds of wide distribution or generalized habits, such as the Song Sparrow and Mourning Dove, nesting even in extensive forest areas, and the smaller woodlands are often invaded by many of the typical orchard and garden species like the Robin, the Chipping Sparrow, and the Yellow Warbler. There is quite an extensive group of birds that seem to find the best conditions for their existence in the forest borders and in brushy pastures and we will discuss them next.

Fig. 87. Sharp-shinned Hawk at its nest, a bird of the forest upper story.

BIRDS OF THE WOODLAND BORDERS

There is a region where the woodlands leave off and the open fields begin, more or less covered with a growth of bushes and vines, that gives shelter to certain typical birds. Where cultivated fields approach the woodlands closely, this border is a mere fringe, but where the fields have been found unfit for cultivation, or where the clearing has been recently done, this type of environment may cover many acres. If it has been used as a pasture, the undergrowth is usually in clumps with grass-land or paths dividing it into innumerable islets of low vegetation, usually with scattered larger trees and often with stumps or stubs of dead trees not worth removing. Clearings in the woods and forests that have recently been burned over have a similar growth and shelter the same birds. It is a transition region between the woodlands and the open country, and, naturally, is often invaded by many of the woodland birds already discussed, but in addition, it has many species that are primarily its own. Many of the birds that we now think of as typical of our orchards and gardens undoubtedly had their origin in this area bordering the woodlands, and some are still found equally abundant in both places.

This area of sunlight and shrubbery is conducive to the production of abundant fruits and insects upon which birds feed, and so we often find that the forest-border birds are more abundant than any other group.

As with the woodland birds, there is some variation in the species using this environment for nesting between the palmetto scrub of Florida and the sweet fern and yew of Canada. The Ground Doves are rare north of Georgia, the Mockingbirds and White-eyed Vireos are scarce north of Pennsylvania, while the Fox Sparrows and White-crowned Sparrows are never found as far south as the United States during the nesting period. Certain species, however, are widespread throughout the eastern United States, and we will confine ourselves largely to them.

Birds of the Ground:

This border country is primarily an environment of bushes, saplings, and vines, and none of the birds that are typical of it nests regularly on the ground. But the woodland Juncos and White-throats are found as often as not along the borders of the woods, and so might be considered as ground-birds of this environment. The Towhee, likewise, is probably more abundant in brushy pastures than in the woods proper and usually nests on the ground. The Brown Thrasher, the Song Sparrow, and the Field Sparrow that regularly nest in low bushes, very frequently hide their first nests on the ground at the base of a bush or tussock, particularly those individuals that nest early before the leaves afford much protection higher up. They really belong to the next stratum, however. The Mourning Warbler and the Yellow-throat, nesting in the rank herbaceous vegetation, might also be included here.

Birds of the Low Bushes:

There is, of course, no sharp line between the low bushes and the higher bushes, and if there were, probably few birds would recognize it. Certain birds, however, are more frequently found nesting in the blackberries, raspberries, and bushes of this type than they are in the taller elderberries and witchhazels. On the other hand, bushes like the thorn-apples, attract birds of both types. Indeed, there is no better place to look for birds' nests than in a pasture lot dotted with thorn-apple bushes.

Some birds always show a preference for certain bushes, so that one familiar with their tastes can glance over a woodland border or a brushy pasture and state immediately where the Chats' nest will probably be found, where the Field Sparrows', where the Chestnut-sided Warblers'. These preferences, doubtless, are different in widely separated parts of the bird's range just as the vegetation is different. Thus, in central New York, the Yellow-breasted Chats restrict their nests to clumps of cornels, spireas, or viburnums that present a dense exterior, but which are rather open within. In Connecticut, on the other hand, they seem to prefer the cat-briars or tangles of other vines, together with the Catbirds and Thrashers. The Indigo buntings build nests similar to those of the Chats, though usually with more leaves in the bottom, but they almost invariably nest lower and in little saplings, tall weeds, ferns or other upright growth. The Field Sparrows and Chestnut-sided Warblers likewise nest low, and often in the same sort of bushes, showing a preference for the short, slender-branched spireas, huckleberries, and red raspberries. Their nests, however, are quite different, that of the Field Sparrow being made chiefly of grasses and rather thick-walled, while that of the Warbler is made chiefly of narrow strips of bark and fibers and is thin-walled. The Field Sparrow's nest is more like a Song Sparrow's, but is smaller, less than 2 inches inside diameter, the Song Sparrow's being about 2½ inches. The Song Sparrow is such an adaptable bird that it often places its nest in exactly the sort of location that the Field Sparrow chooses, though it likewise nests on the ground and occasionally even in apple trees.

Cardinals and Mockingbirds in the southern states, and Catbirds and Thrashers farther north, all belong to this group of woodland border birds and frequently nest low in blackberries or cat-briars or other thick growth. At other times they nest considerably higher, thorny orange trees being favorite places for the Mockingbirds and Cardinals and thorn-apples for the Catbirds and Thrashers. Cardinals' nests are made largely of weed-stems, but Mockingbirds, Catbirds, and Thrashers use twigs for the outer layer and rootlets for the inside. The Catbird's nest is the bulkiest, containing considerable grape-vine bark, rags, paper, or dead leaves in addition to the twigs.

The most distinctive nest built by any of these thicket-dwelling birds is the beautiful hanging-basket of the White-eyed Vireo. It is not very different from the nest of the Red-eyed Vireo in structure, but, so far as I am aware, is usually thicker-walled and always built in a much denser location, such as in berry bushes, and is usually lower. The other Vireos already treated as Woodland birds, often nest along the forest border but none of them nest in the real thickets. The White-eyed Vireo is rare as far north as New York and New England.

Birds of the Higher Bushes:

In addition to the last birds mentioned there are a few that regularly select the taller bushes or higher branches for their nests. The two species of Cuckoos, for example, while occasionally nesting in the blackberries close to the ground, prefer the taller bushes or young saplings for their homes. The Yellow Warbler, too, while sometimes building where you can look into the nest, seems to prefer to get just out of convenient reach. The same is true of the Chipping Sparrow and Mourning Dove that often mount into the trees for their nests. The last three are among those birds which might now be called garden birds, though I believe they had their origin in the woodland borders.

On the highest branches of the thorn bushes, in the open, or the lower branches of the oaks or maples fringing the woods, may be found the nests of the Goldfinches, Waxwings, and Kingbirds. The Goldfinches' nest is one of the felted nests, like the Redstart's and Yellow Warbler's, but it can always be distinguished from them by its larger size and the fact that it is wider than it is high. Kingbirds and Waxwings build very similar nests of grasses, weed stems, string, and bits of cotton or wool, usually saddled on horizontal branches. Fresh nests can be distinguished by the fact that the Kingbird's is wider and shallower, the Waxwing's deeper and usually with a tuft of yellowish grasses hanging from the bottom. Old, flattened nests are sometimes indistinguishable.

Birds that Nest in Holes:

Scattered along the edge of the woods, in the clearings, and in the pasture lots are numerous dead trees and stubs that form the nesting-sites of a most interesting though unrelated group of birds. The holes are usually made by Woodpeckers, almost any species being likely to be found in clearings, though the Redhead and the Flicker are the most abundant ones in the open. The Redheads usually build higher than the Flickers and make slightly smaller holes, but the discarded cavity of either of these species may be used by some other bird. If it becomes enlarged to 3 or 4 inches in diameter, and re-sembles the nesting hole of a Pileated Woodpecker, a Screech Owl or a Wood Duck is likely to use it, or, in the real duck country, a Golden-eye, a Bufflehead, or a Merganser. A 3-inch hole makes a good home for a Sparrow Hawk without any renovation or the addition of any nesting material. Smaller holes will do for Crested Flycatchers, Bluebirds, Tree Swallows, House Sparrows, Starlings, Wrens, or Chickadees. Inasmuch as these birds also nest in the orchard, we will reserve description of the nest which they build at the bottom of the cavities, until the discussion of orchard birds.

In addition to the birds mentioned in these several groups, many of the woodland birds already discussed often move to the border of the woods for nesting, so that it may be well to provide one list

Fig. 88. Birds of the woodlands of eastern North America, showing where each species nests.

where all of the commoner birds inhabiting the different zones of vegetation in and about the woodlands can be seen at a glance. For such reference, the following lists are offered and also a diagram with the nests of the various species indicated by number upon it.

Birds of the Woodlands and Woodland Borders*

(a) GROUND-NESTING BIRDS:

1. Woodcock
2. Bob-white
3. Ruffed Grouse
4. Whip-poor-will
5. White-throated Sparrow
6. Junco
7. Pine-woods Sparrow
8. Towhee
9. Black and White Warbler
10. Nashville Warbler
11. Ovenbird
12. Canada Warbler
13. Veery
14. Hermit Thrush

(b) BIRDS OF THE UNDERGROWTH AND LOW BUSHES:

15. Field Sparrow, and Yellow-breasted Chat
16. Song Sparrow
17. Cardinal
18. Indigo bunting
19. White-eyed Vireo
20. Black-throated Blue Warbler
21. Chestnut-sided Warbler
22. Mourning Warbler
23. Hooded Warbler
24. Mockingbird
25. Catbird, and Brown Thrasher
26. Winter Wren

(c) BIRDS OF THE HIGH BUSHES AND LOWER BRANCHES:

27. Mourning Dove
28. Black- and Yellow-billed Cuckoos
29. Kingbird
30. Acadian Flycatcher
31. Blue Jay
32. Chipping Sparrow
33. Goldfinch
34. Rose-breasted Grosbeak
35. Scarlet Tanager
36. Cedar Waxwing
37. Red-eyed Vireo
38. Blue-headed Vireo
39. Yellow Warbler
40. Magnolia Warbler
41. Myrtle Warbler
42. Redstart
43. Golden-crowned Kinglet
44. Wood Thrush
45. Robin

* Including only the common species of eastern United States. The numbers refer to those on Fig. 88.

(*d*) BIRDS OF THE HIGHER BRANCHES AND TREE-TOPS:

46. Herons, Great Blue and Black-crowned Night
47. Bald Eagle
48. Hawks, Red-shouldered, Red-tailed, Broad-winged, Goshawk, Cooper's and Sharp-shinned, Osprey
49. Olive-sided Flycatcher
50. Wood Pewee
51. Baltimore Oriole
52. Purple Finch
53. Pine Siskin
54. Yellow-throated Vireo
55. Warbling Vireo
56. Cerulean Warbler
57. Black-throated Green Warbler
58. Blackburnian Warbler
59. Pine Warbler

(*e*) BIRDS THAT NEST IN HOLES:

60. Wood Duck
61. Barn Owl
62. Barred Owl
63. Screech Owl
64. Great Horned Owl
65. Woodpeckers—all species
66. Crested Flycatcher
67. Sparrow Hawk
68. Starling
69. House Sparrow
70. Tree Swallow
71. Prothonotary Warbler
72. Carolina Wren
73. Bewick's Wren
74. House Wren
75. Brown Creeper
76. White-breasted Nuthatch
77. Red-breasted Nuthatch
78. Brown-headed Nuthatch
79. Tufted Titmouse
80. Chickadee
81. Bluebird

5

Birds of the Fields and Orchards

Where daisies and buttercups vie with the clover and timothy for possession of the farmer's hay-field, there lives a group of birds quite as distinctive and even more restricted in their distribution than the birds of the Woodlands and Borders which have been discussed in Chapter 4. Some of them, like the Meadowlark and the Bobolink, are known to every farmer's boy, and are as much a part of his life as the hay and the grain and the dusty road to school. But others, less conspicuous, like the Vesper, Savannah, and Grasshopper Sparrows are lumped together by him under the common appellation of 'ground bird.' Still others, like the Henslow's Sparrow, pass entirely unnoticed, their weak voices mingling with the myriad insect notes. There are many birds that are occasionally found in the open fields in search of food or by mere chance, but the ones that make up the 'open-field community' are those that not only get their food there, but also nest there and spend practically their whole lives away from the bushes and trees. Naturally, they often fly to the top of a bush or tree that stands in the field, for it makes a conspicuous singing-place, but a fence-post or a bare telegraph pole suits them just as well, for there is nothing in a tree that is particularly attractive to them. Let us, then, direct our steps along some country road until we get away from houses and barns and bushes and trees and come to the extensive fields of clover and daisies. It will be better if we search out some field that has not been plowed for several years, where the hay is less dense and the 'weeds' more numerous, for this is the type of field that these birds like the best.

As we trudge along the dusty road (and it will be much better if we leave automobiles and paved roads behind us), certain birds will be quite conspicuous. There will be Swallows on the wires, Red-headed Woodpeckers or Flickers on the telephone poles, Kingbirds and Wood Pewees in the apple trees, and Goldfinches on the dandelions by the wayside, but none of these birds belongs to the

community that we are out to study and we pass them by. It is only
when the plaintive whistle of the Meadowlark reaches our ears that
we begin our study of the birds of the open fields. "It's sweet to me,"
he seems to call, and we assume that he means life in the open, and
we are thoroughly willing to agree with him. If we approach the
vicinity of his nest, his note changes and, though still plaintive, it is
only about half as long, as though he were calling to his mate "be-
ware." It is not until we leave that we hear his full song again, and
then it sounds to us as though he were calling "All is well."

One familiar only with the plaintive song of the Meadowlark will
have difficulty in recognizing the various harsh call-notes and a rather
pleasing rattle as originating from the same bird. Ordinarily, the
Meadowlark sings from a fence-post or the top of a tree in the open,
but, occasionally, in a burst of enthusiasm, he mounts upward in the
air on quivering wings and repeats and modulates his song until it
is scarcely recognizable. At such times it resembles more the song
of the Western Meadowlark, which never sings as simple a refrain
as our eastern bird.

It is no easy matter to find the Meadowlark's nest, but the task
grows easier if we have learned the bird's vocabulary, or at least
some of the alarm-notes by which it is possible to guess the general
vicinity of the nest. Then, if we withdraw to a distance, until the
male no longer indicates alarm by his voice, and watch him through
binoculars, he will, sooner or later, fly down to visit his mate at the
nest. Even then, however, it is difficult to find it, for it is roofed over
with grasses and has the opening on one side. I have known careless
persons actually to step on the eggs before discovering the nest.
After the eggs have hatched, the roof does not last long, and by the
time the young are half-grown the nest is usually as open as a Bobolink's or a Vesper Sparrow's.

Examining a Meadowlark in a museum, or observing the bright
yellow breast on any colored plate of the bird, one would think that
this would be a conspicuous mark in the field. On the contrary, one
has to be close to see it, or the bird has to be in full sunlight. At
other times, the yellow is entirely absorbed by the greens and
browns of the grasses, and the bird appears uniformly brownish. It is
the conspicuous white outer tail-feathers that make the best field-
mark, appearing as two square white patches as the bird flies away.

As we approach the daisy field of our choice, a small grayish bird runs ahead of us in the road, awaits our approach, and then flits along a little farther. It is about the size and shape of a Song Sparrow and has the same streaked breast, and a larger spot in the middle, but it is a grayer bird, and when it flies it usually but not always, shows white outer tail-feathers. It is the Vesper Sparrow, one of our birds of the open field. We often find Song Sparrows along the roadside, also, but never far from bushes or brushpiles in which they can take refuge when frightened. The Vesper Sparrow, on the other hand, when alarmed, flies up and away through the open. The songs of the two birds are also somewhat alike, though that of the Vesper

FIG. 89. Meadowlark and its nest.

Sparrow is usually clearer and sweeter and ordinarily begins with two low notes, and then two high notes followed by a trill. It might be expressed by the phrase "Listen to my evening singing." The Song Sparrow's song is less clear, usually begins with three low notes followed by one high, one low, and a trill, and can often be fitted to the phrase "Hip hip hoo-ray, boys, spring is here." There is a third bird that resembles the Song and the Vesper Sparrow in color and markings, the Savannah Sparrow, another of our field birds. It has the same streaked breast with a larger spot in the middle, but its tail is shorter and it has a fairly conspicuous yellow line over the eye and a less conspicuous one below the eyes and through the middle of the crown. Its song, however, is entirely different having more

of an insect quality. It usually begins with two low *tsips* followed
by a high trill and a shorter lower trill which might be represented
tsip, tsip, see, ee, ee, me-ee. The Vesper Sparrow and the Savannah
Sparrow are a good deal alike in habits, both building cup-shaped
nests in slight hollows in the sod, but the Vesper Sparrow usually
prefers more open places in the meadow, often nesting by the roadside where there is some bare ground, while the Savannah as often
as not selects a place in the thick clover.

In addition to the Vesper Sparrow, there is another bird that we
may see running in the roadway ahead of us, the Prairie Horned
Lark. The Lark is somewhat larger than the Vesper Sparrow, less
streaked on the back, and more of a pinkish brown in color. Its most
distinctive characters, however, are the black markings about its face,
the crescent on its breast, the broad bar from the bill to its cheeks,
and the narrow line of feathers bordering the crown, which can be
elevated on either side so as to form tiny 'horns.' The markings are
more conspicuous in the male which, likewise, has a yellower throat.

The Horned Larks are the first birds to come back in the spring
to the northern states, if they have not spent the winter there, often
arriving early in February. By the middle of March they are
often nesting, so that the incubating or even the brooding bird may
get covered by the late snows. The most interesting thing about the
Horned Lark, however, is its habit, in common with the European
Skylark, of soaring. Starting from the ground, often at one's very
feet, the male bird mounts upward on a giant spiral until it is almost
out of sight. Then, as a tiny speck in the blue, it hovers and sings.
The song is not at all comparable with that of the Skylark, made
famous by the poets; indeed, it sounds more like someone climbing
over a wire fence, but the performance which follows is fully as
thrilling as that of its European cousin for, closing its wings, the
Lark plunges headlong towards the earth. Like a plummet it drops,
until one feels sure he will see it dashed to death against the ground.
For hundreds of feet it plunges unchecked; then, within a few feet
of the ground, it spreads its wings, shoots abruptly forward, checking
its momentum, and gracefully alights as though nothing had
happened.

And now we have come to the field, white with daisies and spotted
with black-eyed Susans and devil's paint-brush—a poor hay-field but
a very good place for the birds of the open country. Two or three

Bobolinks are chasing each other about the field, making it resound with riotous song, a grand medley of warbles and banjo-like notes that can be confused with nothing else. The cream and gray and white spots on their upperparts all appear white at a distance and reflect, in turn, the white of the daisies, their black underparts appearing as nought but shadows. We see nothing of the sparrowlike females that are sitting close on their nests, but, if we should, it would pay to watch them until they fly to their homes, for the Bobolink's nest is just as difficult to discover as the Meadowlark's, though it is not roofed over. The thickly spotted eggs are far from conspicuous, especially when the nest is placed in the dense grass or clover. The birds never fly directly to or from their nests, but ordinarily, traverse the 10 to 15 feet nearest the nest on the ground, and out of sight of marauding eyes. So even if you mark exactly the spot where the female flies down, it may take you a half hour to locate the nest.

As we listen to the ecstatic outbursts of the male Bobolinks, it is difficult for us to believe that within a few weeks they will be silent or, at best, announcing their presence by only a metallic *pink,* and that they will change their striking black-and-white suits for the somber clothes of the female. Then, better known as "Ricebirds' or 'Reedbirds,' they will start on a 5,000-mile journey to Brazil and northern Argentina. They seem so devoid of care and so absolutely satisfied with their present environment that one naturally thinks they should stay until the frosts sear the meadows, but, instead, they will scarcely wait until their own young are strong on the wing before flocking to the marshes and starting on their southward flight.

Such a medley of sounds arises from the Bobolinks that we might easily suppose that there were no other inhabitants of the daisy field, but if we can close our ears to their voices, we will soon become aware of many lesser folk adding their bit to the general concert. Were we not already familiar with the song of the Savannah Sparrow, we might attribute all of the tiny trills that we hear to the crickets and grasshoppers; but, having once learned what to listen for, we can soon pick out the songs of three or four of these little short-tailed sparrows, and perhaps locate the birds perched on the tops of some of the taller weeds, their heads thrown back and their little bodies a-quiver with all the enthusiasm of their more musically endowed cousins. If we know just what to listen for, we may be able to pick out the song of a Grasshopper Sparrow among them or off to one side of the field. It is only about half as long as the song of the Savannah Sparrow and of even more insect-like quality, lacking entirely the second and lower trill of that bird, *tsip, tsip, see-eeee*.

If the Grasshopper Sparrow did not sing, or if he sang from the ground, he might never be discovered, so inconspicuous is he; but like all other birds, his song, such as it is, is an announcement to the world and to all other Grasshopper Sparrows that a certain part of the field belongs to him and he will brook no intrusion. Therefore, while making the announcement, he wants to be as conspicuous as possible, and he flies to the tallest weed or fence-post within his territory. At other times, he runs around mouse-like on the ground and is never seen unless flushed, and then but for an instant, for he never flies far before dropping back into the grass. After the nest is started, the male seldom ventures very far from it, so that it is comparatively easy to mark the general location of every nest in a field. It is not so easy to find the nest, however, for it is roofed over like a Meadowlark's, but the whiteness of the eggs catches one's eye much sooner than the eggs of the Savannah Sparrow or those of the Bobolink, which are gray and heavily marked with brown. In most photographs of birds' nests it should be remembered that the vegetation has been pressed aside from the nest so as to make it and the eggs as conspicuous as possible. It seems more than a coincidence, however, that the field birds that lay conspicuous eggs build roofs over their nests.

If one has difficulty in finding the Grasshopper Sparow, he might as well never start hunting for the Henslow's Sparrow, for both in song and habit it is as much less conspicuous than the Grasshopper Sparrow as the Grasshopper is less conspicuous than the Savannah. I have never heard of anyone discovering it for the first time all by himself, though after his attention has been called to it he may discover it in some of his most familiar hunting-grounds. It seems to prefer the oldest and most run-down fields, though occasionally a little colony appears in a good hay-field, along-side of the Savannah and Grasshopper Sparrows. An entomologist listening for unusual insects is more likely to discover this bird than an ornithologist with an ear attuned to bird-voices. *Tisape . . . tisape*, its call sounds to me, usually with quite an interval between the syllables. It is probable each dissyllable *tisape* represents the bird's complete song, and, if so, it is the most unpretentious effort with which I am familiar, comparable only with the voicelessness of the Pelican and Frigate-bird.

After one has learned the song of the Henslow's Sparrow, he will be able to pick out the bird in the field from among the Grasshopper and Savannah Sparrows by its more conspicuous whitish bill and the faint streaks on the sides of the breast, and it will give him no small degree of satisfaction to identify it, though it may not add materially to his esthetic enjoyment of the daisy fields in June.

The nest of the Henslow's Sparrow resembles that of the Savannah, and the eggs are whiter though more heavily spotted than those of the Grasshopper Sparrow.

We have enumerated but seven birds as composing the open-field community and, indeed, they are the most typical members in the northern and eastern states, though we might include the Bobwhite, the introduced Pheasant, the Killdeer, and even the Spotted Sandpiper, were we to list the birds that nest in the fields away from bushes. They spend so much of their lives in other environments, however, that we may well exclude them from this community. Farther south or farther west there would naturally be different members in this community, but whenever one finds the open fields, he will find a circumscribed group of birds designed by nature to live and derive their sustenance therefrom.

The transition from the open fields to the orchard is very abrupt but no more so with its plant life than with its birds.

THE BIRDS OF AN OLD ORCHARD

What bird is it that builds its nest in the orchard? So many times has this question been asked that I am going to try to answer it, partially in reply to the question and partially in an endeavor to add new interest to one of our bird haunts neglected because of its familiarity. In the spring, when the branches are laden with fragrant blossoms and migrating birds flit from flower to flower, no one waits for an invitation to search its recesses for unfamiliar Warblers, but when the petals have fallen and a great sameness comes over the regular rows of trees, we naturally direct our steps toward the more attractive woodlands. It is not until we are gathering fruit in the fall, or until the November storms strip the leaves from the branches and expose the many abandoned birds' nests, that we realize we have missed something, that we have overlooked an opportunity for making pleasant observations at our very doors.

What bird is it that nests in the orchard? It is probably one of about thirty species that regularly nest in orchards in eastern United States, or it may be one of a dozen other tree-nesting birds that some-

FIG. 90. A Flicker at its nest.

times elect orchards for their homes. Most likely, however, if it is a nest that has been merely noticed in passing by an orchard after the leaves have fallen, it belongs to a Robin, or an Oriole, or a Goldfinch, for their nests are the most common and the most conspicuous. Of course the most satisfactory way to identify any bird's nest is to see the bird at its nest, for it permits one to make many more observations than does the mere discovery of the nest after the leaves have fallen. It is not difficult to identify the deserted nests, however, and it makes a very satisfactory class or bird club exercise, for everyone can enter into it and no harm can come to the birds. Furthermore it gives a very good introduction to the orchard and, inasmuch as the same birds tend to return to the same orchard the following year, it prepares one by teaching him where and what to look for the following season. The birds never use the same nests a second season so it does no harm to remove the nests for a school or club collection if desired.

For the sake of convenience in identifying the nests we will divide the orchard birds into six groups: (1) Birds that nest in holes; (2) birds that build hanging nests; (3) birds that build nests containing sticks or twigs; (4) birds that decorate the outside of their nests with bits of lichens; (5) birds that build felted nests of cottony materials; and (6) birds that build nests largely of grasses and straws. We will begin with the birds that nest in holes.

Birds That Nest in Holes

In the modern well-cared-for orchard that is pruned each year and has all dead branches cut out, there are not many places for these birds to nest. The pruning is a desirable practice for the health of the orchard, but it drives away some of the most beneficial birds, so an effort should be made in every orchard to bring them back by putting up bird-boxes to replace the dead branches. In most of the older orchards, however, always enough dead wood appears in the trunks of the trees, where branches have been cut off, to attract the Flickers and Downy Woodpeckers, and they do the carpenter work necessary for the homes of Bluebirds, Nuthatches, Chickadees, Wrens, Crested Flycatchers, Tree Swallows, Screech Owls, and the ever-present Starlings and House Sparrows. Some of their old holes are likewise used by red squirrels, flying squirrels, and deer mice, so that one has plenty of choice in trying to decide what was the last tenant of any hole under observation. The mammals can usually be eliminated, however, by the presence of cherry pits or pieces of nut-shell in the nest, which is usually made entirely of shredded bark.

It is easy to tell whether a Flicker or a Downy Woodpecker excavated the hole in the first place, because the opening made by the Flicker is two inches or more in diameter, while that of the Downy is but one and a half inches. Red-headed, Red-bellied, and Hairy

Woodpeckers make intermediate-sized holes, but they usually confine their operations to larger trees than are found in an orchard. None of the Woodpeckers builds a nest at the bottom of the hole, but merely lays its eggs on the bare chips. If any nesting material is found, it indicates that some other bird has usurped the hole. If there are a lot of sticks or twigs entering into the make-up of the nest, one can rest assured it was made by a House Wren. If it is made entirely of dried grasses, it is probably a Bluebird's; if it contains a cast snake's skin, it is probably a Crested Flycatcher's, and if it contains only a few straws and a few feathers, it is probably a Tree Swallow's nest. If the nest is made of moss and wool and bits of bark, it is a Chickadee's or a Nuthatch's, although the latter bird more often nests in a natural cavity of greater size where there is plenty of room for a large family. Starlings and House Sparrows build rather bulky nests in the cavities, usually made of yellowish straws and feathers, those of the House Sparrow being roofed when fresh. If one finds a lot of feathers at the bottom of the hole and no other nesting material except perhaps a few pellets of bones and fur, he can rest assured that a Screech Owl has been occupying the cavity and that the fur and feathers are remains from his victims. There is a certain romance surrounding every hole in a tree and a fascination to the work of discovering what bird made it and who have been its occupants.

Birds That Build Hanging Nests

A hanging nest is usually one that is supported only at the rim, with the bottom hanging free. Only the Orioles and Vireos build this type of nest, in Eastern United States those of the Vireos being much smaller than those of the Orioles, and less than two inches deep on the inside. The two Orioles' nests are very different, that of the Baltimore Oriole being made of strings, yarn, milkweed fiber, etc., while that of the Orchard Oriole is made of dried grasses. The nest of the Orchard Oriole might almost not be considered a hanging nest, as the bottom often rests against a branch, though it is supported almost entirely at the rim. The three Vireos' nests that are likely to be found in an orchard are practically indistinguishable as to structure, but they are usually placed in different parts of the tree. The Red-eyed Vireo builds near the tips of the lowest branches, the Warbling Vireo goes to the outer extremities of the uppermost branches, and the Yellow-throated Vireo usually hangs its nest in a forked twig fairly close to the trunk or larger branches of the tree, somewhere near the middle.

Birds That Build Nests Containing Sticks or Twigs

Occasionally Crows or Green Herons build their large stick nests in orchards, but such instances are so unusual that they are negligible. The Heron's nest is flat and without any lining, while the Crow's is deep and well lined. Of the smaller nests, the Blue Jay's is the

Fig. 91. A Goldfinch at its nest.

largest and bulkiest, being over three and a half inches inside diameter. It is deeply hollowed, as is also the Migrant Shrike's. Indeed the two nests resemble each other closely, but the Shrike's is less than three and a half inches, inside diameter and usually contains woolly material in the lining, a substance seldom found in the Blue Jay's nest which is ordinarily lined with rootlets. Nests of the Mourning Dove and of the Black- and Yellow-billed Cuckoos are likewise built of twigs and are frequently in orchards, the Dove's more often than the Cuckoos'. All three nests are mere platforms of twigs very slightly hollowed, and the Dove's nest has practically no lining of rootlets or leaves. The Cuckoos' nests can be distinguished from the Dove's by the lining of leaves or rootlets, but I have as yet found no good way of distinguishing the nests of the two Cuckoos.

Birds That Decorate Their Nests with Lichens

There are but two orchard birds that fall into this group, the Ruby-throated Hummingbird and the Wood Pewee, and their nests are very different. That of the Hummingbird is about the size of a walnut and made of cotton or plant down, with a complete covering of lichens or bits of moss; that of the Pewee is about three inches in outside diameter, very shallow, and built of bark fibers and rootlets, with a scattered covering of lichens. Both are beautiful structures and well worth any effort to find them. In the southern states the Blue-gray Gnatcatcher sometimes builds its lichen-covered nest in an orchard. The nest resembles a Hummingbird's but is larger.

Birds That Build Felted Nests of Cottony Materials

Here belong the Goldfinch, the Yellow Warbler, and the Least Flycatcher. The Redstart that builds a nest like the Yellow Warbler, but thinner at its upper margin, seldom ventures into the orchard to nest. The Goldfinch's nest is distinguishable from the others by the fact that it is always wider than it is high, outside measurements, while the Yellow Warbler's and Least Flycatcher's are higher than wide. The Goldfinches nest late and always use thistledown in the lining, but this material is not ready for the earlier-nesting Warbler and Flycatcher. It is more difficult to distinguish the nests of the Warbler and the Flycatcher, but the former usually selects forks of vertical branches, while the latter saddles its nest on a horizontal branch and usually adds bits of paper to the outside of the nest as no law-abiding Yellow Warbler would do.

Birds That Build Nests Largely of Grasses and Rootlets

There are two divisions of this group: those like the Robin, Wood Thrush, and Grackle that always employ a middle layer of mud in shaping their nests, and those like the Kingbird, Cedar Waxwing, and Chipping Sparrow that never use mud. Of the first group, the Wood Thrush and Grackle do not ordinarily nest in orchards in most parts of the country and need not usually enter into consideration. Where they do, the nest of the Grackle can be distinguished by its larger size, being over four inches inside diameter, the others being less. The Wood Thrush's nest can be distinguished by the presence of dead leaves and usually moss clinging to the bottom of it. Of course the Robin's nest is everywhere the most abundant, and practically every nest found in the orchard that contains an inner layer of mud is a Robin's.

Of the other nests built of grasses and rootlets, the Chipping Sparrow's is the smallest and can always be distinguished by a horsehair lining. The Kingbird's and Cedar Waxwing's nests are much alike, both containing little horsehair but usually with some woolly material woven into the grasses and rootlets. The Waxwing's nest is usually smaller and deeper, being about an inch and a half deep, while the Kingbird's measures but an inch in inside depth. The Waxwing's nest usually has some loose yellowish grasses hanging from the bottom, while the Kingbird's is more compact. Occasionally the Rose-breasted Grosbeak and the Scarlet Tanager nest in orchards and their nests resemble the Cedar Waxwing's except that they never contain the woolly materials found in the latter. The Grosbeak's nest is never as well made as the Tanager's, usually having no apparent lining, while the Tanager's is well lined.

Some nests preserve their shape much better than others and frequently one finds the remains of nests that only an expert can identify. At times the lining blows out of a Robin's nest or the rains cause it to settle until it appears as large as a Grackle's. Young Yellow Warblers will sometimes trample down the sides of their nest until it becomes shaped like a Goldfinch's, or only the basal twigs of a Blue Jay's or a Shrike's nest that has blown out of place may remain in the tree and give the appearance of a Mourning Dove's nest. Only well-preserved nests should be saved for the collection and these should be reinforced by sewing them to the branch with black thread or fine copper wire. The Cornell University study collection of birds' nests is kept in metal drawers twelve inches square and four inches deep. The nests are fastened to the branches so that they will not pull loose, and the branch holding the nest is fastened to a heavy card that snugly fits the bottom of the drawer. Whenever it is impossible to preserve the branch on account of its size, or when the nest has been built on the rocks like a Phoebe's, the nest is fastened directly to the card. In the case of ground-nesting birds, a strip of cardboard two or three inches wide is circled about the nest, the overlapping edges fastened with adhesive tape, and the cup fastened to the card in the same manner. Most of the drawers contain but a single nest, but some contain several small ones which are obviously advantageous to have together for comparison, as in the case of the Vireos. The nests are arranged in the order of the A.O.U. Checklist except when an exceptionally large nest, like a Crow's, has to be kept elsewhere and its place marked by a dummy.

6

Bird Communities

BIRDS OF THE MARSHES AND SHORES

Birds of the Marshes

There are some who shun the marshes as the abode of snakes and fever, the haunt of naught but evil, and to them the strange voices which come from its unknown depths are uncanny. The rhythmic waving of the sedges, the cold breezes at evening, and the blackness of its waters portend no good. But there are others who have spent hours wading through its dense growth; who know when the pickerel run and the bullheads nest; who know when the Mallard, the Widgeon, and the Pintail circle over its ponds, and who know in which hollow elm the Wood Duck nests. They know how the Redwing hangs its home and where to find the Coot and the Rail. They have looked into its dark pools and seen the caddice worm carrying its case and have watched the dragonfly nymph stalk its prey. Lucky few who know the marshland and therefore love it!

Early in March when the ice has scarcely thawed from its flooded surface, before the pike have begun to splash and before any birds have come, the notes of a sun-warmed peeper announce that spring is on its way. And next, from out of the clear blue sky comes the low sweet chuckle of the first Bluebird; the joyful 'gurgle-lee' of the Redwing greets one's ears, and towards dusk the wild ducks fly in narrowing circles and alight with a splash among the brown flags. The Geese go honking overhead in a great wedge, and then comes the spring. Each evening great flocks of migrating Redwings settle like smoke into the dried flags and each morning they depart for northern marshes, males first by themselves, and two weeks later the females. All night the shrill notes of the peepers fill the air with a deafening chorus. The yelping of the wood frogs and the lower pulsating choir of the meadow frogs announce that soon the waters will be teeming with tadpoles. The first dragonfly darts after some luckless gnat that has seen fit to transform so early and a small flock of Tree Swallows comes skimming from the south. Let us wait until the middle of April, however, before we don our high boots and start through the marsh, for from that time until the first of June the marsh is at its best.

Fig. 92. Male Marsh Hawk and its nest in the cat-tails.

The earliest cat-tails and water dock have now reached the surface of the water and give the first greenness to the marsh. Large ponds mark where the sedges will later appear for they are slower in starting and the winter fires have left not even a brown stalk to show above the surface. The marsh resounds with the music of the Redwings and many strange calls emanate from tangled places that one is eager to explore. A great liquid call comes from a matted patch of sedges at the edge of the marsh. "Ooble-oob, ooble-oob," like water being poured from a huge jug, these notes preceded by a tapping sound like striking a stake with a mallet. It is the Bittern and, if we are fortunate, we may be able to stalk him and catch him at his work, though more likely we will almost step on him, so inconspicuous is he in his brown plumage. As the tapping starts again one may see his gulping contortions as first he claps his bill and then makes the motions of swallowing with great difficulty, but he never puts his bill beneath the water as is sometimes stated. As one approaches closer, the strange bird instead of flying immediately, may stretch up his long neck and point his long bill toward the zenith, simulating a broken snag projecting from the water. If he is among the brown sedges, he will be practically invisible because his neck is striped with brown and buff and resembles the lights and shadows of the dead vegetation. If one tries to circle about him, he slowly rotates so as to present always his striped neck, but finally frightened, he springs clumsily into the air and sails off across the marsh, gradually drawing his head back on his shoulders and trailing his long legs behind after the manner characteristic of all Herons.

As he disappears from sight a splashing in the water may attract one's attention to a spot where the pike are spawning. The dorsal fins of the huge fish can be seen above the surface as, side by side, they swim back and forth scattering their eggs. They came up from the lake when the ice melted, and they will return when their labors are completed. Big fellows they are, some of them weighing ten to fifteen pounds, and if one remains quiet they may swim so close as to show their broad flat snouts, the snaky yellow markings in their dorsal fins, and the small white spots on their sides. Many times in one's journey through the marsh he will be startled by a great splash almost under his feet as he frightens one of these large fish from its hiding place, and he will be able to follow its wake as it zigzags through the flags.

Numerous spherical bunches of frogs' eggs, held up from the bottom on slender reeds or brush, and tangled, yarn-like strings of toads' eggs are everywhere conspicuous, and the jubilant trills of the toads themselves announce that their breeding season is not yet over though many of the frogs have left the marsh. There are many other sounds, almost as incessant, that one may long be at a loss to explain.

From a tangled mat of brown cat-tails comes a peculiar grinding sound as though someone were gritting his teeth. This is followed by a clicking noise much like an old-fashioned sewing machine, and then out of the top of the flags bursts a little brown ball. Floating upward like a tuft of cotton, it breaks into vivacious music and then drops back into hiding to continue its scolding. It is the Long-billed Marsh Wren and if one remains quiet, its inquisitiveness soon overcomes its timidity and it runs up a reed to get a closer view of the intruder, carrying its tail cocked forward over its back in most impish fashion. Again it floats upward, all its feathers fluffed out and its short wings vibrating so rapidly that they are scarcely noticed. The cause for all this excitement we are not long in discovering, for hung conspicuously among the dead flags is a ball of brown sedge leaves with an opening on one side. Always busy, always mischievous,

Fig. 93. Long-billed Marsh Wren at its nest.

the little Wren has already completed one nest and will doubtless build several more before his mate arrives, but when she does come, she will spurn them all and start a new one of her own.

As one watches the Wren one may be surprised by a loud call on the far side of the tangle: "Ticket, ticket, ticket, ticket," as though an admission fee were to be charged before one could see further secrets of the marsh. It is one of the notes of the Virginia Rail but it will take some careful stalking before one sees the slender dark brown bird with a rather long reddish bill sneaking between the cat-tails, its short tail cocked up, like a tiny brown hen's. It is difficult to make the Rail fly unless it is cornered, and even then it may dodge back between one's feet rather than trust itself on its somewhat feeble wings.

A little later one may be startled by loud clucking sounds, and then a terrific "Wup-Pup-Pup-Pup-pup-pup-pup" announces the presence of a Florida Gallinule or 'water chicken,' a bird about the size of a small bantam, slaty black in color except for its bill and legs. The bill is set off by a large red plate on the forehead and a greenish tip, while the green legs are trimmed with little red bands like garters. White feathers under the tail and white streaks on the flanks usually pass unnoticed, but when the bird is startled, especially with its young, they are made very conspicuous.

Occasionally one may hear a call that begins like the Gallinule's, but ends with almost plaintive cooing. "Wup-Pup-Pup-Pup-pup-pup-pup-caow-caow-caow-caow," it floats across the marsh and it will probably be a long time before one associates the call with the obscure, timid bird we know as the Pied-billed Grebe or 'hell-diver.' It is a little early yet to look for its floating nest and even later, when the bird is incubating, it will be almost impossible to find it, so much does it resemble the small platforms of débris thrown up by muskrats, for the mother bird always covers her eggs before leaving the nest so that passing enemies will not find them.

The Redwinged Blackbirds are scolding everywhere, and one expects to find many of their nests. It is still too early, however, for, although it is a month and a half since the first Redwings were seen, the females that are to nest in this marsh are just arriving and the males are welcoming them. Whenever a female in her streaked coat appears, she is pursued by several males, now close against the water, now high in the air, as though they must display to her their strength of wing. Again, several males may be seen mounting upwards for hundreds of feet, then hovering there on suspended wings like so many skylarks, finally floating back to the marsh with feathers ruffled and epaulets flaming.

It is too early also to hear the whinny of the Sora Rail or the soft cooing of the Least Bittern that will add their charm in May. Nor do the borders of the marsh yet echo the witchery call of the Yellowthroat. But the marsh is a glorious place to be on one of these warm spring days, especially in the morning or towards dusk when one is almost overwhelmed with the abundance of life. And even during the night the marsh dwellers are far from quiet. The frogs and toads maintain a sonorous accompaniment to the varied calls of the birds. The spasmodic notes from excited Swamp Sparrows and the weird calls from startled Rails and Gallinules mingle with the almost incessant chatter of the Marsh Wrens until long after midnight. Then all is quiet for a few hours, but long before the first signs of dawn the activity begins once more. By four o'clock the Song Sparrows are singing about the border of the marsh and a few minutes later the Swamp Sparrows begin their sweet twitter. The stars are still bright when a Short-eared Owl gives its peculiar call and is dimly seen as it circles near. The Sparrows continue to sing for half an hour before the first Bittern sounds it liquid notes. Then the Gulls begin to gabble on the lake, and ten minutes later the Wilson's Snipes begin to bleat and a strange winnowing sound pulsates across the marsh as they perform their aerial evolutions.

It is now three quarters of an hour since the first Sparrow sang, the morning star has sunk below the horizon, and the first signs of dawn have appeared. The Gulls start up the valley for their daily foraging in the fields, and the first Redwing is heard. As though awaiting the signal, hundreds of birds give answer and day is proclaimed. The stars die out and color appears in the east: the greens and yellows change to rose, and the rose to red. A Great Blue Heron leaves his roost in the woods and starts for his fishing grounds. A pair of Teal swing across the field of vision, dark against the sky. A few restless Grackles start up from the marsh, heading for the uplands, and soon the morning flight of Redwings begins. Scattering over the marsh, they do not leave in the compact flocks that are so characteristic of the evening flight. Single birds, more uneasy than the rest, loose groups of seven or eight, and at times slightly larger flocks fly towards the hills to the east and to the west. By eight o'clock most of the Redwings have left, and two hours later one would scarcely know there had been a Redwing in the marsh. If we have spent the night near the marsh, we are content now to leave, for we have experienced one of the most stirring phenomena that nature has to offer. When thousands of other experiences crowd into our lives and dim our memories, one picture will retain its freshness: it will be spring on the marshes and the awakening of the birds.

Let us visit the marsh again in October when the Wild Ducks are coming down from the north.

Flock after flock comes from the north, most of them flying high, and apparently bent only on getting south as quickly as possible before the shallow ponds freeze over. At first so far away that they appear like a thin wisp of smoke against the hurrying clouds, they come on swiftly beating wings, until in a moment they pass overhead and then disappear into the bank of clouds at the south. Very often they are flying low enough so that one hears their wings whistle and can see enough of their color pattern to satisfy himself as to their species. Usually they are silent, but occasionally they answer the calls of their fellows who are feeding in the ponds below, and then it is a great delight to see them break rank and circle over the marsh, trying to make up their minds that they want to delay their journey long enough to refill their capacious crops.

They seem to know well that many of the voices that they hear and the Ducks that they see are not to be trusted and they must therefore determine that all is safe before they descend to the water. Around the marsh they go in great circles, sometimes so low that it seems they must alight, but, just as often, something alarms them and they climb upward again. Three or four times they circle and then, coming up into the wind, they set their wings and start the descent. With wings strongly arched, they drop downward, swinging first to one side of the pond and then to the other until, when about twenty feet from the water, they begin to back-peddle with their wings. Their bodies come to a vertical position, they drop their legs, spreading their webbed toes and their tails at the same time to ease their descent, and, with a big splash, they land in the water. For a few moments they are silent and stretch up their necks to make sure that all is well, and then they begin to talk. One who thinks of Ducks as only quacking will be surprised at the variety of sounds that have to be classified under the one word.

The Mallards and Black Ducks are vociferous in their expressions and their voices are real quacks, the females' louder and more rapid, the males' lower, more subdued, and slower in their repetitions. The Teal have high nasal voices and the Balpates explosive ones, while the cries of the female Wood Ducks resemble nothing more than the midnight wail of a sick baby. Although the voices of the male and female Mallards and Black Ducks are much alike, the males of other species have calls entirely different from those of the females. Drakes of the Pintail and Teal, for example, utter peeping whistles almost like the little tree toads called 'peepers,' the male Baldpate calls *whew-whew,* and the male Wood Ducks cry *hoo-eek-hoo-eek.* In the fall, however, the majority of Ducks are quite silent until after dark, at which time the marshes often resound with their quackings and other varied notes.

It is the Geese that are noisy during their flights, and one can often hear them honking before he can make out the form of their flock. In great wedges they go over, sometimes a hundred or more strong, but usually from six or seven to thirty or forty. And such a racket as a hundred Geese can make, all talking at once! It sounds as though they were all disagreeing as to who should be leader or which way they should go but, nevertheless, they keep to their regular form and disturb not even the rhythm of their wing-beats. They seem to be in no hurry, their bodies rising and falling with the measured strokes of their great wings, and yet it is but a moment before they, too, have disappeared into the clouds and one hears only the faint echo of their voices.

There are other water birds migrating, too. Loons, nearly as big as the Canada Geese, pass over in very scattered flocks, each one, apparently, taking no notice of the others, forty or fifty birds taking up half a square mile of the sky. Cormorants, looking like huge black Ducks with rather long tails, may file by in long lines, flying with rather slow beats of the wings or with alternate flapping and sailing. Yellow-legs and Black-bellied Plover, the last of the season, may wheel by, their wild whistles in full keeping with the spirit of the day. But let us take our stand near some large pond where we can get a closer view of such Ducks as may decide to stop off on their journey and linger to feed for a few hours.

It is seldom that wild Ducks permit the close approach that one enjoys with the land-birds, and one must learn, therefore, to identify them at greater distances. It is only where they have been fed and protected for years that they lose their inherent wildness and fear of man, and approach so close that one can see all their markings in detail. But it is the charm of their wildness that makes their study so inviting, so we conceal ourselves and await their coming. But movement more than anything else attracts their attention and alarms them, so we must be careful about raising our glasses or even turning our heads when they are close, and particularly when they are circling over the marsh before dropping in. Often have I sat motionless in a perfectly exposed place and had the wild Ducks drop into the water within a short distance of me, only to jump with alarm when the slightest motion on my part attracted their attention to me. Indeed, I have had even the wary Black Ducks eating corn from my 'coat tail,' oblivious to my presence so long as I was perfectly quiet. Therefore, whenever the Ducks come at all close to us, in whatever position they find us, we will remain perfectly motionless until they are well past us or, obviously, looking the other way.

In the beginning it is well to learn the three types of Ducks for it makes the identification within each group so much easier. First, there are the Mergansers, or Fish Ducks, or Sawbills, as they are locally known. They have rather long, narrow bills and crested heads, and in flight seem somewhat long and slender of body. Like the diving Ducks, their legs are attached rather far back and they have difficulty in rising from the water, usually 'skittering' along the surface for a short distance. There are but three species in North America, and only the little Hooded Merganser is likely to be found about the marshes, the American and Red-breasted preferring the larger bodies of water or the rivers where fish are more abundant. In October, the males have usually not yet come into breeding plumage, and all three species, males and females alike, are colored the same, having reddish brown heads, gray backs, and white underparts, the two larger species with conspicuous white patches in their wings.

The second group, called the diving Ducks, include the Canvasback, the Redhead, the two Scaups, the Golden-eye, the Bufflehead, the Ring-necked Duck, the Old Squaw, the three Scoters, the three Eiders and the curious little Ruddy Duck. Most of them, like the Mergansers, prefer the larger bodies of water, where they sometimes assemble in huge 'rafts' or flocks of hundreds or even thousands of birds. They feed by diving in deep water for molluscs or aquatic plants, and being less disturbed by the early freezes, they often do not migrate until late in the season. During the latter part of October, however, large flocks of Lesser Scaups, Redheads, Whistlers, and Scoters will be moving and the first of the Canvasbacks are likely to be seen. They do not often stop in a marsh, however, unless it happens to be an estuary from some larger body of water, and we will have to content ourselves with making a guess as to their identity as they pass overhead. All of them have relatively stout bodies and short necks, and their wings are shorter than those of the dabbling Ducks.

The Golden-eyes will be the easiest to identify, for even if they do not fly close enough for us to see the large white patches in their wings, we will be able to hear the whistling sound made by the air rushing through their spread primaries as they rapidly fan the air. This has given them the name of Whistlers by which they are better known in most places. No one has ever discovered a reason why their primaries should spread more than those of other Ducks on the down stroke of the wings, but a study of flight photographs will show that they do, and certainly the whistling of their wings is much louder than with any other species.

The Redheads, Scaups, Ringnecks, and even the Canvasbacks will look much alike to us as they fly overhead, their dark heads, black breasts, and white underparts giving the same color pattern to all four. The Redheads tend to fly in closer formation than the others, and the Canvasbacks often form a V, like the Geese, but these characteristics cannot always be depended upon. The Scoters will appear very black as they go over, darker even than Black Ducks, and, of course, much heavier-bodied and shorter-necked because they are divers, while the Blacks are dabblers. Some of the Scoters will have white in their wings, indicating that the are White-winged Scoters, but the American and Surf Scoters will look just alike from beneath. Young Scoters can be told from the old ones by their lighter underparts, some being very light on the belly.

If Oldsquaws are migrating we cannot miss them because of the striking pattern and the long tail-feathers of the males. From beneath they will appear snowy white, with dark wings and with a broad band of black across the breast. Even the females are quite distinctive with their white underparts and dark wings, though they lack the ornaments of the males. The little Buffleheads and the Ruddy Ducks we are likely to mistake for Teal unless we realize the plumpness of their bodies, for they are much stockier than the Teal, though about the same size, and have none of the lightness and grace of flight characteristic of the latter.

It is the dabbling Ducks that are most likely to circle the marsh and drop into the pond before us—Black Ducks, Mallards, Baldpates, Blue- and Green-winged Teal, Shovelers, Pintails, and Wood Ducks. The Black Ducks and Mallards are the largest and usually the most numerous, though at times the Pintails are nearly as abundant. Unfortunately for ease in identication, males and females of most

Ducks, except the Black Ducks, are very different in their color patterns and the females of all are much alike. To add to the difficulties, by October, only the male Mallards and Wood Ducks have come into their bright plumages and the other males all resemble their females. One might just as well learn the females in the beginning by their size and shape and what few marks they have and then he will be prepared to identify any Duck that he sees.

The Black Ducks and the Wood Ducks will appear the darkest, all of the others being more of a yellowish or rusty brown, while these two appear blackish brown. The white belly and longer tail distinguish the Wood Duck in any plumage, and the silvery white linings of the wings, seen against the blackish body, will always distinguish the Black Duck in flight. Females of the Mallard, Pintail, and Shoveler are all much alike in their streaked rusty brown feathers, the best field characters being the whitish outer tail-feathers of the Mallard, the slender neck and pointed tail of the Pintail, and the broad bill of the Shoveler. The two species of Teal are so much smaller that they will be confused with nothing but each other, and on the water they are almost identical except for size, the Green-wing being somewhat smaller. In flight, the Blue-wing usually shows its pale bluish 'shoulders,' which appear almost white at a distance. Both male and female Baldpates can be distinguished from the other dabbling Ducks by the conspicuous white patches in their wings, those of the male being very pronounced. They likewise differ in not being streaked, the brown of the breast and flanks being of a peculiar uniform cocoa shade.

There is one other dabbling Duck, common in the western parts of the Mississippi Valley but rather rare in the East—the Gadwall. The female Gadwall is one of the most difficult ducks to identify in the field, resembling a slender female Mallard with pinkish edging to the bill.

It is fascinating to watch the Ducks circling the marsh. One forgets all about the weather, or else hopes for more wind and more snow so that even more Ducks will come down from the north. Once on the water it is interesting to watch them feed, tipping up in the shallow water, 'standing' on their heads and pushing with their feet. The dabbling Ducks do not like to dive unless necessary, though, when driven to it, they can do it very neatly. So they push and strain to reach the bottom by tipping, sometimes sending up jets of water from their feet when they push a little too hard. Suddenly something alarms them. Up go their heads, their necks straight as pokers, and they begin edging away from the spot where they have been feeding, trying to locate the source of alarm. If they see trouble coming, up they go, straight into the air 30 to 40 feet before making off in one direction or another. How differently do the diving Ducks behave under similar circumstances! Any sudden alarm causes them to dive, and they come to the surface 40 to 50 feet away, and apparently are flying when they come up. But they cannot rise straight into the air like the dabblers; they must 'skitter' along the surface until they gather enough momentum to rise, and they do not rise high until they have covered a considerable distance. The dabbling Ducks leave a few widening circles to mark the spot they have left, the divers, a long wake.

Of course, it is not necessary to pick out the coldest and most bleak day of October or November to study Ducks. There are Ducks to be found in the marshes throughout October and most of November, though not in such large numbers. Early in the morning and just at dusk they get up and fly around, so that these are the best times to watch them. And always bear this in mind, if the weather in town seems very disagreeable, for those of us who are down on the marsh, it's a fine day for ducks.

If the waters in the marsh have receded leaving the bare mud exposed we may be greeted by an entirely different assemblage of birds from the ducks we have been watching, for over its moist surface are innumerable tiny insects, fresh water shrimps, and the like, that attract the Shorebirds. If the waters in the marsh remain high we will have to make for the seashore, or the lakeshore, or for any extensive low-lying mud-flat that the drought of summer has recently left exposed, for there we will find birds in abundance. We will not choose the bathing-beaches, nor yet the rocky shores, but rather the muddy, oozy areas that are shunned by most people as unsightly and uninteresting. There, running along windrows of seaweed, chasing the receding waves, or making tracks in the soft mud are troops of charming little Sandpipers and Plovers. To the casual observer they all look alike except that some are larger than others. Indeed, even to the real bird observer, trained in the ways of Warblers and Sparrows, they constitute a post-graduate course in bird-study. One need not expect, therefore, to recognize them all the first season. Many of them may pass unrecognized for years until familiarity with the commoner species leads one to scrutinize them more closely and pick out from their very midst species that had previously been unsuspected.

Early in August, many of the returning shore birds will still be wearing some of their spring feathers and can be identified more easily than later on in their fall plumages, when all are clad in varying shades of gray or brown, and when even the Spotted Sandpiper has lost his spots.

As early as the last of June or first of July, some of the Sandpipers start back from their summer homes in the far North, and even where there are no mud-flats to attract them, they can frequently be heard on cloudy nights calling as they pass overhead on their long journeys. By the middle of July, numbers of them have congregated on favorable feeding-areas, even as far south as Virginia, and by the first week of August the migration is in full swing and suitable spots throughout the United States and Canada teem with them. Naturally, some species migrate later than others and some have much more extended migration periods. Seldom, for example, do Redbacked Sandpipers become common in the United States before October, while Sanderlings and Semipalmated Plover may be found from early August until late October. All of the shore birds are great travelers, often flying long distances over the open sea. Regularly, for example, do the Golden Plover fly from Labrador to northern South America, and their western cousins from Alaska to Hawaii, apparently in a single flight, distances of from 2,500 to 3,000 miles. Some of the shore-birds winter along our Gulf Coast, but the majority continue their journeys to northern South America, and some wander to Chile, Argentina, or even to Patagonia.

But let us stand on the nearest shore or mud-flat for a study of shore birds. Perhaps we are already familiar with the Killdeer Plover and the Spotted Sandpiper because they have been with us throughout the summer. At any rate they are good birds to begin with so that we can learn to distinguish quickly between a Plover and a Sandpiper. The most obvious difference, aside from coloration, is the shorter, heavier bill of the Plover, which is somewhat swollen towards the tip. Differences in bills are not always conspicuous but they play such an important part in the identification of shore-birds that we must train our eyes to appreciate them. Of course, the Killdeer does not resemble the Spotted Sandpiper in the least except that both have long legs, for it is brown above while the Sandpiper is grayish olive. Moreover, the Killdeer has two conspicuous black bands across its snowy breast and a white ring around its neck, and it is not forever teetering like the Spotted Sandpiper, though it does occasionally jerk his head. It is this habit of teetering that has given the Spotted Sandpiper many of its local names like 'tip-up' and 'teeter-tail.' The name 'Spotted' Sandpiper is a misnomer in the fall for, while the spots are conspicuous enough on the breast in the spring, when we look for them during August and September we focus our glasses in vain for they are lost during the post-nuptial

Fig. 94. A Killdeer scolding.

molt. The young birds, as well, are without them until the following spring.

There are other birds that resemble the Killdeer much more than does the Spotted Sandpiper, of which the Ring-necked or Semipalmated Plover is by far the commonest. Indeed, this species is a miniature edition of the Killdeer, with the exception that it has but one band across its breast instead of two. The Piping Plover is similar to the Ring-neck but much paler and is almost unknown, except along the Atlantic coast and the shores of the Great Lakes. The larger Golden and Black-bellied Plovers are much more Sand-piper-like in their fall plumage than any of the Killdeer group for they have the same checkered gray and black and white backs typical of so many of the Sandpipers. Especially might they be confused with the Yellow-legs if only coloration were considered, but, fortunately, they have the typical Plover bill and the larger heads and heavier bodies that go with it, while Yellow-legs have the long, pointed bills and the lithe bodies typical of the Sandpipers. The two Plovers resemble each other very closely, especially in the late fall, when there is little yellow left in the plumage of the Golden, and when the black under parts of both species have been replaced by white or whitish. The best field marks are the smokier underparts of the Golden Plover and the black axillars (under the wing) of the Black-bellied Plover that show in flight.

The notes of the different Plovers are exceedingly characteristic but much more difficult to transcribe to paper than they are to imitate by a whistle. Plovers always respond to a whistled imitation of their calls and, when not frightened, will often circle time and again over one's head, searching for the source of the notes. The Killdeer derives its name from its high-pitched *kill-dee, kill-dee,* but it has several shorter notes and a rolling twitter that are used to express different feelings. The Semipalmated Plover has a very mellow, liquid call that might be represented by the syllables *to-where,* the second slightly higher pitched, and the Piping Plover has a series of liquid peeping notes. The Black-bellied Plover has the wildest note of any, a loud clear questioning whistle of three slurred notes that seem to ask the question 'where-are-you?' a question that is best answered about daybreak some stormy morning in late October when the approach of winter drives down the last big wave of Plover and Yellow-legs along with the hurrying flocks of Teal and Pintail.

The identification of the Sandpipers is not as simple as that of the Plovers but it is greatly facilitated by knowing one species well. If one can always recognize the Spotted Sandpiper at sight, in flight or at rest, in spring plumage or fall, and has learned all of its various call-notes, he is in a fair way to learn to know all the species. One should not rely entirely upon its teetering to identiy it, but should recognize its characteristic 'quivering' flight as well, and should see the two narrow gray lines that cross each wing. He should be able to distinguish its call of *weet-weet,* as it takes flight, from the similar *peet-tweet* of the Solitary Sandpiper, and should never forget its sweet twitter, *wee-weet-weet-weet-weet* given with the rising inflection, or *weeta-weet-weeta-weet-weeta-weet* with the accent on the *weet.* The

Spotted Sandpipers are rather solitary, never gathering in large flocks like most of the other species; prefer fresh water to salt, and they are found frequently on small streams as well as about lake-shores or mud-flats. In this respect they resemble the Solitary Sandpiper, a bird that is often overlooked though it passes through in considerable numbers during May and again during July and August. The Solitary is about the only species that one finds around woodland pools, most shore birds preferring exposed beaches. It is frequently attracted to the shores with other Sandpipers, however, though it usually keeps by itself. It resembles the Spotted Sandpiper more than it does its closer relatives, the Yellowlegs, but it is a trifle larger and darker, has a spotted back, a white eye-ring, and shows conspicuous white on its outer tail feathers, like a Meadowlark when it takes flight.

The Greater and Lesser Yellowlegs resemble each other like the Hairy and Downy Woodpeckers, almost feather for feather, both being gray above spotted with white, and white below with light streaks on the sides of the breast and with conspicuous white tails and rumps. It is often easier to identify one of these birds by its call than by its size when there is nothing to compare it with, the call of the Lesser Yellowlegs consisting of but two or three clear flute-like whistles while that of the Greater Yellowlegs is usually of four or five similar but louder notes. A bird that is overlooked by many experienced bird students because it so closely resembles the Lesser Yellowlegs is the Stilt Sandpiper. It is really a trifle smaller and has a more pronounced white line over the eye. Adults have darker legs and slightly barred flanks but these differences are not visible on the immature birds. The call-note of the Stilt Sandpiper is not so full and clear as the Yellowlegs', resembling more that of the Solitary Sandpiper.

The most abundant and the smallest of the Sandpipers that trot along the beaches are of two species, the Least and the Semipalmated. They are appreciably smaller than the Spotted Sandpiper and never engage in teetering. The Least Sandpiper has a brower back, greener legs and a somewhat slighter bill that one soon learns to recognize. They often occur together in flocks, making the difference noticeable, but sometimes the Leasts feed farther back from the water's edge on the drift or in the sparse vegetation. The difference in the notes of the two species is about as great as the difference in their bills, that of the Semipalmated being heavier or hoarser. The two birds collectively are known as 'Sand-peeps' and are familiar sights along the beaches from July until October, sometimes assembling in flocks of several hundred birds.

Slightly larger than the Semipalmated Sandpiper, and very much whiter, is the Sanderling, conspicuous because of its nearly pure white head and large white patches in its wings. It prefers the sandy beaches where it often associates with the Semipalmated and becomes very tame.

About the size of the Sanderling, but marked more like a Semipalmated, is the White-rumped Sandpiper which differs, however, in having a few indistinct streaks on its breast and a conspicuous white bar above its tail in flight. It, likewise, sometimes assembles in large flocks by itself but is more often discovered mixed in with other species. The Baird's Sandpiper is less common in eastern North America and would ordinarily pass for a White-rumped in the fall. The middle of the rump is not white, however, and the breast is more thickly streaked so as to appear almost like a band. The Red-backed Sandpiper (Dunlin) is likewise very similar in its fall plumage but can always be distinguished by its slightly decurved bill. Somewhat larger than any of these birds, and much browner on the back and with its throat and breast heavily streaked with brown, is the Pectoral Sandpiper or 'Grass Snipe' or 'Krieker' as it is variously known. Its back pattern and its method of flight are somwehat similar to the Wilson's Snipe, but the latter bird has a very much longer bill. The Dowitcher resembles the Wilson's Snipe more than does the Pectoral Sandpiper because of its very long bill and habit of probing in the soft mud. The Snipe usually seeks the protection of the vegetation fringing the mud-flat, however, while the Dowitcher ventures right into the open. The Dowitcher shows a black-and-white barred rump and tail when it flies, while the Snipe shows brown and rufous.

Of the larger shore birds, it is a rare treat nowadays in the northern states to come upon a flock of Curlews with their decurved bills, or Godwits with their upturned bills. The Willet, with its conspicuous black-and-white wing pattern that is entirely concealed when the bird is at rest, is rare away from the sea-coast and the Knots that formerly assembled in flocks of hundreds are in most places still very rare, though with all the other species they have shown a marked increase since they were removed from the game list.

But it is not only the true shore birds that one will find along the beaches during August, for these mud-flats make favorite feeding places for the wading birds as well. The stately Great Blue Herons stalk through the shallow water, while the Little Green Herons crouch low as a school of minnows approaches. The secretive Bittern occasionally ventures out upon the open flat and at dusk the Night Herons can be heard making for the spot from their roost in the woods close by. When all has been quiet for some time, the Rails, or even a Gallinule, may venture out from the adjacent marsh. Of course, the Grackles and Redwings assemble there to feed upon the stranded minnows and crustaceans, and, curiously enough, Savannah Sparrows, leaving their upland fields, now become one of the dominant birds of the shore. A little later in the season there will be Pipits, and Rusty Blackbirds, and the first of the Snow Buntings, and the sharp eye may detect a Nelson's Sparrow darting through the bulrushes like a mouse.

7

Bird Behavior—Ethology

There is a flock of Grackles at the feeding station below my window as I start this chapter. They are mostly birds hatched this spring and are now moulting into their first winter plumage with spots of fresh iridescent feathers here and there. They travel together as a flock but they do not seem very friendly toward one another and are frequently bickering and fighting—each one trying to claim ownership of the whole feeding log. Sometimes they clinch bills and strike each other with their wings or rise into the air and scratch each other with their feet or even roll off the log together, striking and scratching.

Some of the younger Grackles open their mouths at the approach of another bird as though they were still begging food from their parents but the incoming bird's chest goes up and he knocks the begging bird over the head with his bill. Then the beggar's bill goes up and they face one another with a glassy stare as though trying to intimidate one another. Altogether they waste a good deal of time and neither one gets anything to eat.

What they are really doing is building up a 'peck-order' in the flock so that when it is recognized there will be no more fighting and each bird will recognize his superior at a glance and make way for him. When their parents came to the feeder this spring, fights seldom occurred—their behavior was all ritualized so that when a second bird approached the first, each would throw up his chest, point his bill toward the sky and glare at the other bird. Usually this was sufficient and one would back off. If not, one of the birds would puff out all his feathers, spread his wings and give his vocal challenge as well as his visual and this was usually sufficient so that the 'childish' fighting that goes on with the immature birds seldom occurred.

The flock of Grackles that frequented the feeding station was a

117

smoothly running organization where each bird recognized where he belonged in the 'peck-order,' which of his neighbors he had to respect and which ones he could dominate, so that little time or effort was wasted on actual fighting. The birds were free to feed as soon as their superiors left, and they could have more time for the more immediate business of finding a mate. This, too, had become a stereotyped procedure calling for a very definite song and display of plumage, etc. Indeed a bird's whole life seems to be governed by one series of rituals following another in a definite

FIG. 95. Intimidation display of White-breasted Nuthatch used in driving a House Sparrow from the feeding log.

sequence over which the bird exercises relatively little conscious control. Some of the patterns improve with practice or by learning from others, but most of them seem more or less innate for each species—connected with the genes—so that they are inherited from one generation to the next.

Closely related birds usually have similar patterns of behavior but each species has certain characteristics within the pattern, both visual and acoustical, which tend to prevent hybridization as surely as the color of the plumage itself. When hybrids do occur, inherited behavioral patterns are often antagonistic to one another so that frustrations occur in the hybrid generation. The individuals are less well adapted to life and either do not survive or are unable to find mates.

On the pond here at the Sapsucker Woods Laboratory (where I am writing) we have a hybrid Redhead x Shoveller that is very confusing to all the other ducks as well as to himself and most of the observers watching him. At times he dives with the Redheads, at others he guzzles with the Shovelers and most of the time he swims around with a jerky motion that is characteristic of neither diver nor dabbler. This spring he felt the urge to do a little courting when all the other drakes were hard at it. In general male ducks have a ritualized procedure the most striking incident of which is what Lorenz calls the 'Grunt-whistle' for the Mallard and which is very similar in all the dabbling ducks. At this time the male stands up vertically in the water and throws his head down onto his breast at the same time giving a little whistle and a grunt. The similar ritual in the diving ducks calls for throwing the head back toward the tail so that the back of the head strikes the back. As the head comes forward again the drake utters his characteristic sound which in the Redhead is "Carr-r," in the Canvasback "Cuck-oo" and in the Golden-eye "Beard." Our hybrid tried to combine the salient features of each pattern, if that is possible, rising in the water like a Shoveler and then throwing his head back on his shoulder like a Redhead, a mixed pattern not recognized by any species—so that no duck paid him the slighest attention.

I once had the opportunity of watching a hybrid Prairie Chicken x Sharp-tailed Grouse that frequented a booming ground of the Prairie Chicken in Wisconsin. Apparently his booming was good enough to be recognized by his neighbors for what it was intended though his air sacs were lavender like a Sharp-tail's instead of orange-yellow. When he boomed, his nearest rival would come running over and challenge him to a fight in characteristic Prairie Chicken poses. He answered, however, by spreading his wings and raising his tail in Sharp-tail fashion and then started to dance. His rival would immediately lose interest, turn around and go back to his own little territory, thus showing the importance of the complete ritual in courtship behavior. No female came to the booming ground while I was watching but I am sure she would have responded as did the male with a complete lack of interest.

Dr. William C. Dilger, my colleague at the Laboratory of Ornithology, has been studying for several years the behavior of a group of African parrakeets belonging to the genus Agapornis. He has eight species of the genus in the Aviary, each one of which meets the exigencies of life with a pattern of behavior characteristic of that species. Dr. Dilger has worked out these patterns very carefully. In the wild state, these birds occupy different parts of Africa so they do not come in contact with one another and have no occasion to hybridize. In captivity, however, when they are given no choice, certain of them, in spite of the fact that their plumages are quite different, hybridize freely and produce vigorous offspring that nest freely. It is interesting to observe, however, how the parental behavior patterns, as inherited by the young, conflict to produce frustrations. For example, it is customary for all of them to cut narrow strips of bark (or paper in captivity) about $1/4''$ wide and $6''$ long as material for nest building. The females of certain species (Agapornis fischeri) for instance carry this paper to the nesting

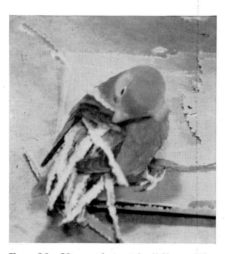

FIG. 96. Unusual nest-building. The Rosy-faced Parrakeet carries nest material tucked in the feathers of the lower back.

box in the bill like most ordinary birds. Others, however, like (Agapornis roseicollis) tuck one end of the strips under the feathers of the lower back. These feathers are different in some way from those of most birds and normally will hold from five to ten of the streamers before the female flies to the box. The hybrid young apparently inherit the 'tucking' instinct but not the ability to hold the nesting material successfully. So the hybrid female spends a great deal of time cutting and tucking—only to have the paper promptly fall out whenever she moves. Finally she grabs one strip in her bill and flies to the nest box. When she returns for more material, she continues the 'tucking' pattern, not learning very much from the experience.

There is a group of New World Flycatchers belonging to the Genus Empidonax which, to our eyes, look very much alike. (The Least, Acadian, Traill's, Western, etc.) Indeed, two of the species look so much alike that taxonomists lump them together and the ones from Alaska to Maryland are even placed in the same subspecies (E. traillii traillii). It is common knowledge, however, that the southern birds have a distinct 'song' and easily distinguishable nests. The northern birds call *"Phe-be-o"* and make bulky nests of grasses; the southern birds call *"Fitz-beu"* and make compact nests of cottony materials. In certain overlapping range areas of New England, New York, Michigan and further west the two types occur side by side with no apparent intermediates or hybrids. Experiments by Dr. Robert Stein in playing the songs of one group back to the other indicate that there is no recognition between them and that they behave as two different species as they may well be.

Thus we begin to see the importance of the study of bird behavior and the many surprises that are in store for the keen observer. The study of Ethology is so comparatively recent, however, that, as might be expected, a new vocabulary is arising and various interpretations are given to the same facts of observed behavior. When such divergent fields as psychology, physiology, ecology, taxonomy and good old-fashioned natural history are all involved, it is little wonder that conclusions are somewhat confusing. The interested student will read some of the illuminating papers of Lorenz, Armstrong, Lack, Tinbergen, Howard, Poulsen, in Europe and those of Emlen, Dilger, Kendeigh, Lehrman, Nice, Rand, Whitman, Wolfson and others in this country, before he feels qualified to interpret all the varied aspects of bird behavior that come under his observation.

Even then he will be at a loss to explain some of the things birds do, like 'anting' for example when birds rub ants and sometimes other materials on their feathers. A good beginning will be made by reading Chapter 5 of *Recent Studies in Avian Biology*, "The Study of Behavior in Birds" by John T. Emlen, Jr., published by the University of Illinois Press under the sponsorship of the American Ornithologists' Union.

We are doubtless safe in assuming that it is essential to the bird's way of life that it be endowed with an innate pattern of behavior that may be perfected through use but which covers all its natural activities. The general pattern is transmitted from parents to off-spring as surely as the color of the feathers or the length of the bill. Like such physical characteristics, the pattern is not complete at the time of hatching but is given expression as the bird matures and gains the use of its eyes, ears and physical means of reacting. The various behavioral aspects of this pattern are released by certain elements of the environment ordinarily to the distinct advantage of the bird. For example, young Robins in the nest, before their eyes are open, respond to any jarring of the nest such as might be caused by the returning parent, by stretching up their necks and opening

Fig. 97. A female Orchard Oriole indulges in "anting" (rubbing ants on its feathers) a behaviorism not understood by ethologists.

their orange mouths. The orange mouths serve as releasers to the parents to feed and to place the food where it belongs. A week later, after the young have gained the power of sight, a similar jar to the nest causes the same birds to crouch and hide in the nest (as though in the presence of an enemy) until they actually see the parents or hear them call. Then they open their mouths and give a call that is now necessary as a releaser for the feeding reaction of the parents. After they have left the nest and the parents have to find them, in the trees, this 'hunger call' is much more important in helping the parents to find them, but the gaping orange mouth is still necessary to release the feeding reaction.

The innateness of the stimuli and the releasers was nicely shown by Tinbergen in his work with Herring Gulls when the small young gaped for a red spot on a cardboard bill and the parents tried to feed pink paper mouths set up alongside the young. Of course these 'blind instincts' are soon affected by the learning process and some young recognize, as their parents, the first larger creature that takes care of them. Lorenz's incubator-hatched goslings quickly attached the parent relationship to him and followed him about as though he had laid the eggs and sat upon them for a month. He calls this "imprinting" and it can produce strange bed-fellows.

Some of these innate propensities are cyclical and are apparently governed by the activities of certain of the ductless glands like the pituitary or the thyroids or the adrenals or the gonads, they themselves being governed by releasers from the sun or other unknown factors of the environment or by internal metabolism. The various activities of the mating season, for example, such as song, courtship, display of plumage, mating, nest building, incubation, etc. varied as they are in the different species, are released at only a certain season of the year and in a definite sequence.

In a few species like the Cowbirds, the Honey Guides and certain Cuckoos, and Weaver Finches, the sequence is interrupted at the nest-building stage and the birds have become social parasites, laying their eggs in other birds' nests. Some birds accept the Cowbird's eggs, some throw them out and some bury them in the bottom of the nest by building a second story over the offending egg. Those species which refuse to accept the Cowbird's egg, however, will usually accept a young Cowbird if it is placed in the nest, responding to its food call as if it were identical with its own nestlings. The accompanying photograph of a House Wren feeding a young Cowbird larger than itself (Fig. 100) was secured in this way, since the House Wren always throws out the Cowbird's egg if the bird is able to get into the nesting cavity or if an experimenter puts the Cowbird's egg in the Wren nest.

In some birds, especially evident in those in which the males are brilliantly colored, the acquisition of bright colors by the females is merely inhibited by the hormone estrogen secreted by the ovary and when the ovary is removed the female acquires male feathers and male behavior at the next molt.

The song of a bird, in addition to attracting females, is a challenge to any other male bird of its species to keep out of his territory and birds with near neighbors sing more than those that do not hear others of their kind singing. In our project of recording the songs of our native birds, we sometimes take advantage of this behavior pattern by playing the bird's own song back to him which usually results in bringing the bird right down to the loud speaker where his song can be recorded much more satisfactorily, especially in noisy environments. If a mirror is added to the speaker, the challenging bird will often fight the mirror as well as do his best singing. When we hung the loud speaker on the fence post where a Bluebird was building a nest and played his song back to him, it produced an unexpected reaction in that when the Bluebird could not find his rival, he attacked his own nest, in what might be called a redirected aggression, and started throwing out all the grasses his mate had so laboriously gathered.

Another unexpected reaction occurred when we tried to stimulate a group of three Whooping Cranes to call. They are usually very quiet during the winter and so unapproachable that the only record of their voice we had secured was by sneaking up on a pair in a fog. Since the recording was not very satisfactory we planned to play it back to the group of cranes that occasionally came to a fresh-water pond on the Aransas refuge. We, therefore, concealed ourselves in a blind with a parabola and its microphone aimed at the far side of the pond where the Cranes occasionally came to drink. We concealed the speaker on the near side of the pond and waited two days for the Cranes to come. They finally came in silently and remained silent during their drinking and feeding. Then we turned on the tape we had previously recorded in the hope it might stimulate them to utter some kind of an answering call which we could record. The effect of the recorded sound was instantaneous. It was obviously an alarm note and it released no answering call but the birds jumped into the air and headed for distant parts without uttering a sound.

There is no end to the experiences which one could recount in studying the behavior of birds but just what the explanation should be, in each case, is not always clear. As Emlen states *"stimulus* and *response* are the basic attributes of environment and organism respectively in this relationship," and "Because of the stereotyped and relatively inflexible nature of many of their responses, birds have proven to be excellent subjects for analyzing the inherited and acquired components of behavior." The student of bird behavior will therefore have many rewarding experiences and can expect a good measure of surprise and entertainment in his studies, but one should become thoroughly familiar with the basic principles of ethology and with the bird being studied before intelligent interpretation can be made.

INSTINCT AND INTELLIGENCE IN BIRDS

A few years ago I was taking some motion pictures of a male Redstart feeding its young on my children's hands. After the first few minutes he paid little more attention to them than he would to the trunk of a tree on whose branches his young might have been perched. Young birds when they first leave the nest require a great deal of food and constant feeding, and nature gives their parents an instinct to provide that food at all costs. In the case of this male Redstart, its food-providing instinct completely over-rode its fear of man, as it so often does with many of the male Warblers, and it went about its work of filling the hungry mouths as though no one were present. The female Redstart, however, behaved quite differently. Her food-providing instinct was at its highest

FIG. 98. A "redirected activity." A female Redstart feeds young Robins when fear prevents it from feeding its own.

pitch while the young were still in the nest and when they left the nest it was inferior to that of the male. Her fear instinct was greater and she dared not come close enough to us to feed her young.

Some might say that the female was more intelligent and recognized us as enemies or that the male was more intelligent and recognized us as friends. But let me relate the rest of the story and I think everyone will realize how purely instinctive is this parental care of birds, automatically regulated by the calls and action of the young.

It so happened that a pair of Robins had a nest on the garage some 25 feet from the young Redstarts, and at every approach of their parents they called lustily for food. Nor was it only at the approach of their parents—any sound of scratching on the roof would cause their heads to pop up and their mouths to stretch in anticipation of being filled. And so when the female Redstart, by chance, alighted near the nest, she was met by the same clamor for food that would have greeted the Robins. The call was quite different from that of her own young and the mouths were many times as large as the ones she was accustomed to fill, but here was a chance to

FIG. 99. The Male Redstart's parental instinct is stronger than its sense of fear.

satisfy that food-providing instinct which her fear of us had prohibited her from satisfying in the normal way, and so she deposited her load of green 'worms' into the throat of the hungriest young Robin. Soon it became her regular practice. She would find a couple of worms, make a few advances toward her own young, and then fly directly to the young Robins and feed them. At times the adult Robin was at the nest when she arrived, and then she fluttered about the nest, as though trying to drive the Robin away, until the Robin left and permitted her to feed. As far as we could see the little Redstart seemed just as satisfied with herself after having delivered the worms into the throats of the young Robins as she would have been had she fed her own off-spring. The search for food, the delivery of it in response to certain reactions of young birds, and the return for more food were all automatic without conscious design.

It may be objected that the case of this female Redstart was exceptional and that the male was behaving in the more normal way. But when I put the young in a cage of small-mesh wire, where they could easily be seen and heard but could not be fed, the male likewise fed the young Robins. True, he made every effort to feed his own young, but when he alighted near the Robin's nest and was greeted by the food-call and the open mouths, he could not resist the instinct to attempt to fill them.

The question is often asked, "Do birds have any intelligence or are they governed entirely by instinct?" and I have related this incident as a good example of instinct. Instinct is defined as "an innate propensity to certain seemingly rational acts performed without conscious design"; intelligence as "quickness of understanding." The test of intelligence should be the rapidity with which an animal responds correctly to a brand-new set of conditions, conditions which do not occur in nature frequently enough in the experience of the species in question to develop, through the course of natural selection, a set of automatic responses to those conditions.

The Redstarts ordinarily care for their young in a rational way and feed them as if by conscious design so long as conditions are normal. But interpolate the human element or the cage, outside of the experience of the Redstart species, and acts are no longer rational but resolve themselves into automatic responses to certain stimuli.

And so if we analyze the daily life or the seasonal life of any bird, we will find it made up or at least governed by, a series of instincts which guide the bird more quickly and accurately through its routine than could any amount of intelligence. First there is the instinct to migrate with a guiding sense of direction, then there is the instinct to select a nesting 'territory,' to sing and to defend its territory against aggression; then the instinct to mate and to build the nest, to lay a certain number of eggs, to incubate those eggs, to care for the young, and so on through the season. So long as conditions remain normal these duties are performed much more accurately and quickly than as though the bird had to take thought and register intelligence over each one. The proper reactions for each set of conditions are 'born in the bird' and require no teaching or even powers of observation on the part of the bird, though doubtless many of the responses improve with the greater experience of the bird. They constitute what is often called the "Behavior pattern" of the species.

At another time I had the experience of watching a young Pied-billed Grebe hatch from the egg. Poor, bedraggled, little striped creature, for an hour or more it was too weak to make much of any response to life except to lie where it fell from the shell beneath the breast of its mother who had in the meantime returned to her nest. But after it had dried off and acquired a little strength, and before its brothers and sisters were yet out of the shell, it edged its way out from under its mother's breast and began to climb up over her flank feathers, seeking a resting-place on her back beneath her wings. Had it been a duck or a chicken or almost any other bird it would have been satisfied to snuggle into the feathers of its mother's breast or flanks or under her wing for warmth, but it was a Grebe, and young Grebes are brooded on the backs of their parents, so Nature had provided it with the instinctive desire to climb and it knew where it belonged without ever having to be told.

So long as conditions are normal, these instincts guide the lives of their masters in a most perfect manner, but when conditions are suddenly changed and the bird is confronted with experiences, new, not only to the individual but to all its ancestors as well, they are of no avail. Intelligence is called for and then it will be found that different birds react in very different ways according to their varying degrees of intelligence.

The Cowbird is a species in which the mating instinct is apparently developed at the expense of the instinct to care for the young. A few years ago when Dr. Herbert Friedman was studying this species intensively, we kept a lone male in a large flying-cage where he could be easily observed. After he had become accustomed to his new quarters, a 'stuffed' female Cowbird was wired to one of the branches within the cage. The bird was not well mounted nor fastened very securely to the branch, so that it soon slipped into a very unnatural pose. This made no difference to the male Cowbird.

He apparently recognized it as a female Cowbird and immediately his instincts were aroused and he sang and displayed his plumage before it as though it were the most charming individual of the species.

The parasitic habit of the Cowbird in laying its eggs in the nests of other birds is an intelligence test which Nature is herself carrying-on on a large scale. In the history of birds this parasitic habit is a comparatively recent development. Were it older, the responses of all the individuals of each species of parasitized bird would be more

Fig. 100. A House Wren will feed a young Cowbird but never accepts a Cowbird's egg placed in its nest.

uniform. When sufficient time has elapsed for an instinct to have developed, if there are still ornithologists in the world, they will observe that each species reacts uniformly to the intrusion of the Cowbird's egg. They will either all accept or all reject and not, as today, when some Vireos bury the egg in the bottom of the nest, and some hatch it and rear the young Cowbird instead of their own. Today, I believe it is still largely a matter of individual intelligence whether a bird rejects the Cowbird's egg or accepts it as its own. The bird's instinct, as at present developed, inspires it to incubate any egg or feed any young which it finds in its nest. Those birds which are more intelligent recognize the difference between their own eggs and that of the Cowbird and then, according to their relative intelligence, they take various ways of getting rid of it. A House Wren is accustomed to punching eggs and pitching them out of nests so that when she feels the large egg in her nest she will ordinarily throw it out. A Yellow Warbler, on the other hand, is not accustomed to handling eggs this way, and though she may be intelligent enough to recognize the difference in the eggs, she is not intelligent enough to develop such a new activity. She does know how to build a nest, however, and to cover up any twigs that may stick into the bottom of the nest, so if she has not yet laid any of her own eggs, she will either desert her first nest with the Cowbird's egg and build another, or she will build a new nest on top of the Cowbird's egg. The varying responses of different species and different individuals to the intrusion of the Cowbird's egg and young, form a very fruitful field to one interested in animal behavior, but we cannot dwell longer on them here.

That birds show varying degrees of intelligence, both as to individuals and as to species, there can be little doubt, but it is often difficult to tell where instinct leaves off and intelligence begins. With regard to the egg-destroying activity of the House Wren, apparently all Wrens do not react in the same way toward their neighbors. Some individuals regularly destroy competition within their territory by punching holes in the other birds' eggs, while others live on amicable terms with them. In some localities, apparently, all of the Wrens have learned the trick; in others, perhaps, none. My home, apparently, lies on the border-line, for one spring the Wren that lived on the lawn west of the house broke up a Scarlet Tanager's nest and a Chipping Sparrow's before I removed his box, while the Wren on the east side lived amicably, or almost so, with a Redstart, a Robin and a Phœbe that were nesting close by. I am disposed to believe that the activity has not yet become instinctive but is the expression of a rather intelligent bird. And it is one of Nature's laws that the intelligent shall inherit the earth.

Another activity of the House Wren that is often looked upon as an indication of intelligence is its feat of manipulating a long twig through a small hole. It may well be that some Wrens are much more skillful than others in this trick, but it seems to me that the House Wren must have met with this problem ever since it acquired the habit of building its cumbersome nest in a cavity, and that by this time it is just as instinctive as the weaving of the Orioles, the plastering of the Cliff Swallows, or the gluing of the Chimney Swifts.

One of the greatest changes of conditions which a bird may be subjected to is that of captivity, and the way birds respond to it is rather a good index to their relative degrees of intelligence. I have at my home a small pond, where I have kept under observation from time to time a few wild Ducks of a dozen or more species. One wing is pinioned so that they cannot fly, and a low fence keeps them from wandering. Here they soon become accustomed to the near approach of people and behave much as they would in the wild state. This does not mean that they all behave alike. Each has its characteristic calls and displays of plumage and courtship performances leading up to the laying of the eggs. Then there is a big difference. Those individuals that have been raised in captivity select their nesting-sites, lay their eggs, and proceed to incubate in the normal way, while those that have been raised in the wild and trapped when full grown, stop short at egg-laying, and, without exception, decline to select a nesting-site or even to lay an egg in the water. They may be absolutely docile, tamer than many of the hand-reared birds, so that they will eat out of one's hand, and yet they refuse to lay eggs. Hand-reared Ducks of the same species, living by their sides, under identical conditions, on the other hand, go ahead and deposit eggs in the normal way. Here is a problem in avian instincts that has puzzled me for many years, and for which I have as yet no very satisfactory explanation.

These same water fowl show varying degrees of intelligence, with the Black Duck and the Goldeneye at the head of the list and the Wood Duck at the bottom. I am often led to wonder if the seeming stupidity of the Wood Duck had not something to do with its increasing scarcity.

It is too bad no one ever performed an intelligence test on the Labrador Duck, before it became extinct, for, perhaps, it was the most stupid of its family. With the exception of the Wood Ducks the various Ducks all soon learn to distinguish not only the person who feeds them, but, likewise, whether or not he wears rubber boots. Rubber boots are always the signal for them to swim to the far side of the pond in alarm, whether or not I advance to the edge of the water. Nor will they ever come to feed while I stand on the shore wearing boots. A few minutes later, however, should I appear in shoes, they will flock to my feet. But not so with the Wood Ducks. They never differentiate. They are as likely to come up and feed before boots as before shoes, and if alarmed they seldom learn the cause of their alarm and they stay alarmed without discrimination, for days at a time. The other species soon learn that they cannot fly and if alarmed when on shore run to the water for safety, but the Wood Ducks always try to fly and turn somersaults in their haste.

The most intelligent bird with which I have had any experience is the common Crow, both in the wild state and in captivity. Of course Crows have their instincts which govern their routine life just as other birds, but they are not such slaves to them and they are much quicker at understanding new situations than any other bird with which I am familiar. I could write a book on the interesting and often amusing sparks of intelligence that have flown from various Crows that we have reared in captivity. Wild Crows are credited with developing games to amuse themselves, of playing pranks on one another or on some other bird, and, if it is possible in a 'dumb animal,' I should be willing to credit them with a sense of humor. One of our pet Crows learned to laugh as well as to talk, and used his laughter so appropriately on numerous occasions that I could scarcely credit it all to coincidence. He was very observant and when children were not present he used to roll their balls and play their games by himself. He was fond of teetering which he accomplished by running up one side of the see-saw until it went down and then turning around and running up the other. New situations were continually presented to him, new to the Crow species as well as to this individual, where no instinct could guide him, and he met them, not as did the Redstart, but rationally, with intelligence.

8

The Migration of Birds

Did you ever wish for the wings of a bird that you might fly away to the Southland and escape the cold winter? That was the wish of our fathers before fast locomotives and big automobiles and speedy planes were invented. "Oh for the wings of a bird!" I do not know that anyone ever mentioned the particular kind of wings that he preferred. Most people, when they are dissatisfied with the weather, will accept almost anything that is a change or that will enable them to go quickly to some place where the weather is different. And yet what a difference it would make if you wanted to go to Florida and got the wrong wings. You might much better take the wrong plane. Suppose, for example, you were given the wings of a Ruffed Grouse. You would start off with a rush from the front door; you would travel with great speed and think you were going straight for Palm Beach but, after a few flights, behold! you would land at your own back door. On the other hand, if you were blessed with the wings of a Golden Plover, you might start for Florida and never stop until you got to northern South America. So the next time you begin wishing for wings, and before you decide what kind of a bird you want to be, get out your 'Manual of Birds' and find out if that bird travels to the place to which you want to go. You will find it a good lesson in geography as well as bird-study. Indeed, it might well furnish the material for a bird-geography game to be used in the schoolroom or the bird club.

When we look through frosted windows at our northern Christmas landscape and hear the tinkling notes of the tiny Golden-crowned Kinglets or see the friendly little Chickadees all fluffed out among the snow-laden branches we wonder at the law of nature that holds these tiny atoms of bird-life among the northern blizzards, yet sends the sturdy Robins and Blackbirds scurrying south long before snow flies. We can understand readily enough why the

Robins and Blackbirds leave us. Indeed, it would seem quite natural if every creature with wings left such a land of apparent starvation. Neither is it difficult to understand why birds that nest in the far north, like Snow Buntings and Tree Sparrows, should be content to spend the winter with the snow and ice of our northern states, but that Chickadees and Nuthatches, that have spent the warm summer with us, should elect, of their own free will, to hazard the winter, is beyond our comprehension. That the same, identical Chickadees and Nuthatches do spend the entire year about one place in the northern United States has been repeatedly shown by banding them in winter and finding the banded birds at their nests not far away the following summer. Of course, it does not prove that all Nuthatches and Chickadees are sedentary, and it may be that some, especially those in the northern part of their range, do migrate southward. But is it not remarkable that any should choose to remain where zero weather prevails and food must, of necessity, be scarce?

There is a theory that at one time North America was practically without bird-life. Great continental glaciers had descended from the north into what was later to become the United States making the country uninhabitable by covering even the highest hills with hundreds of feet of solid ice. Then something else happened; perhaps the earth, in its whirl through space, changed its axis. At any rate, the ice melted, the glaciers receded, and the country became once more ready for plant and animal life. Where was it to come from? First, perhaps, from the South, from the land that had been unaffected by the glaciers, and then later from the North, for there is evidence that, following the Ice Age, even Greenland and Iceland had temperate or subtropical climates.

If we study the relationship of the birds that are found in North America today, we find that many families, like the Warblers and Vireos and Hummingbirds, have most of their representatives in South and Central America, and have no close relatives in Europe, Asia, or Africa. Other families, however, like the Nuthatches, Chickadees, Creepers, and Kinglets have their relatives in the Old World. It is reasonable to think that the former had their origin in the South while the latter came into North America from Europe or Asia by a northern route. Now if we consider our winter birds we will find that the majority of them belong to these Old World families. Some of them, however, like the Tree Sparrows, Snow Buntings, Woodpeckers, Gulls and Waterfowl, belong to families that are widespread over the surface of the earth. Even here, however, the species that remain in winter are ones most closely related to European species, so that we are probably safe in assuming that our birds came from European stock. If we explain the fall migration of birds as a returning to their ancestral homes, we can easily see how those that came from the South find migration easy when the cold weather comes on, while those that came in from the North have their escape cut off. Furthermore, we can well understand how birds of northern origin can be hardier than those whose ancestors were nurtured in the tropics. So, perhaps, it is not so remarkable, after all, that some birds, like the Chickadees and Nuthatches and Downy and Hairy Woodpeckers and the Ruffed Grouse, stay with us in the northern states for Christmas, and that other birds, like the Snow Buntings, Tree Sparrows, Redpolls, Crossbills, Grosbeaks, Creepers, and Kinglets, from further north, join them at their frugal board.

But what of the summer birds? Why should the Veery continue its flight to northern South America while the Wood Thrush stops in Central America, and the Robin and Bluebird be content with our own southern states? Why should the Bobolink feel that it has to fly all the way to northern Argentina for winter, while many of the other Blackbirds stay, occasionally, as far north as New England? Why should the Golden Plover leave the little Piping Plover on the shores of the United States while he makes for the pampas of Argentina? Why should the Arctic Tern, that nests often as far north as northern Greenland, be dissatisfied unless it can spend Christmas south of the Antarctic Circle? It is a strange and complex problem which makes even a check-list of birds fascinating reading if we stop to contemplate the anomalies of bird distribution and migration.

It is not only a scarcity of food that drives the summer birds southward at the approach of winter. If it were, they would stop as soon as they reached a bountiful food-supply, and they would not leave their summer homes during September or August or even July, when insects are at their peak of abundance. There must be some other instinct that impels them, an instinct like that which draws together the scattered members of a family at Christmas-time.

Perhaps they are returning to their ancestral homes to "eat, drink, and be merry." Their children are grown up; their family cares are over for the time being; what more natural than that they should return to a land where they know they will find others of their kind? The distances to be traveled seem long to us because we are clumsy and do not enjoy flying. Watch the Pigeons dart from the tower, rush this way and that way, rise, fall, circle, and return to the tower without ever touching the ground. Can anyone doubt that they enjoy flying?

One summer we raised a little Black Tern until it learned to fly and finally left us. All day long it was free to go where it pleased and at night it would come back and get into its cage and we would close the door. In the morning when we opened the door, so anxious and excited would it be to try its wings that it would often not touch its food until after it had performed its evolutions over the tree-tops. There was no doubt in the mind of anyone watching it that it really enjoyed flying and that it could cover long distances without fatigue and without becoming satiated with the joy of flying. Very likely then the birds really enjoy these migratory flights. The distances do not seem long to them, and they travel much farther than is necessary merely to get food.

One of the most interesting facts to contemplate in studying the winter birds is that you may be watching the same individual birds year after year, for it has been shown, by banding birds, that some species, at least, tend to return to the same place every year to spend the winter. For example, three Tree Sparrows visited my window feeding-shelf from January until March. There were numerous Tree Sparrows in the near-by country but I never saw but three at a time at my feeding-station, and I gradually came to recognize them as the same three birds. During January I caught these birds, one after another, in a Sparrow trap and placed bands on their legs. In March they disappeared, presumably starting northward for their nesting-ground in northern Quebec or Labrador. In January of the next year, Tree Sparrows again began visiting my window. At first there was only one, and I caught it on January 4. Lo! it was wearing band No. 51550 that had been placed on its leg the preceding January 17. Unfortunately, on January 18, it was killed by a cat. Its place was soon taken by two other Tree Sparrows, both wearing bands. One of these was caught January 13 and was discovered to be the same bird banded the preceding January 20, and the other, captured January 29, was the one banded on January 27 of the preceding year. Thus all three of them had returned. No one knows how scattered these three birds may have been during the summer, but some instinct drew them together after traveling over a thousand miles, and they met on the self-same window-sill. Strange as it may seem, they brought no others with them, and the two survivors were the only visitors to my window the following February, though hundreds of other Tree Sparrows frequented the woods and fields not far distant.

FIG. 101. A banded Tree Sparrow. The aluminum band bears a number and the statement "Notify F. and W. L. Service, Washington, D.C." Nearly 11,000,000 birds have been thus banded with more than 800,000 "returns."

The fourth winter I was in the South myself and had no opportunity to learn what Tree Sparrows returned, but a neighbor, Professor E. L. Palmer, caught one of the two survivors in a trap at his feeding-station. What a personal interest it lends to the birds and what added impetus it should give to our winter feeding stations when we realize that the birds recognize the kindness bestowed upon them and search one out on their long journeys to pay a 'party call' or to become regular members of the family. What a community of interest it would give if you only knew whose Florida garden your House Wren visited during the winter or from whose feeding-station in Georgia the Chipping Sparrow, that nests by your porch each year, derives its winter food. And how natural does it seem to fight for bird-protection when you know that the particular Bobolink that enlivened your meadow and destroyed the army worms that threatened your field, instead of returning next spring, to carry on his good work, has fallen before the gun of some worthless pothunter.

When the high tide of the spring migration comes, it is about the middle of May and nearly three months have passed since the first Horned Larks started northward over snow-covered fields. The March Robin brings forth its crowd of admirers, the call of the Bluebird draws a response from others, but when every hedgerow and thicket resounds with musical voices, and even the trees of the city streets flash with brilliant Warblers, everyone likes to stop and listen and notice the unusual number of birds. We cannot help wondering whence have come these little wanderers, where they are going, and what is the meaning of their journeys. In great waves they come from the South, flood us with beauty and song for a few days, and then pass on. Wave after wave moves over us during the course of the month, until June arrives, when the last immature birds hasten on to their nesting ground and leave us with only our summer birds until the fall migration brings them back once more.

A little observation from year to year shows us that these May birds are extremely regular in their appearance and disappearance. One can soon learn just when to expect each species, and, if the weather is normal, it will often arrive on the day set. The earlier birds, such as the Robin, Bluebird, Blackbird, Canada Goose, Meadowlark, and Mourning Dove, which come during March, are much less regular because of the idiosyncrasies of the weather. If there were no such thing as weather, if food were always equally abundant and if there were one great level plain from the Amazon to the Great Slave Lake, the birds would probably swing back and forth as regularly as a pendulum and cross a given point at exactly the same time every year. For this migrating instinct is closely associated with the enlargement and reduction of the reproductive glands, a physiological cycle which, under normal conditions, is just as regular as the pulsing of the heart and records time as accurately as a clock. With most species the organs of mature birds begin to enlarge before those of birds hatched the preceding year, and those of the males before those of the females. Because of this, the male birds arrive first and are followed by the females and later by the immature birds. With some species, like the Robin, Bluebird, and Phœbe, there is very little difference in the time of arrival, but in the case of the Redwinged Blackbird, often a period of two weeks, or even a month, intervenes. This may be a wise provision of nature to secure a nesting-area that will not be overcrowded, for once the male has established himself—and it is often at the same spot year after year—he drives away all other males of his species from the vicinity, awaiting the arrival of the females, and particularly his mate of the previous year. But with the later migrants, such as the shore birds, that have a long way to go, the females usually arrive

WATERBIRDS

Red-Throated Loon

Puffins

Holboell's Grebes

WATERBIRDS

Great Blue Heron

Great White Heron

Whooping Cranes

WATERBIRDS

Pintails Tipping

Redhead Diving

Pair of Wood Ducks

WATERBIRDS

Standing Flamingo

Flying Roseate Spoonbill

Purple Gallinule

with the males, and, with some species, courting takes place en route and they arrive at the breeding-ground fully mated and ready to nest.

The early migrants are those that have spent the winter entirely within the United States. This is true of all the March birds in the northern states, but, during the last of the month, the first birds from the West Indies and Mexico begin to arrive in the southern states. About the middle of April, many of the birds that have wintered still further south begin to arrive, including the Swallows, the Spotted Sandpiper, the Black and White Warbler and the Waterthrush. The last of April and first of May brings even to the northern states the initial wave of birds from Central America, and perhaps even northern South America, and about the middle of this month, when occurs the height of the migration, thousands of tiny Warblers, Vireos, and Flycatchers that have been wintering on the slopes of the Andes, or the pampas of Brazil, are winging their way overhead to Labrador, Hudson Bay, and Alaska. The shortest route which one of the last to arrive, the Blackpoll Warbler, can traverse is 3,500 miles, while those which nest in Alaska travel over 5,000 miles. Some of the shore birds, which bring up the close of the migration in late May or early June, have undoubtedly come from Chile, or even from Patagonia, and they still have several thousand miles to go, so that, before they reach their nesting-grounds again, they will have traveled 16,000 miles since leaving in the fall. The 'champion long-distance migrant' of them all, however, is the Arctic Tern, the extremes of whose nesting and wintering ranges are 11,000 miles apart, so that some may have to travel 22,000 miles each year.

Fig. 102. Screech Owl, a permanent resident.

This constrains us to wonder how these tiny wayfarers are able to travel such tremendous distances and still return so accurately to their homes. That many of them do this has been proved by placing numbered aluminum bands on their legs, so that they can be recognized from year to year. Not only has this been demonstrated, but it has likewise been shown in the same way, that many birds spend the winter in exactly the same place year after year, as in the case of the Tree Sparrows already mentioned.

At one time it was thought that they followed well-marked highways in the mountains, rivers, and coast-lines, surveyed, as it were, by their ancestors and unfailingly followed by all descendants. But now it is believed that these highways are followed only so far as they afford abundant food, and when the food-supply lies in some other direction, they are regardlessly abandoned. What is it, then, that guides them mile after mile in their flights, flights made mostly under the cover of darkness, and often at altitudes varying from 2,000 to 5,000 feet above the earth? A sense of direction, it is sometimes called, an instinct for recording directions as accurately as a compass, which we, having only so crudely developed in ourselves, are at a loss to understand; an instinct which permits birds to travel north, south, east, or west and not lose their bearings. For the migration route of most birds is not directly north and south, and many preface their southerly journeys by long flights directly east or west. The Bobolinks and Vireos of the northwestern states, for example, leave the country by way of Florida or the Gulf Coast, and first fly directly east to the Mississippi Valley, to join the others of their kinds before starting southeasterly. The White-winged Scoters, which nest about the lakes of central Canada, upon the completion of their nesting duties, fly directly east and west to the Atlantic and Pacific where they winter. Some Herons preface their migrations by long flights, even to the north, so that frequently American Egrets and Little Blue Herons are found in the northern states during August and September.

The Arctic Terns which nest along the east coast of Labrador probably cross the Atlantic to join their Scottish cousins before proceeding southward, for birds banded by Mr. Oliver L. Austin, Jr., at Turnevik Island were recovered at La Rochelle, France, and at Natal, South Africa, and two banded by Oscar Hawksley at Machias Seal Is., Maine were recovered in Scotland and S. Africa.

With birds that travel such enormous distances, it is interesting to note their rate of advance. While it is possible for birds to travel great distances without a rest, as witnessed by the fall flights of the Turnstone from Alaska to Hawaii, or of the Golden Plover from Labrador to northern South America, distances of over 2,000 miles across the open sea, they do not ordinarily progress far in single flights. The spring advance of the Robin, for example, averages only 13 miles a day from Louisiana to southern Minnesota. The rate increases gradually to 31 miles a day in southern Canada, 52 miles per day by the time it reaches central Canada, and a maximum of 70 miles a day when it reaches Alaska. It should not be inferred

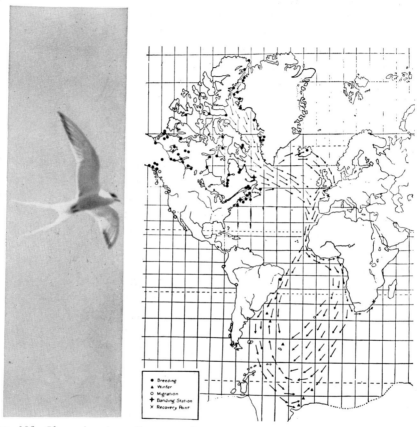

Fig. 103. Champion long-distance migrant, the Arctic Tern and its migration route.

from this that each Robin does not ever migrate less than 13 or more than 70 miles a day. Probably they often fly more than a hundred or two hundred miles in a single flight, as do, undoubtedly, many of the smaller birds, but after each flight they dally about their resting-place for several days before starting on again, and this brings down the general rate of advance.

There is considerable evidence for believing that the period of delay bears a direct relationship to the amount of fat stored as fuel under the skin or in the tissues and that optimum weight is the stimulating factor. They never take off without a 'full tank.' This would likewise explain why the fall migration starts while food of all kinds is most abundant and does not wait for cold weather.

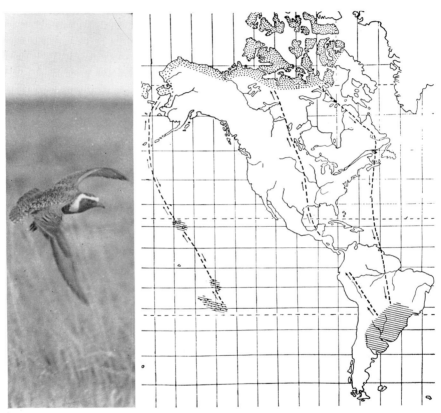

Fig. 104. Another long-distance migrant, the Golden Plover and its route.

The rate of speed at which birds travel is rather difficult to estimate, except in the Homing Pigeons, which can be timed from one place to another, or in the Ducks and Geese, whose conspicuous flocks, traveling high over cities and towns, can be easily followed. The championship speed for Homing Pigeons has been recorded as 55 miles an hour for a period of four hours. A Great Blue Heron has been timed by a motorcyclist keeping below it and found to be travelling 35 miles an hour. A flock of migrating Geese has been found to be traveling at a speed of 44.3 miles per hour and a flock of Ducks at 47.8 miles. The speed of smaller birds is usually less, although when they mount high in the air and start on their migratory flight, they probably fly faster than the birds one so often passes flying parallel to a passenger train or an automobile.

With the development of aviation we are gathering more and more information regarding the speed of flying birds and a British aviator, Col. Meinertzhagen has published in *The Ibis* the following speeds of birds as observed by him.

Small Passerine birds, 20-37 miles per hour.

Members of the Crow family, 31-45 miles per hour.

Geese, 42-55 miles per hour.

Ducks, 44-59 miles per hour.

Tame Pigeons, 30-36 miles per hour.

Starlings, 38-40 miles per hour.

Falcons, 40-48 miles per hour.

Waders, 34-51 miles per hour.

The greatest speed recorded with any attempt at accuracy is that of two species of Swifts in India timed by E. C. Stuart-Baker with stop watches over a two mile course. He reports them in *British Birds,* Vol. XVI, 1922, p. 31, as traveling at the rate of from 171.4-200 miles per hour.

The vast majority of birds migrate during the night; some migrate both by day and by night; others only by day. The latter are, for the most part, birds that find their food in the open and can feed as they travel. Such are the Robin, the Kingbird, and the Swallows. Other birds like the Sparrows, Vireos, Warblers, and marsh birds, that find their food among the trees or in dense vegetation, migrate entirely by night. The necessity for this is shown when they arrive at the Gulf of Mexico or other large body of water where it is impossible to get food of any kind. If they started early in the morning, so as to be across by night, they would not be able to get much food before starting, and by the time they reached the other side, it would be dark and again impossible to feed. Thus an interval of thirty-six hours would elapse without food, a period that might result disastrously for many birds because of their high rate of metabolism. If, however, they spend the day feeding and migrate by night, their crops are full when they start, and, when they arrive at the other side, it is daylight and they can begin immediately to glean their living.

During these migrations by night birds are attracted by any bright, steady light, and every year hundreds and thousands dash themselves to death against lighthouses, high monuments, and buildings. When the torch in the Bartholdi Statue of Liberty was kept lighted, as many as 700 birds in a month were picked up at its base. On some of the English lighthouses, where bird destruction was formerly enormous, 'bird-ladders' have been constructed, forming a sort of lattice below the light where the birds can rest instead of fluttering out their lives against the glass. Again, in crossing large bodies of water, birds are often overtaken by storms, and as their plumage becomes water-soaked, they are beaten down to the waves and drowned. Sometimes thousands of birds are killed by a single storm. In recent years the higher radio towers that reach upwards over a thousand feet and into the nocturnal flyways of the migrating birds have taken a tremendous toll. In a single night one such tower in Kansas killed 585 birds and another in Georgia 5,000-7,000. The ceilometers on the air fields have at times been far more destructive because the pillar of light under certain foggy conditions proves so irresistible to migrating birds that they circle about in it until they strike one another or fall exhausted to the ground. After one such night (Oct. 7-8, 1954) over 50,000 birds were killed on the airfield at Warner Robins Air Force Base, Georgia and 25,000 at Hunter Field, Georgia. But of course the vast majority of birds sweep on and arrive at their destinations in safety.

And so, if one steps out on a cloudy night, when the birds are migrating low to escape flying through the moisture-laden clouds, he will hear their strange calls, only faintly resembling their familiar daytime notes. Then he can picture to himself the thousands of winged travelers returning from a sojourn in the tropics and pushing on through the black night, guided by some strange sense of direction to their old homes. Then he can think over the past ages through which this migrating habit has evolved to the days when all North America basked under a tropical sun, and birds darted among the palms and tree ferns without ever a thought of leaving the homes of their forefathers. Then one can picture to oneself the coming of the Ice Age and the destruction of all the life that could not adapt itself to the changed conditions or flee before them.

One sees the birds pushed gradually to the south, encroaching upon those already there. One understands the crowding that must have ensued, and how these birds spread northward again as the glaciers receded, only to be pushed back once more by the coming of winter. One contemplates how, with the withdrawal of the ice and the evolution of the seasons, these migrations, by repetition through the ages, became permanent habits or instincts; and, with the ensuing modifications in the contour of the continent, and the changes in the location of the food-supply, many variations developed in the migration route of each species which seem inexplicable today.

One pictures these things to himself; one understands a little better the great mystery of the bird's life; and, perhaps, one appreciates somewhat more fully the presence in our thickets and gardens of these songsters, whose lives are ever one series of hazards and hardships, and yet which, withal, are so expressive of the happiness and joy to be derived from nature.

Many years ago I made an intensive study of the migration of the Redwinged Blackbird.* It was a good bird to study because the plumages of the males and females are so distinct and because the adult birds can be distinguished from those hatched the preceding year, even in the field. Moreover, they occur in open places where they can be watched, and they migrate mostly by day. For three years I followed the Blackbirds migrating through Ithaca, N. Y., very intently, letting other birds take care of themselves, and I finally discovered what I thought was the schedule which they followed. I have watched them casually since and, as yet, have found no reason for changing the schedule which was laid out for them at that time. It might be of interest to republish at this time the summary of the spring migration of the Redwing at Ithaca, in the hope that someone will check it for another locality or, better still, work out the schedules for other species.

Summary of the Spring Migration of the Redwing at Ithaca, N. Y., in 1911.

    I. Vagrants . . . . Feb. 25-March 4
    II. Migrant adult males . . . . March 13-Apr. 21
    III. Resident adult males . . . . March 25-Apr. 10
    IV. Migrant females and immature males . . . . March 29-Apr. 24

* Abstract of Proceeding, Linn, Soc. of N. Y., Nos. 24-25, 1911-13.

    V. Resident adult females . . . . Apr. 10-May 1
    VI. Resident immature males . . . . May 6-June 1
    VII. Resident immature females . . . . May 10-June 11

The dates given in the table are for the single year 1911 and indicate the migrating period of each group of birds. The actual dates
would naturally vary considerably from year to year, but the order
of arrival of the different groups should remain the same. Thus, the
first birds to arrive are usually 'Vagrants,' birds that have been
wintering in the near vicinity and which do not represent the beginning of the true migration. Many years they are not recorded.
The true migration begins with the arrival of the migrant adult
males, that is, adult males that are going to nest further north, and
they are followed by the males that are going to nest in the immediate vicinity. Whether this is true for other species than the Redwing is yet to be determined, as is also the question whether the
adult birds come before the immatures.

Female Redwings always come much later than the males (sometimes as much as six weeks intervene), but this is not necessarily true
for all species. With many birds it is difficult to distinguish the males
from the females, and impossible to tell the immatures from the
adults in the field. It is likewise very difficult to tell the resident
groups of birds from those that are merely passing through, and,
until we have a large number of birds banded or marked in some
other way, it will require most diligent, continuous watching of the
actions of individual birds to determine this point. The bird-banders
who have been successful in banding all of the nesting birds about
their traps will doubtless be the ones to give us the most definite
information on this point. With birds like the White-throated
Sparrows, in which the adults and immature birds are conspicuously
different, it should not be difficult to determine which come first
and which stay the longer. With the Redstarts, the males, the females
and the immature males are noticeably different, and one should be
able to determine nearly as much by intensive observation as was
determined for the Red-winged Blackbird.

Nearly everyone interested in birds keeps a bird calendar or record
of the spring arrival of the birds.* Some observers keep a list only of
the first arrivals; others maintain a daily list. This year make a special
effort to determine when the first females appear and when the

* See Chapter XIV

individuals that are to nest in the vicinity arrive. Each year the members of my household vie with each other in maintaining a calendar of the arrival of the birds on our grounds. It was begun in a spirit of play but now I find that we have information of considerable value about the birds that nest here. A comparison of our dates of arrival with those that are kept for the entire region by a corps of observers shows many things and emphasizes the well-known fact that what is true for one species is not necessarily true for others. Our Robins, for example, do not arrive for many days, sometimes weeks, after Robins have invaded the region, while our House Wrens and Redstarts are often the first to be recorded.

After one has watched the birds of one neighborhood for several years and knows where each one nests and raises its family, he looks forward each spring for the return of individual birds as much as for the first record of the species. The Robin that sings from the gable and drives other Robins from the front yard, the Chipping Sparrow that nests in the shrubbery by the porch, the Bluebird that nests in the bird-box on the post, and the Catbird that scolds from the berry-patch are expectantly awaited, and their return should be as conscientiously recorded as that of the first arrival in the spring. The discrepancy in the dates should be explained, and how long, if at all, does the male have to wait for his spouse to arrive?

Of course, it is not always the same bird that returns to the same spot each year. Bird-banding has shown us this as well as the fact that in a great many cases it is the same bird, so that we must learn not to generalize upon single experiences, no matter how interesting and illuminating they may seem. My first returns on banded Chickadees indicated that the same birds remained in the vicinity throughout the year, but since then many banded birds have disappeared in March, not to reappear until the following December, showing some kind of migration. My first returns on banded Canvasbacks were all from the vicinity of the place where they had been trapped one or two years before, indicating that they spend the winters in the same place year after year. But then came several returns from birds banded at the same time and place, but shot in Maryland and North Carolina. How shall we explain it? Either our wintering Canvasbacks are not as constant as I at first supposed, or else when the Ducks were trapped, during the last of February, a northward migration had already set in, and we had caught some Carolina

Canvasbacks with the Cayuga Lake Ducks. But at least it shows that it is not safe to generalize from a few observations. Nearly everyone would be willing to venture a guess as to whether the males precede the females in the spring migration, whether the old birds precede those hatched the previous year, and whether the migrant individuals pass through before the residents arrive. But let us gather the facts first for each of our common birds, and although one species behaves in a certain way, let us be very cautious before concluding that all others do the same.

The greatest pleasure and fascination in the study of the return of the birds come in the discovery of the first arrivals of the different species, and we vie with one another to be the first to see the Robin or the Bluebird or the Phœbe. But when the rush of May comes, the competition is truly at its height to see the first of each species to return. It would be impossible for one person to follow the migration of every species intently enough to determine, in one year, the relative times of arrival of the males, females, adults, immatures, migrants, and residents. Almost anyone can determine the dates for one species, however, in addition to following the general migration. Would it not be well, then, for each observer to select one bird that he will follow intently throughout the season and see if he can determine these facts about it? The bird selected should be a common one for the locality, and preferably one in which the sexes are easily distinguished and in which the immatures differ from the adults sufficiently to be recognized in the field, such as the Red-winged Blackbird, Orchard Oriole, Purple Finch, Goldfinch, White-throated Sparrow, Myrtle Warbler, or Redstart. Robins and Bluebirds show age and sex differences which the careful observer can distinguish but the spring plumages of most birds are so similar that even an expert cannot separate them according to age.

Since the foregoing chapter was first written, much added information on the migration of birds has been gained through bird-banding, through controlled laboratory experiments and through watching migrating birds across the moon at night and, still more recently, on radar screens.

Nearly three million birds have been banded in North America alone with thousands of returns emphasizing some of the statements made here as well as pointing out the wanderings of immature birds and the definite flyways developed by many species, especially the waterfowl.

Professor Rowan's experiments in locating the stimulus for the migratory urge in the activity of the pituitary gland stimulated by the increased sunlight of the lengthening days of the spring or the total amounts of light received has opened up a very promising field of study—as well as the control that optimum body weight has on delays enroute as pointed out by Wolfson and Odum. More recent studies on Bird Navigation by Griffin, Yeagley, Kramer, Matthews, Ising and others have uncovered many conflicting facts that seem to indicate that the great secret has really not yet been solved.

Brief clear summaries of these recent studies can be found in "Fundamentals of Ornithology" by Josselyn Van Tyne and Andrew J. Berger.

9

The Courtship of Birds

Selection of Territory

In our discussion of migration we learned that ordinarily, with each species, the males precede the females; the adult birds the immatures; and groups of migrants that are to nest farther north, usually precede the ones that are to nest in the region under consideration.

As soon as the resident males arrive they select definite areas in which the nests will later be built. These areas, I called "domains" in my studies* of the Red-winged Blackbird but some years later they were very fittingly, called "territories" by H. E. Howard in his book "Territory in Bird Life," and the name has been very generally adopted. The resident male spends most of his time in the territory which he selects and drives out every other male of his species. He may even drive out the migrant females when they arrive, but just as soon as the group of resident females arrive, his mating instinct is at its height and he endeavors to convince one of them to accept the territory which he is so valiantly defending.

The size of the territory depends largely upon the food habits of the species and secondarily upon the abundance of the species in the vicinity. If a bird regularly secures the food for its young in the immediate vicinity of the nest, it requires a larger nesting territory than one which regularly flies to a distance to feed. Thus Song Sparrows and Robins and Catbirds will have larger nesting territories than Terns or Herons whose nests may be nearly touching. Even in the case of these social birds, however, it will be found that each nest has a definite territory about it on which other Terns or Herons are not allowed to trespass. Some species, however, are regularly much less territorial than others.

* The Red-winged Blackbird: A Study in the Ecology of a Cat-tail Marsh, A. A. Allen. Proc. Linn. Soc. of N. Y. No. 24, 1911-13.

Some birds have separate nesting and feeding territories and apparently recognize, also, certain neutral feeding areas. Thus a pair of Great Blue Herons may claim only a few feet of nesting territory in the colony while they are defending a whole lake shore as a feeding territory. A pair of Kingfishers may claim the fishing rights to half a mile of stream, their nest being in a sand bank a half mile in another direction, and they will drive away any other Kingfisher from this part of the stream. A little lower down there may be a neutral territory where several Kingfishers feed and still farther down will be the territory of another pair. Similarly with the Robins about one's garden. The whole area may be divisible into several Robin territories with a pair defending each, or there may be some neutral ground not claimed by any particular pair where all feed in peace.

Early in the season there may be a good deal of fighting or bickering along the boundaries of adjacent territories but sooner or later the different pairs come to recognize each other's boundaries and serious quarrels are few. In most places the number of nesting pairs of any species is remarkably constant. Immature birds arriving later than the adult birds find the desirable territories all occupied and they either move on or they fill in the gaps caused by the death of some older bird. It is probable with such species as show no noticeable increase in their numbers or extension of range that all of the immature birds are absorbed in this way. Birds like the Starling, however, that are very prolific produce more than enough young to fill the gaps and they are rapidly extending their ranges.

The northward extension of range that has been occurring in recent years, of the Cardinal, Carolina Wren, Tufted Titmouse and Blue-gray Gnatcatcher is probably being accomplished in the same way by yearling birds.

When the resident male has selected his territory he begins to strive for a mate. This is done by song, by display of plumage, and often by curious antics or aerial evolutions or other courtship performances. We will first consider song and substitutes for song.

Song and Call-Notes

There can be little doubt that the voice in birds has been developed, as in other animals, as a means of communication. This does not necessarily imply an elaborate thought mechanism nor even an extensive vocabulary, but merely a means of communicating their feelings. Anyone who makes an extensive study of the call-notes of one bird, however, will be impressed with the number of modulations, and these may correspond to different words. The barnyard fowl, for example, in leading her chicks about, is continually calling to them in various notes. One announces food, another announces

danger, another calls them to brood, and so on. What is true of the domestic fowl is true of all birds, only most of us are not familiar enough with them to recognize the differences, and even if we do recognize differences, it is almost impossible to represent them with words.

Certain of the call-notes are apparently recognized by all birds, while others may or may not be understood by other species. When a Robin discovers a Hawk or an Owl, it gives a certain note, and not only do all the Robins of the vicinity flock to the spot, but birds of other species as well, seem to recognize the 'rally call.' Another call which is apparently recognized by

FIG. 105.
Swamp Spar-
row singing.

all species is the distress call. This can easily be imitated by moistening the knuckle of the bent forefinger or the back of the hand and kissing it very lightly, so as to produce a distressing sort of squeak. It usually requires a little practice to do it well, but with experience one can produce such a realistic call that birds of all species will flock to the spot to learn the trouble. During the nesting season the writer has had as many as thirty different kinds of birds in sight at one time, and some of them within arm's length, by calling thus from concealment. Like the cry of 'wolf, wolf,' however, continued use of the 'squeak' at one spot destroys its efficacy.

Another call that is apparently recognized by more than one species, is the food-call of the young, particularly the call that is developed when the young leave the nest, so that their whereabouts will be known to the parents. The call is very insistent with some young like those of the Cowbird and Baltimore Oriole. The writer has observed a Redstart returning with food for its own young, to be waylaid by a young Cowbird that was being raised by a Red-eyed Vireo, and actually to give the food which it carried to the young Cowbird, so insistent were its cries. Upon another occasion, where two Robins were nesting side by side, unusual enough in itself, one of the Robins deserted its own young, which were just hatched and had not yet developed the food-call, to assist in the care of the other young which were just leaving the nest and whose cries were very insistent. (See also Chapter VII, p. 125, Instinct and Intelligence.)

The calls of birds are apparently inherited, for young birds hatched in incubators or under other birds seem to have the calls of their own species. Their songs, however, are apparently largely influenced by imitation, and birds never hearing the songs of their species may develop very different songs. In species with wide ranges, the individuals in different localities may develop local dialects recognizable by keen-eared observers. The adaptability of birds' voices in this respect varies considerably. Some birds like Parrots, Mynah birds, and members of the Crow family, learn a variety of sounds readily and are easily taught to imitate the human voice. Other birds can be taught to whistle tunes or the songs of different birds, and birds like the Mockingbird, Catbird, and Starling seem to do this naturally and are well known as mimics.

In the development of birds from their reptile-like ancestors, undoubtedly the call-notes arose long before songs, for true songs are still confined to what are considered the higher Families of birds, i.e., those above the Flycatchers, the so-called "Oscines." The lower Orders of birds have substitutes for song, some of which are just as elaborate as the songs of many of the Corvidæ or Icteridæ, which are considered true singing birds. The laughing of the Loons, the cooing of the Grebes, the whistling of the shore-birds, for example, are much more musical than the guttural notes of the Crow or the shrill, hissing notes of the Cowbird. Nor can one always determine the musical quality of the song by the elaborateness of the structure which produces it, for the vocal apparatus of some of the lower Orders is more complicated in some ways than that of the true singing birds.

The voice of birds is not produced in the larynx as it is in man, but in a structure called the syrinx, which is located at the lower end of the trachea, usually where it divides into the bronchial tubes. Here are located the membranes which vibrate, as do the vocal cords of mammals, to produce the sounds. Without going into details of structure, it might be mentioned here that in the true singing birds, called Oscines, these membranes are controlled by from five to seven pairs of muscles, while in the lower Families the number of controlling muscles is less. The sounds are produced entirely by the air rushing past these membranes, causing them to vibrate, the rapidity of the vibrations and the corresponding sounds produced being controlled by the tension of the muscles. Undoubtedly the larynx and the tongue more or less modify the sounds, if we can judge from their motions during singing. There are, however, among the higher Families, no sounding boards such as are developed, for example, in the trachea of the male ducks. The syrinx of a male duck is a curious looking object because of the great shell-like swelling of the lower end of the trachea, which gives resonance to the mating-call. In addition, certain species have accordion-like enlargements of the middle of the trachea, features which are never developed among the true songsters.

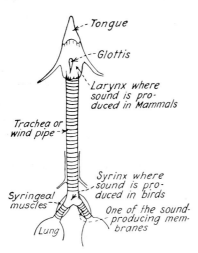

FIG. 106. A bird's "voice box" is not in its larynx.

The songs of birds, like the bright plumage of many, is undoubtedly a secondary sexual character, and has been developed as a means of bringing the sexes together, and of actual species recognition. Many species, like the Empidonax flycatchers, resemble each other so closely that it has been shown that voice is more important than plumage in preventing hybridism. On the other hand, the Golden-winged and Blue-winged Warblers which do not look much alike but whose songs are similar frequently hybridize. As one might expect, song is best developed in the males and largely confined to them.

The females of a few species, however, occasionally sing nearly as well as the males, but their songs are usually much more subdued. Female Cardinals, Rose-breasted Grosbeaks, and Purple Finches are noted for their vocal ability, and a number of tropical American Wrens sing delightful little duets with their mates. (See 'Impressions of the Voices of Tropical Birds' by L. A. Fuertes, *Bird Lore*, November-December, 1913, or "My Tropical Air-Castle," by F. M. Chapman, D. Appleton, 1929.)

Song is usually concomitant with the breeding season. With some birds, like the Redwinged Blackbirds and the Warblers, it begins with the northward movement in the spring, and they are singing their full songs when they pass through on their spring migration. Others, like the Thrushes, seldom sing until they arrive on their nesting-grounds. Similarly, song ceases soon after nesting is begun, or at least by the time that the young leave the nest. Thus, Bobolinks and Orioles cease singing the last of June or early in July, and other birds follow suit shortly afterward, except those that nest late or have more than one brood. During the moulting season of August and September, practically all birds are silent, except those indefatigable songsters, the Song Sparrows, the Wood Pewees and the Red-eyed Vireos.

Inasmuch as the object of song is to announce the bird's presence, the bird usually chooses a very conspicuous place from which to sing, thicket-loving species like the Brown Thrasher and Song Sparrows leaving their hiding-places and mounting to the tops of the bushes or trees to express themselves, and field-loving birds, like the Meadowlarks and Vesper Sparrows, mounting to the tops of fence-posts. Many terrestrial birds that can find no prominent place from which to sing, develop the habit of flying up into the air to sing flight-songs, that of the European Skylark being one of the most beautiful expressions of nature. The performance of our own Horned Larks, previously described, while less musical, is no less remarkable. Birds of almost any species occasionally indulge in flight-songs when no perch seems to satisfy them and they bound into the air on quivering wings to give vent to their feelings. Especially is this true of the Ovenbird whose ordinary song of *teacher, teacher, teacher,* is introduced by some wild ecstatic notes that one would never guess were produced by the same bird. Its flight-song is given usually just at dusk, or after dark, and the singer often mounts high above the trees during the performance. Some of the most impressive moments that the writer has ever experienced have been in the forest at dusk when the silence was interrupted only by the bell-like cadence of the Hermit Thrush and the wild, ringing flight-song of the Ovenbird.

The singing of birds at night, by its very incongruity, always awakens our interest. The European Nightingale has been lauded since ancient times because of its nocturnal outbursts, but it is not alone in this habit. Aside from the Owls and Whip-poor-wills, that one naturally expects to be active at night, one may hear during the height of the mating season, the song of almost any bird ringing out on the night air as though the songster could not restrain himself. Yellow-breasted Chats are particularly noisy at night and, on the marshes, the Wrens, the Rails, and the Gallinules seem to take on renewed activity when darkness falls. Robins, Song Sparrows, Chipping Sparrows, Catbirds and other familiar species often cause our gardens to echo in the dead of night, and the Mockingbird of our southern states is said to do its finest singing on moonlight nights.

Birds frequently become greatly attached to certain perches from which they sing, the Robin to a certain gable, the Mockingbird to a certain chimney, the Thrasher to a certain tree-top. The accompanying photograph of a Swamp Sparrow (Fig. 105) was secured by observing that the bird always came to a certain reed in the marsh to sing. To our eyes it looked just like a thousand other stalks, but the Sparrow had formed the habit of always singing there and the presence of the camera did not deter it. The Ruffed Grouse returns to the same log to drum day after day and season after season, and Flickers and other Woodpeckers often return to the same tin roof or other resounding surface, year after year.

The drumming of the Ruffed Grouse and the tattoos of the Woodpeckers can not be called songs, but they are substitutes for song and serve exactly the same purpose. The Grouse frequently comes to his log on moonlight nights, or at least before dawn, even in the rain, and he frequently drums every five minutes for several hours. When getting ready to drum the bird selects the same spot on the log and faces in the same direction each time. He does not beat the log with his wings nor do his wings strike his breast nor do they hit each other behind his back, as has frequently been asserted. The sound is produced entirely by fanning the air. The bird stands stiffly erect with his tail down and begins with a few deliberate strokes of his wings. The first two are short and produce no sound, the third produces a dull thump as do the next twenty, gradually increasing in rapidity until one can no longer count them and the thumps blend into a whir. The first strokes are directed forward and downward but the later ones forward and upward forcing the bird backward until his tail is pressed so tightly against the log that when the drumming ceases it springs upward as if in recoil. The sound produced is of such a low frequency (40 cps) that it seems no louder at a distance of 200 feet than it does at 200 yards.

Another mechanical sound that takes the place of song is the *"winnowing"* of the Woodcock, produced by the air whistling through the outer three primaries which are much attenuated. The performance can seldom be observed until after dusk when it is difficult to see just what is happening, but the birds can be heard calling first from the ground—a sharp nasal *"peent,"* followed by a very low *"cuck-oo"* which is audible for less than 50 feet. The bird next mounts into the air on a great spiral, *winnowing* or *chippering* as he rises, his wings apparently fanning the air more rapidly than in normal flight. When almost out of sight he flies in great circles alternating the weird wing *chippering* with vocal notes like the syllables *quit, quit, quit.* The bird then zigzags back toward earth silently or with five or six vocal quits at the first part of the descent.

Fighting

The song of a bird is primarily an announcement to the female of the presence of the male and a challenge to other males of his species to keep out of the territory which he is guarding. The male birds, as previously stated, ordinarily precede the females on the northward flight, and, arriving on the breeding-grounds, proceed to select the territory in which the future nest is to be built and over which he exercises absolute dominion so far as his species is concerned, unless driven out by a more powerful rival. If any other male of his species dares to intrude, he is immediately driven away. An amusing incident, illustrating this, took place in front of one of my windows, where I maintain a feeding-log.

It seems that a certain male Song Sparrow had decided to have a nest in an adjoining hedge and had been announcing the fact by his cheerful song for several days. Whether he already knew about the feeding-log near the window I do not know, but one unfortunate day he ventured to it, and when he did so, discovered his own reflection in the window. He thought it was another Song Sparrow trespassing upon his territory, and in a fury he dashed into the glass to drive it away. Nor did the fact that the window met him as hard as he met it check his ardor. He kept at his task of driving away the other bird all that day and all the next, barely taking time to eat or to announce to the world that he was still defending the hedge. Indeed, as the days rolled by and he continued to fight his reflection, we grew worried about him and tried every means of discouraging him, to no avail. He had discovered that another Song Sparrow claimed every down-stairs window on that side of the house, and he continued to fight. There were so many windows that it gave him little time to eat or to sing, with the result that he went without a mate from early April until the middle of May. When at last a female settled in his territory, he grew less pugnacious and ventured to the windows only a few times each day to make sure that his rival did not steal a march on him. Cardinals in the northern states are likewise very territorial and fight windows or mirrors or hub-caps or pieces of red cardboard with equal viciousness. Robins are often

FIG. 107. A Cardinal mistakes its reflection for an intruder in its territory.

seen fighting cellar windows and we had a most amusing experience with a Ptarmigan on the Tundra of Hudson Bay that discovered its reflection in a mirror.

With some birds this zeal of the male in the defense of his territory seems to be quite essential, for the female, which accepts him, seems to be much more devoted to his territory than she is to him. Should a stronger male come along and drive away her first mate, she accepts the new suitor with perfect equanimity. I have observed this with Robins, Redwinged Blackbirds, and House Wrens. Indeed, in the case of the Wrens, the victor was already the lord of a nest-box a short distance away, so that he found himself presiding over two families that season.

Whether the varied songs of birds have any effect upon the females other than to point out a nesting territory which will be guarded, is open to question. However, when S. Prentiss Baldwin placed a cardiometer in a House Wren's nest he discovered that every time the male sang, the pulse rate of the female went up. Female Redwings and other birds have likewise been observed to quiver their wings and give evidence of some feeling when the male sings. Certainly the males of most species have recourse to other methods of bringing the females into a synchronous mating cycle than merely singing to them, and it is some of these methods that we wish to consider. Before leaving the combats of the males in defense of their territory, however, we should mention the 'tournaments' for which some birds, such as the European Ruff, and the Black Cock, as well as our own Prairie Chicken, and Sharp-tailed Grouse are noted. With these birds it is customary for all the male birds of the neighborhood to assemble at a suitable place and engage in sparring matches. Each male Prairie Chicken selects a certain spot on the 'booming ground' to which he returns each morning at dawn. There he struts around with wings down and tail up and the long 'pinnae' erected like rabbit ears. He cackles and hums before he inflates his orange air sacs preliminary to booming. The boom is a challenge to his neighbors as well as an announcement to the distant females. After the drum his nearest neighbor usually approaches and they crouch a few feet apart and glare at one another with more cackling and humming until one rises and starts to boom. This stimulates his neigbor to fly at him with the intent of seizing him by the back of the neck and flipping him over onto his back. This is seldom accomplished because they usually meet in the air breast to breast with a slap of the wings and come back to earth ready to repeat the performance.

The Sharp-tailed Grouse have a similar booming ground and glare at one another while crouched face to face but instead of fighting, they arch their wings stiffly and whirl around in a curious, quick-stepping dance. The dance stimulates the other males and sometimes a dozen will be dancing at the same time—running, stopping, pirouetting and rattling their erected tail feathers in unison.

Just as important as the singing and fighting in the courtship of many birds is the display of plumage. Some species have special plumes, wonderfully modified and beautifully colored, which are worn only during the breeding-season, and which are seen to advantage only during the periods of courtship; others, like the Prairie Chicken and Sharp-tailed Grouse, have large air-sacs which can be distended beneath brilliantly colored skin; while still others can claim little by way of adornment though they make up for it by curious antics.

Of the birds which have special plumes to display, the Peacock is perhaps the most familiar. The greatly elongated, eyed feathers which are ordinarily spoken of as the "tail" are in reality the upper tail-coverts, the real tail of ordinary stiff blackish feathers being entirely concealed. It is interesting to watch a pair of these gorgeous peafowl on a spacious lawn and see with what deftness the male displays his charms to the female. They may be walking quietly side by side when one's attention will be attracted by the rattling of quills as the male shakes out his feathers and prepares to spread them. A few quick-stiff-legged steps brings him ahead of his consort and then, with a beautiful sweep of his long 'tail,' he wheels in front of her and at the same instant lifts and spreads the most beautiful fan that nature has ever fashioned. It is no wonder that he is venerated by the inhabitants of his native jungle.

The Peacock belongs to the Pheasant family, the males of all of which are noted for their brilliant plumage and their curious displays. The display of the Golden Pheasant, a native of western-central China is conspicuous in every aviary. Even when at rest he is a gorgeous bird with his scarlet breast, his brilliant yellow back bordered by red, his emerald-green shoulders, his bright orange cape banded with purple, his silky yellow crest, and his long flowing tail. But when, like the peacock, he takes a little run ahead of the female, spreads his fan-like cape, apparently shifting all of his brilliant feathers to her side of his body, and opens his arched tail, splashing it with the red of his upper tail-coverts, one marvels at the unconcern of his sombre-colored mate. His brilliant yellow eye gleams over the top of his cape, but it gets no response from her, for she either appears perfectly unmoved or she dodges back without so much as giving him a glance. The display of the Lady Amherst Pheasant is very similar, but the numerous other species have each their characteristic courtships which are easily watched in an aviary or on a game-farm. I once watched a wild Ring-necked Pheasant displaying before his mate. He began by pecking the ground as if to attract her attention and there followed a little stamping. With his head still down, the wing toward the female was lowered to the ground carrying the spotted flank feathers with it. The tail was then spread and the back feathers shifted, as in the display of the Golden Pheasant, until the picture which was presented to the female was that of a perfectly gorgeous shield, almost heart-shaped, the iridescent bars and spots making a beautiful pattern on an orange and maroon background.

The display of our native Ruffed Grouse is no less interesting though less brilliant. As in the color plate, both wings are drooped to the ground and the fan-like tail is lifted as with the more gorgeous Peacock. The iridescent black ruff feathers which normally lie almost concealed on the sides of the neck are then lifted until they make a perfect circlet like a large Elizabethan ruff, into which the head fits. The cock bird struts beside the hen until the spirit moves him to enter into the final stage. He then begins to peck at the ground and to shake his head from side to side, uttering short, hissing sounds with each twist. Finally, with a short quick run, he gets in front of the female, and, shaking his head so rapidly that the ruff is but one continuous iridescent blur, he turns quickly, stiffening his legs and turning his tail laterally so that she will get the full benefit of the climax of his effort. At the same time, his short notes that have kept time with the shaking of his head grow into one loud prolonged hiss.

Some of the most elaborate displays of nuptial plumes are those of the Birds-of-Paradise which may be observed at the larger Zoological Parks. The first Blue Bird-of-Paradise exhibited at the New York Zoological Park surprised even the most experienced aviculturists by its unique display. For, instead of hopping up and down on his perch and erecting his plumes into a beautiful cascade as was expected of him, he hung upside down from his perch and shook out his long flank feathers until he formed an exquisite azure lyre with a dark maroon center. The astonished keeper thought the bird was having a fit.

Lest it be thought that only foreign birds or birds with unusual plumes or brilliant colors display in an interesting way, mention should be made of the curious effort of the Cowbird, a plain little blackbird with a brown head. So far as colors go he has nothing to boast of, but, for an unadorned bird, he certainly makes a supreme effort at a nuptial display. Cowbirds are very easily watched because they are often in small flocks and take delight in sitting in the exposed tops of trees where, early in the season they are quite conspicuous. The juxtaposition of another Cowbird, male or female, starts one off. He points his bill toward the zenith and compresses his feathers, looking like a broken stick. The next moment, however, the feathers all over his body stand on end, he spreads his wings and tail, and with a shrill hissing whistle he falls forward with quivering wings in an apparent fit of extreme nausea. So far forward does he fall that he oten has difficulty in regaining his balance.

The display of the White-breasted Nuthatch is less often observed but is no less interesting because, in addition to showing every one of his feathers to advantage, he has the pretty little trick of making a present of food to the female. This is what happens at my feeding-station every year when the warm days of early April start the buds to swelling. Together the two Nuthatches come to the tree nearby, uttering low conversational notes, the female almost coy in the way she follows the male and edges away when he comes too close. Suddenly the male swoops to the food-shelf, seizes a sunflower seed, and is back to the waiting female with scarcely a pause. With wings and tail spread and feathers fluffed, he presents the tidbit to her as though it were a choice bouquet or a box of chocolates. Occasionally he pauses at the food-shelf long enough to remove the seed coat from the seed so that it will be ready to eat, but this is by no means a regular part of the ceremony. The display of the little Chickadee is very similar, though given apparently with less bravado, and he does remove the seed coats from the sunflower seeds before presenting them.

But the courtship of birds is not complete with song and fighting and display. There are many birds which supplement their displays with curious evolutions in the air, with what well might be called dances, and with other performances that will have to be called 'antics' for want of a better word. The evolutions of the Horned Lark and the Woodcock have already been described. The Wilson's Snipe gathers momentum as he sweeps high over the marsh and has seemed to me occasionally to turn over on his back while on set wings, producing a winnowing sound, supposedly by the air rushing through the outermost spread tail-feathers. The Marsh Hawk 'loops the loop' over the spot in the marsh where the female is perching, sometimes making several loops in succession, like gigantic backward somersaults. The ecstatic flight-song of the Oven-bird is no less thrilling, though, because it is given most often in the quiet of night, the singer is seldom seen when he leaves his lowly roost and mounts high over the trees. Neither would one guess its composer were it not for the fact that, as it falls back to the trees, it finishes its flight song with its customary notes of 'teacher-teacher-teacher.'

The rhythmic stiff-legged dance of the Sharp-tailed Grouse as they whirl about their cackling ground with erected tails and arched wings is a definite courtship performance. So are the promenades of the Cayenne Lapwing of South America. The clustering and waving of wings of the flocks of Jacanas on the tropical marshes and the dances of the Cranes and the Albatrosses are all examples of courtship performances. At least they undoubtedly had their origin as such, though they are today often indulged in at other times. Space will not permit of their description here, and, after all, they are perhaps less interesting than the actions of our more familiar birds. Enough has been said to indicate the sort of thing to look for and the greatest pleasure and the greatest satisfaction come from making an original discovery on the courtship of some common bird. Make a point of watching a pair of Flickers and try to describe their interesting courtship. Robins, Song Sparrows, Grackles, Redwings, Purple Finches, Hummingbirds, practically all of our commonest species, will take on a new interest when one becomes absorbed in trying to observe their complete behavior patterns during the courtship period.

The Mating Cycle

Some years ago I became greatly engrossed with the problem of raising Ruffed Grouse in captivity and in so doing was able to observe carefully many individual birds throughout the entire breeding cycle. In so doing I gained a new insight into the significance of plumage display and territoralism and the other features of the breeding cycle which it would be difficult to gain in any other way. The results of these observations were published in the AUK, Volume LI, pp. 180-199 under the title "Sex Rhythm in the Ruffed Grouse (Bonasa umbellus Linn.) and other Birds." Briefly summarized, I learned that the actual mating period of the male as well as that of the female is very short, although recurrent, and that the whole pattern of behavior represented the endeavor of nature to bring together two birds in exactly the same rhythm or stage of the mating cycle. The establishment of territory serves to avoid unnecessary competition and disturbance as the mating period approaches. Song is an easy method of avoiding competition as well as attracting the mate. The display of plumage is at first entirely for intimidation and is performed for males as well as females. Should a foolish female venture into a Grouse territory at this stage, she might be killed by the intimidating male which at this period merely wishes to establish dominance. Soon, however, he comes into the actual mating period when he becomes very gentle, does not attempt to defend his territory, and will mate with anything resembling a female Grouse in the submissive posture. During this stage he pays no attention to other males and does not attempt to defend his territory so that it is important that all competitors should have been completely intimidated and eliminated before this stage overwhelms him. In a few days he usually reverts to the aggressive stage again when he is interested only in killing rivals and intimidating females.

In experimenting with a number of other species (Lesser Prairie Chickens, House Wrens, Song Sparrows and Yellow-breasted Chats) the same sort of behavior was observed and I was led to the conclusion that the whole pattern of behavior in the spring cycles of birds in general is activated by this need for bringing together two birds in exactly the same stages of the reproductive cycle and keeping away other birds of their kind when they arrive at the mating stage.

10

The Home Life of Birds

Nests and Nest Building

At no time of the year are birds more interesting than during the nesting period. The throngs of migrating birds bring out their hosts of followers during April and May; the morning and evening choruses of courting birds draw a response from others during May and June; but the nesting birds are the most fascinating to the quiet observer. The hunting for the nest and the watching of the daily life about the birds' homes hold thrills that are never known by those who put away their glasses when the migration is over.

In the beginning it might be mentioned that most birds are monogamous, that is, they have the same mates throughout the period of the dependency of the young. With birds the entire cycle from birth to maturity occurs within a comparatively few weeks. The home is built, the eggs are laid, the young are cared for until they become entirely self-supporting; with many birds, all within the period of a month or six weeks. With the human species this cycle of events requires anywhere from twenty-one to forty years depending upon the number of children. It is fair, then to say that birds are monogamous, even though they may change mates from year to year, or even between broods, as is sometimes the case, so long as they do not maintain two mates at the same time. Some birds, particularly those that do not migrate, probably retain the same mates year after year and, even among migratory birds, the same two birds may resort to the same nesting-spot year after year and remate. We have little definite information upon this subject, however, and it is one of the problems upon which 'bird-banding' should throw much light.

In the spring of 1929, for example, a banded female Chickadee returned to the same nesting box in my garden where she raised her brood the previous year. She brought with her, however, a different male. As discovered by Dr. W. K. Butts, however, by the time the

Fig. 108. A female Scarlet Tanager feeds its young.

eggs were laid she had still a different mate and it was a fourth mate
that finally helped her rear the young. A pair of banded Song
Sparrows, on the other hand, that raised three broods together in my
garden in 1928 returned in 1929 and raised three more broods
successfully together. In this, as in most aspects of the home-life of
birds, there is as much individual difference as there is with the
human species, which makes it difficult to generalize upon but rather
fascinating to observe. Indeed the similarity of their lives and actions
and responses to our own is so striking that it has led some nature
writers to endow them with an intelligence and power of thought

Fig. 109. A much-mated Chickadee.

that is not justified by the facts. Some birds are remarkably faithful to one another while others have much greater attachment for the nesting-site than they have for their mates. If one of a pair of Canada Geese is killed or permanently separated, the other may remain single for years and perhaps never remate. On the other hand, with the majority of birds, if one is killed, a new mate is secured within a few hours.

Among some captive Canada Geese which I watched for ten years I had one case of a female remating upon the death of her mate, and one case of actual polygamy when a new gander introduced into the flock was unable to make up his mind the first year and mated with three geese though thereafter he was as monogamous as all the others.

A few birds, like the Pheasants and, probably, most Grouse, are regularly polygamous and others, like the House Wren (and probably other species of Wrens), Redwinged Blackbirds, Great-tailed Grackles, Meadowlarks and doubtless other species, are frequently so; and individual cases of polygamy can be expected occasionally with almost any species, should there chance to be a preponderance of females, a condition which, however, rarely obtains. Polyandry, the mating of one female with more than one male, may likewise occasionally happen, particularly if a stronger male is able to drive away one that is already mated. It is not regularly the case with any bird unless it be the Cowbird, and of its domestic relations we still know too little to say definitely.*

A few birds are socialistic: they build a common nest in which several females lay eggs and then share the duties of incubation and rearing the young. This is particularly true of the Anis of tropical and subtropical America. Many of the African Weaver Birds and the Palm Chats of Santo Domingo are socialistic to the extent of building a common roof beneath which each pair builds its nest. There are slight indications among our Swallows that they may be learning socialism, for I have seen a family of young Rough-winged Swallows being fed by three adults.

Occasionally a male bird, unable to secure a female of his species in the territory which he is defending, will adopt another species so to speak and even drive away the rightful male. I have known this to happen with a Carolina Wren which took over a family of

* See *The Cowbirds*, by Herbert Friedman-Chas. Thomas, 1929.

House Wrens. He started by feeding the incubating female and was so assiduous in feeding the young that not only did the male desert but finally the female also and left him in full charge.

I have also photographed a male Prothonotary Warbler (see color plate) near Ridgway, Ontario feeding a brooding female Yellow Warbler and helping feed the young, the male Yellow Warbler finally deserting his duties. He repeated this performance for several years and even learned the song of the Yellow Warbler. So far as is known, there was not another Prothonotary Warbler within fifty miles.

After the birds are mated the first project, of the female at least, is the building of the nest. The male has already selected the general nesting area or territory in which he has been singing and which the female has accepted by accepting him. It is her duty, however, to select the actual site where the nest is to be built and to do most, if not all, of the building. In the case of the Killdeer, however, and perhaps all shorebirds, it is the male that selects the actual spot where the nest is to be built and makes a little scrape or hollow in the ground where he does much calling and displaying. This is especially true of the Phalaropes in which the males not only select the nesting site and build the nest but do all the work of incubation and care of the young.

With Woodpeckers also, the male takes the initiative in starting the nesting cavity and seems to do most of the work of excavation.

With most, if not all, species of Wrens, the building of 'dummy nests' by the *males* is a common practice but it is apparently part of a courtship performance or a method of marking out his territory, for they are never used by the female. The male House Wren, for example, arriving before the female, proceeds to fill every nesting-box and cranny in the vicinity full of sticks and may even build rather well-shaped nests. When the female arrives and accepts him for a mate, however, she does not at the same time accept the home which he has built; for even though she may decide to use one of the boxes where he has already started a nest, she usually proceeds to throw out all of the sticks which he has laboriously brought in before starting a nest of her own.

I have never known of any passerine bird in which the males and females worked equally at nest-building though with many of the common birds the male makes a pretense at helping and with the common House Sparrow the male may do even more than his share. It is ordinarily the male's duty to see that no other male or even female of the same species intrudes in the territory and this takes so much of his time that, though he may accompany the female back and forth on her trips, he has little time or inclination for gathering nesting material. Judging from the way the female usually treats his occasional offering of nesting material, it would seem that he does not know the proper material when he sees it. Among Cormorants and Herons it is common practice for either sex, returning to take its place on the eggs, to present the incubating bird

Fig. 110. A male Prairie Warbler feeds its mate on the nest but male Warblers never incubate.

with a piece of nest material which is incorporated in the nest before exchange of places occurs.

This brings up the question of what determines the proper nesting material for each species. Practically all birds build nests that are characteristic of their kind. The materials vary somewhat in different localities depending upon what is most convenient but, in general, House Wrens use twigs, Bluebirds use grasses, Yellow Warblers use cotton, and so on, though often curious substitutes are employed. We have, for example, a Wren's nest built largely of hair-pins and wire clippings, and a Robin's nest in which the customary grasses were replaced by long, narrow strips of paper from a nearby paper factory. But only such materials are used as permit the bird to build the type of nest characteristic of the species. Baltimore Orioles normally weave their nests from vegetable fibers such as the inner bark of milkweed. They will take light-colored pieces of yarn or string or horsehair just as readily but never, to my knowledge, do they use sticks, straws, or grasses, though grasses are regularly used by the Orchard Oriole. Marsh-birds regularly use the dried sedges or rushes or marsh grasses; field-birds use grasses and horsehair; woodland birds use dead leaves, mosses, and rootlets, and so on. The materials with which a bird comes most often in contact are the ones employed in nest-building provided they conform to the general type of nest characteristic of the family.

Birds that spend a great deal of time on the wing and come less into contact with any sort of nesting materials and nesting-sites show the greatest diversity both as to site and materials. Among our common Swallows, for example, the Barn and Cliff Swallows build nests of mud about barns or cliffs; the Tree Swallows build nests of straws and feathers in holes in trees or bird-houses; the Bank Swallows build similar nests at the end of holes which they excavate in sand-banks; and the Rough-winged Swallows utilize old Kingfisher burrows or natural crannies about cliffs or bridges or drain pipes.

The factors that control the selection of the nesting-site are primarily the necessity for concealment, accessibility to the feeding-ground, and protection from the elements. If birds were capable of worrying over the probabilities of the destruction of their homes, their 'heads would be white' before their nests got started. As it is, they go about the selection of the site instinctively and finally decide upon one which is usually well concealed from their ordinary enemies such as cats, crows, hawks, owls, jays, grackles, wrens, weasels, skunks, raccoons, squirrels, rats, and snakes, as well as being fairly well protected from wind and rain, and accessible to their feeding ground. The large percentage of nests that are broken up, however, attests the many dangers that ever beset the bird's home and the bird's life. I think it is no exaggeration to state that less than 20 per cent of the nests which I find each year endure until the young leave of their own accord. I would even venture to say that not one in ten of the nests that are started succeed in housing the young to maturity.

FIG. 111. Evolution of birds' nests, from the simplest to the most complex.

1. Nighthawk
2. Black Skimmer
3. Black-necked Stilt
4. Meadowlark
5. Green Heron
6. Red-shouldered Hawk
7. Catbird
8. Chipping Sparrow
9. Yellow Warbler
10. Goldfinch
11. Yellow-throated Vireo
12. Baltimore Oriole

The many ways in which birds circumvent their enemies by building their nests in inaccessible or inconspicuous places, or by decorating them with bits of paper, cobwebs, or lichens so that they will look like something else, would make quite a story in itself, but we must pass them over and merely mention the birds that have changed their natural nesting-sites to suit changed conditions. Some species are not adaptable and when conditions change they vanish;

others are able to make the best of changed conditions and may even increase. Such are the Robin, all of the birds that build in nesting-boxes, the Phœbe, and the Barn and Cliff Swallows that formerly nested only on cliffs but are now so familiar about our dwellings. The Chimney Swift that has almost forsaken the hollow trees for the chimneys is another good example of adaptation. One often hears of birds nesting in unusual places, such as moving street-cars or traveling cranes, under wagons left standing, in clothespin bags, and in the pockets of scarecrows, but they are always of these adaptable species. It is almost beyond the realm of possibility to have a Yellow-breasted Chat or a Cuckoo or even a Catbird behave in such a manner.

Before leaving the subject of nesting we should try to answer the question of why most birds build nests. Some we know still lay their eggs on the ground without any nest whatsoever, and they manage to persist or else we would not have any Nighthawks or Whip-poor-wills. The same is true of many of the sea-birds like the Auks and the Murres. At the other extreme are the Orioles and the Weaver Birds which weave such elaborate nests. Between the two (Fig. 111) we find all gradations of nest structure from those that merely scoop out a little depression to keep the eggs from rolling, like the Killdeer and Least Tern, or those that add a few grasses by way of a lining, like the Spotted Sandpiper and Stilt, to those that build rather elaborate domed nests on the ground like the Meadowlark and the Ovenbird.

Of the birds that have raised their nests above ground to escape floods or terrestrial enemies, there are some that lift them merely by building a platform of dead leaves, like the Veery, or the Rails and Gallinules in the marsh; others build crude platforms of sticks in trees or bushes, barely sufficient to keep the eggs from rolling to the ground. Such are the nests of the Herons, the Doves and the Cuckoos. Crows, Hawks and Catbirds have advanced a step further, for while they still use sticks they build deeply hollowed nests and line them with softer materials. Nests of the Yellow Warbler, Redstart, and Goldfinch, made entirely of soft materials, doubtless represent a still higher stage in the evolution of nests that culminates in the beautifully woven structures of the Vireos, Orioles, and Weaver birds. Such is the present status of birds' nests, probably indicating the various steps through which the more complicated nests have passed. If we would understand the real origin of nest-building, however, we must go back to the earliest birds when they first arose from their reptilian ancestors.

Doubtless their habits of egg-laying at that time were about the same as those of reptiles today. Turtles bury their eggs in the sand; lizards hide them in holes in stumps or decaying logs; snakes bury theirs in decaying vegetation; and alligators build actual nests of the

FIG. 112. Kingfishers (below) and Bank Swallows both dig burrows but the Kingfisher builds no nest. Why?

same material like muskrat houses in which they hide their eggs. Incidentally they are the only reptiles which are said to take an interest in the welfare of the young later on. But, as in all other reptiles, the eggs are hatched by the heat of the sun or from the decaying material. Now it must be remembered that reptiles are 'cold-blooded' creatures and are not affected by great changes in their bodily temperature. A turtle basking in the sun may have a blood temperature nearly boiling while the temperature of the same animal hibernating in the mud may be near the freezing point. As its temperature drops, it becomes more sluggish, but its health is not affected. The warm-blooded birds and mammals, on the other hand, can endure but a very slight change from the normal temperature of their blood, especially upward, without ill effect. What is true of the grown bird is nearly as true of the embryo developing within the egg. Its temperature must be maintained or it will not develop and will soon die. There are a few birds, such as the Megapodes of the Australian region, which have reverted to the ancestral method of burying their eggs in the sand or in piles of decaying vegetation, but they lay their eggs at a time when the temperature is remarkably uniform in the places which they select. All other birds have to depend upon supplying the heat from their own bodies; that is, they have to incubate their eggs. The longest stride in the change from the reptile to the bird and the one which affected their habits even more than the development of wings and feathers, was this advance from a changeable to a constant temperature, from 'cold-blooded' to 'warm-blooded.' We have not the space, nor is it appropriate here, to go into all the differences which this change brought about, but we can point out that the need for incubating the eggs which followed gave rise to the nest-building habit. Birds that had been in the habit of nesting in holes in banks or trees where they could remain with their eggs with no great inconvenience, were doubtless less affected. They did not have to learn how to build nests, except in so far as they had to learn to dig their own excavations instead of accepting natural cavities. Such is the habit of the Woodpeckers and the Kingfishers today. They excavate their nesting cavities but they build no nests within for their eggs.

Birds that had been in the habit of burying their eggs, however, and now had to lay them on the surface of the ground where they could be incubated, had other problems to meet. There were the floods, the cold wet ground, the numerous terrestrial enemies, all threatening to destroy the eggs. It is easy to imagine, therefore, that those individuals that learned to raise their nests off the ground were the ones that persisted until the habit was formed. The first nests were doubtless very crude and the beautiful structures with which we are familiar are probably the result of a gradual evolution, as already indicated.

We have stated that nests are ordinarily built by the female birds though the male often makes a pretense at helping and, in the case of the House Sparrow, the male does more than the female. The time required depends a good deal upon the time at the disposal of the birds, but, with ordinary birds, like Robins or Blackbirds, it is about six days. Three days are spent on the outside and a like time on the interior. The same bird, however, if the first nest is destroyed while the eggs are being laid, might build an entirely new nest in a single day. A pair of Phœbes, on the other hand, under observation one spring, began repairing an old nest fully a month

FIG. 113. Getting ready to incubate, a Killdeer exposes its brood spot. This is divided in all the shore birds by a line of feathers down the middle.

before any eggs were laid. Usually the nest is completed the day before the first egg is laid.

Incubation does not ordinarily begin until egg-laying is completed, so that all of the eggs will hatch at about the same time. Otherwise the first young to hatch would have an unfair advantage over the others in the nest. Occasionally one finds Owls or Bitterns beginning to incubate before all of the eggs have been laid, but they are, perhaps, less regular about egg-laying than most birds. Most birds lay one egg each day at about the same time but larger birds, like the Hawks, Owls, and Geese, have intervals of two days.

As the time for incubation approaches, the bare area on the middle of the breast becomes suffused with blood and is termed the 'brood spot,' and the bird becomes 'broody.' In the shore birds, the brood spot is divided into two by a line of feathers down the middle.

Ducks and Geese which have practically no bare area on the breast pull out the down from that region so as to bring the eggs in direct contact with the skin. Incidentally, this down forms a blanket with which the eggs are always covered when the bird leaves them to feed.

When both birds are colored alike, they usually, but not always, share equally the duties of incubation, but when the male is brighter than the female, he is not often seen on the nest, the Rose-breasted and Black-headed Grosbeaks being exceptions. Ordinarily, the male either stands guard on the edge of the nest until the female returns from her feeding excursions or else he brings food to her. Sometimes he feeds her on the nest but more often he calls, as he approaches, and she flies out to meet him. The easiest way to find a Marsh Hawk's nest is to listen for the returning male and then note from what spot the female flies up to meet him and take the food from his talons. The care of the female by the male is carried to the extreme by the African Hornbills in which species the male walls up the opening in the hollow tree with mud until only the female's bill can be protruded. He then proceeds to bring her all her food and likewise that for the young later on, for she remains imprisoned until the young are nearly full grown. So great is the task of providing the entire menu for the whole family, we are told, that he becomes excessively thin and often succumbs during inclement weather.

FIG. 114. Nest, eggs, and down of a Pintail's nest. Ducks do not have bare brood spots so must pull out the down.

With a few birds the males do most or all of the incubating and care of the young. This is said to be true of the Emus and the Cassowaries of the Australian Region, the Rheas and Tinamous of South America, of the Ostriches, at least in captivity, and more particularly of our own Phalaropes. In the case of the Phalaropes the males not only do all of the domestic chores, but they are likewise smaller and less brightly marked than the females, apparently a complete reversal of the sex characteristics.

The *period of incubation* depends largely on the size of the egg and the nature of the young, larger eggs and those from which precocial young hatch requiring longer periods. Perhaps also, the varying normal temperatures of the different species influences the period of incubation and the length of time the eggs are left unattended while the parents are feeding. The actual time varies from 11 days in the case of the Cowbird to from 50 to 60 with the Ostrich,

Fig. 115. A Cowbird laid an egg in this Redstart's nest (left), and see what happened—one young Cowbird, no young Redstarts.

or even 70 to 80 with the Emu. Sparrows require 12 to 13; Thrushes, 13 to 14; Hens, 21; Ducks from 21 to 30, depending largely on the size; Geese, 30 to 35; etc. An apparent exception is the Hummingbird which requires 14 or 15 days but has the smallest egg of all. This may be due to the fact that she receives no help whatsoever from the male and the eggs may become unduly cooled during her feeding excursions, for it is a fact that unusual cooling of the eggs delays the hatching if it does not entirely prevent it.

The extremely short period of the Cowbird is perhaps an adaptation to its parasitic habits, for if the young Cowbird hatches ahead of its foster brothers, it has a better chance of getting most of the food and either starving them to death or ousting them from the nest.

Young birds are assisted in getting out of the shell by what is called the 'egg-tooth,' a hard calcareous tubercle which with most species develops on the upper mandible and which is used as the cutting tool in 'pecking' the egg. The bills of all embryo birds are very soft, making such an instrument necessary. This egg-tooth occasionally persists for several days after hatching and is quite conspicuous on some birds. Many birds, particularly Grouse and Quail, cut a neat little cap from the larger end of the egg with this egg-tooth, but others break the shell irregularly in the middle. Most

FIG. 116. Egg tooth on a newly hatched Sandhill Crane. Tooth cuts through the shell.

birds are very careful to remove the empty shells from the nests, either swallowing the fragments or carrying them off to a distance. Birds such as Grouse and Water-fowl having precocial young, that do not stay in the nest for any time after hatching, usually do not remove the empty shells. Shore birds, however, regularly do so.

During the period of incubation the eggs have to be turned once or twice a day so that they will be heated evenly and so that the membranes will not adhere to the shell and prevent the free passage of air to the interior. Some birds turn the eggs with their feet, and others with their bills, usually at the time when the female returns from a feeding excursion.

THE EGGS OF BIRDS

One who is familiar only with the eggs of domestic fowls has no idea of the variety of the colors, shapes, and sizes of the eggs of our native birds. It is no exaggeration to state that no pigment color exists that is not represented by some tint or shade on the egg of some bird, though, of course, there is little of the brilliancy that makes birds' feathers so attractive. Indeed, it is commonly believed that all birds' eggs are protectively colored. Whether this is true or not we shall take occasion to discuss later, but certain it is that from the snowy white eggs of the Woodpeckers or the deep-blue eggs of the Thrushes, there occurs almost every conceivable combination of ground-color and marking until we come to the eggs of the Loons that are often so dark as to appear almost black. The change that has taken place in the development of our present-day birds from their reptile-like ancestors in glorifying them with feathers and giving them a blood of uniform temperature, has likewise brought about this change in the coloration of birds' eggs, for those of all reptiles are white or parchment-like without pigments.

It is interesting to consider again the evolution of the bird from

Fig. 117. Yellow-billed Cuckoo's egg (larger and paler) in a Blackbilled Cuckoo's nest.

the reptile in studying the varied colors and shapes of eggs as they occur today. For here also we see that the change that took place from the so-called cold-blooded or variable temperature condition of the reptile to that of the warm-blooded or constant temperature condition of the bird entailed not only great changes in the method of caring for the eggs but also in the eggs themselves. There was never any need for the reptile to lay protectively colored eggs because it regularly buried them out of sight in the sand, in decaying vegetation, or in holes in trees. Here it left them for the heat of the sun to hatch. It mattered little how much the temperature varied so long as they finally received sufficient heat. But after the change to a warm-blooded condition had occurred, it was necessary for the birds to maintain the eggs at a constant temperature, and, as the heat of the sun could not be depended upon for this, it became necessary to supply the heat from the bird's own body and the habit of incubating them arose. It was then (with rare exceptions) no longer possible to bury them and, of necessity, they were laid on the surface of the ground or in cavities where the old birds could be with them. At this time all birds were doubtless laying white eggs, like those of reptiles, for there had been no reason for the development of color. And there was yet no reason for the development of color on the eggs of birds nesting in dark cavities, nor has there ever been since in birds like the Woodpeckers, Kingfishers, and their allies which nest in holes to this day and still lay pure white eggs. But with the birds that began laying their eggs on the ground it was quite a different matter, for white was very conspicuous and attracted the attention of their numerous enemies. Doubtless these first birds found it necessary to cover their eggs, even as do the Grebes today, when they had to leave them. Then, through the process of natural selection, pigments, inclining to make the eggs less conspicuous, gradually developed, and such eggs as those of the Terns, Gulls, and Gallinules resulted, which are colored like the ground or the materials of the nest and are obviously protectively colored. The nests themselves were crude affairs and attracted no attention. They were unsafe, however, in times of storm and flood, and they gave but little protection to the young birds. Fortunately, however, the young were hatched covered with down and were able to run about so that they used the nest for only a short time.

As birds progressed and it became advantageous to have the eggs hatch in shorter periods and to give greater care to the more helpless young, it became necessary to build stronger and more comfortable nests, and these, by their very size, were necessarily conspicuous unless they could be hidden. Many birds then learned great skill and cunning in concealing their nests or in selecting inaccessible places for them but the fact should be brought out here that, with the building of any nest, it no longer availed the bird to lay a protectively colored egg, for whatever concealed the nest would likewise conceal the eggs. It is a fact in nature that a structure exists only so long as there is need for it, and that as soon as the need passes, the structure gradually degenerates, though it usually persists through a great many generations. Examples of this are the tonsils and appendix of man which undoubtedly at one time played a very important part in our metabolism but which have long since ceased to be necessary and are in the process of degeneration. So, in the coloration of birds' eggs, while the pigment was originally developed as a protective measure before the birds built elaborate nests, the need for those colors has gradually passed away with the higher types of birds that lay multi-colored eggs, and the colors are in the process of degeneration. The degeneration has progressed more rapidly with some species than with others and has resulted in the great variety of ground-colors and markings that we find today, most of which must be considered conspicuous. The rate of degeneration is remarkably uniform with most species, however, and so we find now that each species lays a characteristic egg and each family has a type of egg from which there is little deviation. Thus, all Robins lay plain blue eggs and so do a great many of the Thrush family. Spotted Sandpipers lay brownish eggs spotted with black and so do most of the shore birds; Crows lay greenish eggs spotted with black and so do the Ravens and the Jays; Orioles lay bluish white eggs streaked with black and so do most of the Blackbird Family; Warblers lay whitish eggs spotted with brown; Vireos, white eggs with only a few black specks, and so on. Occasionally one finds a nest in which the eggs show a great deal of variation, as that of a Song Sparrow or a Swamp Sparrow or other bird in which the eggs are plain blue instead of heavily spotted; but these variations are so sporadic that they serve but to strengthen in our minds the belief that the colors are in the process of degeneration. Again one sometimes finds eggs of the Goldfinch or the Phœbe, which are usually unspotted, showing obscure speckles. In this they show the relationship to the other members of their respective families for most Sparrows and most Flycatchers lay spotted eggs. This is called reversion or atavism, the individual female bird having inherited the pigment forming glands from a remote ancestor —its own mother probably not having them.

Another fact that has perhaps hastened the change from a protectively colored to a conspicuous egg, is the fact that a conspicuous egg today often benefits the species. It is a well-known fact that most birds do not begin incubating until the laying of the last egg, and that in the meantime the eggs lie exposed to all of the enemies living in the vicinity. It might be thought, therefore, that a protectively colored egg would be beneficial. On the contrary, if the bird has selected a nesting-site where some enemy is likely to find the nest sooner or later, or if the nest has not been properly concealed, it is far better that it should be found at this stage than later, as there would be less delay in building a new nest and laying more eggs. Nature provides that the bird has very little attachment for its nest during the period of egg-laying, and practically all birds desert it upon the least

Fig. 118. Atavism in the eggs of a Goldfinch which are normally plain bluish white with no markings.

provocation. Too close approach, the disarrangement of a single leaf or anything that suggests to the bird that its nest has been discovered before incubation has begun is usually sufficient to cause it to desert the nest and start again somewhere else. After incubation has once begun, the same bird will permit of a great many liberties, and its attachment for its nest increases as incubation progresses, reaching a maximum at the time of hatching. A conspicuous egg, therefore, may well be a benefit to the species building a too conspicuous nest by saving it valuable time during the short nesting period and enabling it to choose a safer place for its young before the season is too advanced.

It has already been stated that hole-nesting birds, like Woodpeckers and Kingfishers, lay pure white eggs, but there are certain exceptions to this rule which give added strength to it and also to the theory accounting for the degeneration of the pigment in birds' eggs. The exceptions are birds like the Wrens, the Nuthatches, the Chickadees, the Crested Flycatchers and the Bluebirds which build nests at the bottom of the cavities and lay spotted or blue eggs. The fact that they build unnecessary nests at the bottom of the holes shows that they have come to a hole-nesting habit comparatively re-

Fɪɢ. 119. Eggs of Ostrich, Hen and Hummingbird, showing size variation correlated with size of bird.

cently, for they must have first learned to build their nests in the open. The fact that they still do build nests and lay colored eggs indicates only the slowness of the course of evolution. It is interesting to note in passing, however, that the eggs of the Bluebird are the palest of all the Thrushes, sometimes practically white, disclosing the trend of evolution in changing what was once, doubtless, a protectively colored egg back to a pure white one.

It would not be feasible here to discuss the identification of birds' eggs by their color or size, for many kinds can be distinguished only by specialists. The only safe way for an amateur to identify most eggs is by identifying the bird that laid them, though with a little experience one can identify at sight most of the well-marked eggs.

The size of birds' eggs varies with the size of the bird, from those of the Hummingbird, which are about the size of beans, to those of

Fɪɢ. 120. A kiwi and its egg—the largest egg relative to the size of the bird.

the Ostrich, which are nearly the size of a man's head. Precocial birds, whose young are hatched in a much more advanced state than the altricial pirds, necessarily lay relatively larger eggs since development has to proceed farther in the egg and more food yolk has to be stored. The largest egg for the size of the bird is laid by the New Zealand Kiwi. The weight of the single egg averages one-third that of the bird. Not so large but still rather extreme as compared with the size of the bird are the eggs of the shore birds. The eggs of the Upland Plover, for example, are about twice the size of those of the Meadowlark, though the birds are about the same size, and those of the Spotted Sandpiper are about twice the size of those of the similar-sized Catbird (see Fig. 121). Precocial birds like the Grouse, which lay a large number of eggs, lay relatively smaller eggs than the shore birds.

The average number of eggs laid by birds in temperate climates is four and in the tropics half that number. The number has doubt-

FIG. 121. Spotted Sandpiper and Catbird with their eggs showing the different relative sizes in birds having precocial and altricial young.

less been fixed through the course of natural selection so that it compares favorably with the number of dangers to which the eggs and young are exposed. Thus, sea-birds, like the Murres, that nest on inaccessible cliffs where there are few enemies, lay but a single egg, while the game-birds and water-fowl whose eggs and young are exposed to a great many enemies lay from ten to twenty. While the number in a complement with each species, is subject to but little variation it is not at all indicative of the fecundity of the bird, for, when the nest is broken up, birds will ordinarily lay again and sometimes will continue laying throughout the season until they are finally successful in raising their young. The case of a Flicker that laid 71 eggs in 73 days has been cited many times, and it is not uncommon now-a-days to develop a strain of domestic hens that will lay over 300 eggs in a season, though if the eggs are not removed, they ordinarily stop laying and begin to incubate when they have laid fifteen to twenty.

The shape of birds' eggs varies from those that are quite long and slender, through those that are oval or sharply pointed, to those that are nearly spherical. Those of the Hummingbird and Ostrich show extremes of shape as well as size. The large eggs of shorebirds are sharply pointed, so that they will fit together like the pieces of a pie and be more easily covered by the incubating bird with its two brood spots separated by a line of feathers. Those of the Murres are pointed for another reason—to keep them from blowing off the rocks where they are laid without pretense of a nest. The ordinary shape of birds' eggs is ovoid, a shape which keeps them from rolling freely and yet which makes them fit together and be most comfortable for the incubating bird.

The parts of the bird's egg are the same as those of the egg of the domestic fowl or the same as those of most animals, for that matter, consisting of the yolk, the albumen, and the shell, with their respective membranes. The yolk is formed entirely in the ovary of the bird, the albumen in the upper two-thirds of the oviduct, and the shell in the lower third, the pigment ordinarily being the last thing added; though with some birds, like the Emu, the successive layers of shell are each pigmented and colored differently from the exterior.

THE YOUNG BIRDS, THEIR GROWTH AND CARE

Young birds at hatching are of two general types. They are either precocial or altricial. Precocial young resemble young chickens in that they are wide awake when hatched, are covered with down, and are able, very soon after drying off, to follow their parents in search of food, a large part of which they find by themselves. Altricial young, on the other hand, are naked or almost naked when hatched, their eyes are not yet open, and they are cared for in the nest by their parents for periods varying from a week or ten days with terrestrial sparrows, to nearly a year with the Condor and the Wandering Albatross.

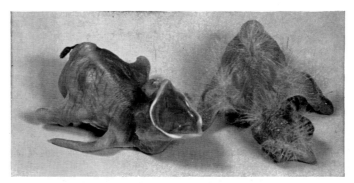

Fig. 122. Altricial young of Waxwing (left) and Goldfinch.

In general, terrestrial, diving and swimming birds have precocial young, while arboreal birds and birds that search their food on the wing, have altricial young. Among the former are the Loons and Grebes, the Ducks, Geese and Swans, the Shore Birds, the Marsh Birds, and the Fowl-like Birds. Some young, such as those of Gulls and Terns, may remain in the nest or, at least, have food brought to them for weeks, but in other respects are entirely precocial, being wide awake, covered with down, and able to run about shortly after hatching. Other young, such as those of Hawks, Owls, Night-hawks, and Whip-poor-wills, and even Herons, are covered with thick down when hatched but otherwise they are quite altricial, being blind at first and quite unable to help themselves for a long time. At the opposite extreme among altricial young are those of the Flicker, the Kingfisher, the Jays and the Waxwings, which are en-tirely naked. Some Woodpeckers have a few hair-like feathers when hatched, and those of the Cuckoo are thread-like. Young Cuckoos and Kingfishers are worthy of attention again when they come to attain their first real feathers for, unlike most birds, these remain in their sheaths until nearly full grown. For a time the young birds seem covered with tiny lead pencils, and the transformation to the fluffy feathers, by the breaking open of the sheaths, is very rapid, requiring but a few hours. With other young birds, the transformation from almost naked young into fluffy feathered creatures is gradual. Whatever down there is, is pushed out on the tips of the incoming juvenal feathers which begin to break their sheaths before they are a quarter grown. In the case of a Red winged Blackbird, for example, the 'pin-feathers' have pushed the down entirely out and are well grown by the end of the fifth day, and on the sixth, the sheaths of the 'pin-feathers' have begun to break. Three days later the feathers have unfolded sufficiently to hide most of the bare spots, and by the eleventh day the young bird is apparently fully feathered, except around the eye, which area, in Blackbirds, is

Fig. 123. Altricial young of Kingfisher (at right) and Swallow-tailed Kite showing variation in the amount of natal down.

the last to be clothed. Of course, the feathers continue to grow after the eleventh day, but the young bird has left the nest and is already able to fly short distances. The change, however, has been gradual, requiring several days, while in Cuckoos and Kingfishers it seems to occur within a few hours.

When the young hatch they are not fed immediately, the time elapsing before the first feeding varying with different species. The method of feeding likewise varies. Many birds are first fed by regurgitation. The parent bird swallows the food and gives it to the young in a partially digested state. Some, like the Mourning Doves and Goldfinches, continue this process as long as they feed the young: Herons and Bitterns swallow the food also, at least as

FIG. 124. Young Redwings five and ten days old.

long as the young are in the nest, and one never sees one of these
birds returning to its nest with anything in its bill though its throat
may be loaded. Waxwings use their crops as regular market-baskets
and return to the nest with their necks bulging with a variety of

FIG. 125. Female Ruby-throated Hummingbird with its short-billed young in a
teaspoon over its nest.

FIG. 126. Ruffed Grouse (precocial young) hatching.

small fruits and insects, mostly in a good state of preservation. Jays use their throats in a similar manner but, with the majority of common birds, this method of feeding is continued only a short time, if at all, and it is a familiar sight to see the parent birds returning to their young with insects or fruit in their bills.

The commonest method of feeding is that of the old bird putting its bill, containing the food, far down into the throat of the young. This prevents any live insect from escaping. In birds that regurgitate food, however, there are several different methods of transferring the food. In birds like the Pelican and Cormorants, which bring

FIG. 127. Ruffed Grouse five and ten days old.

back fish in their throat-pouches, the old bird merely opens its bill and permits the young to rummage around inside. Sometimes they almost disappear down the throat of the old bird. With the Herons, the old bird turns its head on the side and the young grasps the bill with a scissors-like action, dilating its lower mandible so as to catch whatever comes out of the throat of the old bird. To the onlooker, it appears like a very clumsy performance, but little food seems ever to be wasted by spilling. Young Mourning Doves have swellings at the corners of the mouth which the old birds press when they interlock bills, to inspire the proper swallowing action of the young. I once tried to raise a crippled young Dove and could not make it swallow anything, even that which was forcibly put into its throat, until I discovered the nervous adjustment between the swellings and the throat muscles. After that it was easy, for I merely had to touch the swellings and it was like pressing a button. The little bird's mouth flew open and the throat muscles commenced to work even before the food entered the bird's mouth.

With all birds there is a nervous adjustment to prevent overfeeding. Birds do not feed their young in rotation, as one might expect, but ordinarily they feed the hungriest one first and continue to feed him until some other one gets hungrier and stretches its neck further and cries louder. This might result in overfeeding the largest young one but, fortunately, when the young bird has had enough, its throat muscles refuse to work. So after each feeding the old bird looks down into the throat of the young one (the young bird, if well, keeps its mouth open for food as long as the parent is about), and if the last bug is not promptly swallowed, she fishes it out again and gives it to one of the other young. It is this habit of feeding first the one with the longest neck and widest mouth that results in the fatalities to the righful young in a nest where there is a young Cowbird, for the Cowbird always has the longest neck and the widest mouth and gets all the food.

After the young have left the nest the old birds are not so particular about putting the food far down the throat of the young, for the young bird has soon to catch insects or find food for itself. It is interesting to watch a family of young Swallows learning to catch insects on the wing. So long as they are in the nest, they are fed like other young, having the food placed far down their throats, but once they leave the nest, such caution ceases. It is but a short time before the old bird merely sweeps by the young one and drops the food into the open mouth without stopping, and when the youngsters are able to fly, the same operation is employed in full flight. It is as though the old birds were teaching the young to catch things out of the air. Young Duck Hawks learn in much the same way to strike their quarry in full flight. When the young are able to fly, the old birds merely swing by the nesting-ledge with the food in their talons, and the young ones fly out, turn over beneath the old bird, and strike at the food as though it were being carried along on its own wings.

FIG. 128. Young Common Cormorants taking food from parent's gullet.

The amount of food which birds, especially insectivorous species, require, is always a surprise to one observing it for the first time. The well-known experiment of feeding a young Robin all the earthworms it can eat at the time it leaves the nest can scarcely be improved upon. The result with the original Robin experimented with was that it consumed 14 feet of earth-worm in one day. Experiments with young Crows have shown that they require at least *half their own weight* of food each day merely to exist, and that they can easily consume food equivalent to their full weight each day when they are growing rapidly. Many young Crows that are kept in captivity, as well as other young birds, are starved to death because their owners do not realize how much food is required. They do not eat very much at a time but their digestion is so rapid that their parents feed them almost continuously from daylight until dark, and, as E. H. Forbush has said, they eat the equivalent of at least eight full meals each day. If one wishes to be duly impressed by the amount of food required by a young bird, he should put up an observation blind by a nest of young birds of almost any species. Quite naturally they do not require as much food when they are newly hatched as when they are ready to leave the nest. Birds that feed by regurgitation and those which bring back large pieces of

food naturally do not feed as often as those which make the trips to
the nest with only their bills full. Hawks usually feed only about
once an hour; Hummingbirds, once in twenty minutes; but a pair
of Chickadees that I watched at their nest made 35 trips to the nest
in 30 minutes. A pair of Rose-breasted Grosbeaks are recorded as
feeding their young 426 times in 11 hours, and a House Wren,
1,217 times in the 15 hours and 45 minutes of daylight.

When the young are small, and until they have developed their
coat of feathers, they require frequent brooding by the old bird
to keep them from getting cold and likewise to keep them from
getting too hot if the nest is exposed to the sun. Altricial young
are never brooded after they leave the nest but precocial young

Fig. 129. Chestnut-sided Warbler brooding young under breast and wings.

are brooded for five or six weeks (or until they grow the juvenal
feathers), wherever it strikes the fancy of the old bird, though seldom
in the nest which they have left. A pair of Canada Geese, however,
that I had in captivity, took their goslings each night back to the old
nest to be brooded, though it was not much more than a depression
in the ground. Florida Gallinules, and doubtless other marsh-birds,
as well, often make new nests or rafts of rushes on which to brood
their young. Wood Ducks, Grebes, and Swans often take their
young on their backs and brood them beneath their wings. Indeed
the Grebes often take this method of conveying their young to safety,
closing their wings down tight upon them and diving with them.
The Woodcock, on the other hand, is said to convey its young between its thighs to suitable feeding-spots, and it is apparently a

common practice with Rails to seize their young by any convenient appendage and rush them to safety.

The varying degrees of attachment for their young which birds show and their methods of expressing it are always interesting to observe. Few birds seem to feel much of a parental instinct when the young are freshly hatched. The instinct increases daily and reaches a maximum at the time the young are ready to leave the nest. The same is true of the bird's instinct to incubate. When the eggs are freshly laid the birds will desert them readily, but at the time they are hatching, even the most timid birds will cling to the nest in the presence of danger. Bird photographers should always

Fig. 130. Young Pied-billed Grebe climbing onto mother's dry back to be brooded.

bear this in mind and never try to photograph birds at their nests when they are just beginning to incubate or just beginning to brood. Most Hawks, Herons, Cormorants, Pelicans, Yellow-breasted Chats, and Mourning Doves have their parental instincts very poorly developed and readily desert their eggs or young in the presence of danger. Most Chickadees, and a great many Warblers and Vireos, on the other hand, have their parental instincts so highly developed that they pay no attention to dangers while they are incubating or brooding. At least they will permit very close approach and even let you stroke them while they cling to the nest. Between the two extremes there are all gradations, no two birds behaving exactly alike in the defense of their nests or young.

Many birds feign being wounded in an attempt to lure one away from the nest and drag themselves pitifully over the ground in the hope that the enemy will follow them and lose track of the nest or young. Other birds dart at one's head and attempt to inflict blows with their bills, their wings, or their talons, while the majority merely express their distress by loud calls which attract all the other birds to the vicinity.

Fig. 131. A Blackburnian Warbler's incubation instinct is stronger than its fear of man.

It is interesting to observe the varying times at which fear first develops in the young birds. It is apparently instilled into them by their parents, for when eggs from wild birds are hatched under domestic birds, the young seem never to develop the sense of fear for human beings. There are some exceptions to this statement, however, especially among some precocial birds which are extremely timid even when hatched under very quiet hens and lose their fear very gradually. In the wild state, precocial young seem to respond to this fear instinct as soom as they have dried off and are able to run. With altricial young, on the other hand, it is not until they are developing their feathers, a few days prior to leaving the nest, that they crouch and try to hide at one's approach. Before that time, they stretch up their necks and open their mouths for food just as freely for a human being as for their parents. At about the same time the young birds apparently come to a realization of the meaning of the different calls of their parents, and crouch for one note, stretch up their necks at another, or remain passive for a third. Anyone at all familiar with poultry knows of the various calls of the old hen to her chicks. Her vocabulary is not extensive but no one would deny the fact that she has a method of conveying many different instructions. They all crouch when she cries 'hawk,' they scatter when she cries 'cat,' and they rush to her when she cries 'food,' etc. Other birds are just the same but it takes a discerning ear to catch the differences in notes, and it is impossible to put them in print. Distress calls are usually recognized by all species of birds and they fly to the scene of trouble. Whether the other notes are understood by all species, or whether each species has its private lan-

though some of the shaky voices that we hear in the fall may possibly be from early hatched birds.

The time required for the young bird to acquire its full plumage varies with different species. Ordinarily, by the time the wing-feathers are full grown, the body feathers of the juvenal plumage begin to drop out and the first winter feathers come in. If the male and female are alike, this plumage, which is usually fully acquired by September, will be almost indistinguishable from that of the adults, but, in brightly colored species, having the male and female different, it will resemble the female or the male in winter plumage. The next spring it will have a complete or a partial moult of its body feathers to bring it into its breeding dress just as in the adult. Immature Scarlet Tanagers, Goldfinches and Indigo birds then closely resemble the adults, being only slightly less brilliant. With some of the Warblers, however, like the Redstart and Myrtle, and with the Purple Finch there is but a slight moult and the immature male still resembles the female with a few or none of the male feathers. This often results in the recording of female birds singing. Some birds seem to require even more than two years to attain their full brilliancy of plumage, but ordinarily, except for large birds like the Eagle or the Peacock, after the second year, the health of the bird will affect its plumage more than its age.

11

The Adaptations of Birds

Modification for Flight

One of the most wonderful cases of adaptation to be found in all nature is that of the flying bird. The modifications which the entire structure of the bird has undergone in its development from the ancient lowly reptile have been controlled primarily by the requisites of an efficient flying-machine. Other needs have been sacrificed or made subservient to the requirements of flight, so that today, except for degenerate forms, the bird stands as the ideal heavier-than-air flight mechanism. It is little wonder that man, in his endeavor to learn to fly, went to the bird and tried to invent wings that would lift him from the ground. But wings, alone, do not make the bird nor account for its ability to defy the action of gravity. A man with wings is no more a bird and capable of flight than is a hat because it has feathers. It is not alone the fact that birds have wings that makes them capable of flight but it is the hundreds of little and big adaptations of their bodies, their legs, their tails, their heads, their very bones, that lift them from the ground and drive them successfully through the air. It was not until these principles were thoroughly understood and applied that a successful airplane was flown.

When one visits a museum or a large aviary where birds from all parts of the world are assembled, one is at first led to believe by their various sizes and shapes that they have little in common except wings and feathers. But when one examines them at all critically, he discovers that the apparent diversity of form is quite superficial, and that down underneath they are all fundamentally alike. Their different methods of securing food have given rise to different bills and feet, which we will consider shortly, but aside from these conspicuous parts, their structures are very similar. Let us see, therefore, what are the main requirements of an airplane and how these are met by the bird.

1. LIGHTNESS: Above all else, a flying-machine must be light. The materials used must be as light as compatible with strength and there must be no unnecessary materials or parts. So, in a bird, we find, developed from the crude reptilian scales, the structures called feathers, which are as delicate as they are beautiful, but which, withal, are the strongest structures for their size and weight known. We cannot take space here for a full discussion of their wonderful variety of form and color; we can merely call attention to their lightness, their strength, their durability, the beautifully accurate way in which they grow on the bird's wings and body, so that each one has a particular place and a particular manner in which to lay; overlapping certain other feathers and in turn being overlapped, producing the intricate color patterns of some birds and yet at all times, giving the greatest protection to the bird and involving no unnecessary weight. Neither can we stop to discuss the arrangement of the flight quills which give the greatest possible resistance to the air on the downward stroke of the wing and the least resistance on the upward or non-effective stroke. We can merely suggest running one's fingers or a pencil through the flight quills of a fowl to show how easily it passes one way and with what resistance the other. And we will return shortly to a fuller discussion of feathers.

Then there are other ways in which a bird is made light. Examine the cleaned bones from a fowl that has served its purpose at Sunday dinner, not one of the bones, but all of them, for there are many lessons to be learned therefrom. One of the things that impresses us first is their unusual lightness. If we break one of them we see the reason: the marrow that fills the bones of mammals is absent, the bones are hollow, and their walls, moreover, are thin. Here is another great saving in weight. They are, likewise, connected by air-sacs with the lungs and filled with air. These air-sacs fill every available space within the body of the bird that is not occupied by some organ and when they are all filled with air the bird becomes much lighter for its size.

Examine a bird's mouth and one finds not the slightest vestige of a tooth. The first birds had them but they all disappeared ages ago because they were heavy and required heavy jaws to support them and heavy muscles to manipulate them. A real, efficient flying bird could not have all this extra weight, so 'Mother Nature' devised another method of grinding the bird's food and today it is done in the stomach, which is called the gizzard, and the bird's head weighs but little.

The first bird, likewise, had a long lizard-like tail with feathers along the sides but this, too, was heavy and so gradually it became shortened until today all of the feathers are borne on one bone and the skeleton of the tail is very short. And so if we went on considering each and every part of the bird, we would discover how it has been made as light as its required strength permits.

2. STRENGTH: If lightness were the only requirement of the flying-machine, it would be a simple matter to construct one, but, unfortunately, great strength is likewise needed, and it is the combination of the two that is so difficult to achieve. The framework of the machine must be extremely strong to withstand the tremendous strains, and so we find, with the bird, that its framework or skeleton is the most rigid of all animals. Bones fuse together to provide greater strength and are reinforced by the development of new bones from mere bumps or processes to act as props. One cannot fully understand the many beautiful ways in which the bird's skeleton is strengthened unless he has some knowledge of the skeletons of other animals with which to compare it, and so here we can merely call attention to the rigidity of the bird's backbone and pelvis, the box-like form of the thorax with the ribs firmly fastened both to the backbone and to the breast bone, and further strengthened by overlapping processes. The familiar 'wishbone' is nothing more nor less than the two collar-bones fused together to give greater strength to the attachment of the wings, and so on.

If one examines the breast-bone of a bird, he discovers that it is not flat as in man, but has a relatively enormous ridge down the middle for the attachment of muscles, the familiar breast muscles or white meat of the fowl. These are the powerful muscles that manipulate the wings, relatively hundreds of times more powerful than the similar muscles in man.

3. COMPACTNESS: A third requisite of a flying-machine is compactness; the heavier parts must all lie close to the center of gravity. There must be no great weight on the wings or the tail or it will not be steady. This is most strikingly accomplished in the bird. We

have already spoken of the shortening of the tail, the loss of teeth and heavy parts of the head, and the location of the flight muscles on the breast-bone instead of on the wings. These are all adaptations, not only to make the bird lighter, but also to bring the weight close to the center of gravity. What is true of the wings is likewise true of the legs. Birds do not have fat calves. Most of the muscles are on the upper leg close to the body, and they are prolonged to the tips of the toes as very light tendons, just as is done in the wings. The body itself is short and deep for the same reason of bringing the heavy liver, gizzard, and intestines as close to the center of gravity as possible.

4. POWER: A fourth requisite of a machine that will fly is power. Until gasoline and the gasoline engine were discovered, flight was impossible because all the known engines and fuels were too heavy. Great advance has been made in recent years in improving the engines, making them lighter and more powerful for the amount of fuel used, but still the great problem and the greatest drawback to long-continued flights has been the weight of the fuel. An ordinary airplane can carry sufficient gasoline to drive it only a relatively few hundred miles before it has to descend or refuel. Atomic reactors produce much greater power for the same weight and the range of planes as well as submarines has been greatly extended but I doubt if they are even yet as efficient as the birds. Think of the Golden Plover that starts on a non-stop trip from Nova Scotia to northern South America or from Alaska to the Hawaiian Islands, distances of over 2,500 miles, with only the fat stored up on their bodies to serve as fuel. Surely gasoline is not the last word in fuel for airplanes.

If one watches a captive bird closely, he can see the feathers of its breast and elsewhere pulsating in accord with the throbbing of the heart. If one counts the pulsations, he will learn how rapidly the heart of a bird beats compared with that of man, indicating how much more rapidly all of its processes work. The bird's temperature is normally nearly ten degrees higher than that of man, which means that its tissues are burned up and replaced much more quickly, and it means that energy in the form of muscular power is liberated much more rapidly. What a strange misshapen creature man would be if he had relatively the muscular power of a bird.

And so in these four respects, in their modifications for lightness, strength, compactness, and power, all birds are much alike in spite of their many apparent differences. But all birds do not fly alike or in equal amounts, nor are their modifications all carried to the same extreme. As is well known, some birds, like the Ostrich, the Penguin, and the Kiwi have lost entirely the power of flight; and birds like the domestic fowl are far inferior in this respect to the Hawk or the Eagle.

It is interesting to note the differences in the flight of various groups of birds and to try to find correlations in their structures. Thus, if we consider the wings of a Bluebird or a Robin as of normal or average proportions, and their method of flight by continuous beating of the wings, that which is normal to most birds, we find four general modifications correlated with specialized methods of flying. The first of these is that found among terrestrial birds like the domestic fowl, or the Ruffed Grouse that seldom fly except to escape their enemies, when it is necessary that they should be able to rise quickly and fly very rapidly for short distances. The type of wing developed among this class of birds is one that is much shorter and rounder than the average, and it is moved much more rapidly. It would be a distinct disadvantage for a bird that has to fly long distances to have this type of wing as it would soon tire, but it is approximated in many of the Flycatchers and such Hawks, as the Sharp-shinned and Cooper's, that ordinarily lie in wait for their prey and dart out after it. With this type of wing they are able to develop full speed almost immediately. The wings of Rails are likewise of this type though, because of lack of use, their breast muscles have been reduced and their flight is weak. In the case of the Ruffed Grouse it has been shown that three or four flights, equalling perhaps a half mile altogether, so fatigues the bird that it can no longer fly.

The second type is very different being a large, broad, rounded wing, such as is found in the Eagles, Buzzards, and larger Hawks. It is adapted for soaring, and birds having this type of wing can maintain themselves in the air sometimes for hours without flapping their wings, merely by taking advantage of the upward currents of air and adjusting their wings accordingly. A third type of wing found among birds, that likewise enables them to take advantage of the air-currents, is the long, narrow wing, found best developed among the Albatrosses and Man-o'-war birds, but also among the Gulls and Terns and other sea-birds that are on the wing a large part of the time. Among the Hawks, the Marsh Hawk and the Fish Hawk have longer and narrower wings than the others and they seldom soar and never lie in wait for their prey but spend their time sailing back and forth over the water or over the fields, for the long, narrow wing is best adapted for what may be called gliding. The fourth type is that of the pointed wing, usually broad at the base and moderately long. This wing is best adapted for speed of long duration and is that found among the Swallows and the Falcons, birds which pursue their prey on the wing and strike it at full speed. They need to have full control of their flight at all times and to develop great speed, and the moderately long, pointed wing seems best adapted for this. Thus one might go on analyzing the differences among the wings of birds and perhaps find a reason for even the minor differences that are known to occur.

The Feathers

In the whole field of nature there is no structure more distinctive of any group of animals than the feathers of birds. We define the Class Aves, or birds, as warm-blooded Vertebrates more or less covered with feathers, but the mere mention of feathers is really sufficient to distinguish them from all other animals. Nor is there any structure more highly specialized or better adapted to the functions which it has to fulfil than the feather. There is little question that the feathers of birds represent the highly modified and greatly specialized scales that covered their reptilian ancestors, but so glorified have they become that it is necessary to study their development in the embryo to see the faintest resemblance.

During its development, the feather receives its nourishment and blood-supply from the dermis or lower layer of the skin, but when the feather is full grown, this is discontinued and the feather becomes a dead structure composed entirely of material from the inner or Malpighian layer of the epidermis. Its hollow base fits over a tiny papilla at the bottom of the pit in which the feather sets. This papilla is composed of both layers of the integument, and its cells lie dormant until the feather is pulled out or drops out by the process of moulting. This stimulates their activity, and once more the Malpighian cells of the epidermis supply the materials out of which the feather is manufactured, and the dermal cells supply the

nourishment. The exact way in which the beautiful leaf-like apend-
age is developed inside the slender cylinder, which we commonly
call the 'pin feather,' is difficult to explain in a few words, but it is
easier to understand after we know the parts of the mature feather
and their relations one to another. Let us, therefore, examine the
mature feather and see of what it is composed. The contour feathers
covering the birds' bodies are ordinarily more complete than the
specialized flight and tail-feathers or any of the ornamental plumes,
so we will select one of these, such as the flank-feather of a Grouse
or of an ordinary fowl.

Superficially, the feather bears a general resemblance to a leaf with

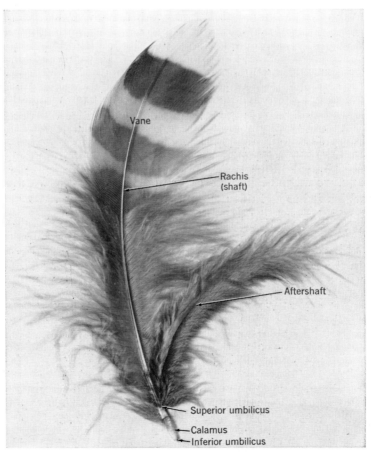

Fig. 134. Flank feathers of a Grouse showing parts of a complete feather.

its petiole, midrib, and expanded portion, but the resemblance goes no further. A careful examination of the 'petiole' portion of the shaft that fits into the skin shows it to be hollow except for a little dried pith that encased the dermal tissue while the feather was growing. This portion is called the *calamus,* and at its inner end it has a minute opening, the *inferior umbilicus,* through which the blood-vessels entered while the feather was alive. The outer end of the calamus is marked by another minute pit, the *superior umbilicus,* located at about the point where the web of the feather begins and the shaft becomes solid. The solid portion of the shaft or the midrib of the feather is called the *rhachis* meaning ridge. On each side of it is the expanded portion of the feather called the *vane, web,* or *vexillum.* The exposed part of the vanes is comparatively firm and stiff and resistant to anything being pushed through it, but the portion covered by the overlapping of other feathers is soft and downy. At the juncture of the calamus and the rhachis and just below the superior umbilicus, the contour feather of the Grouse bears a replica of the main feather called the *aftershaft* or *hyporhachis.* In a few birds, like the Emeus and Cassowaries, this

FIG. 135. Feather magnified to show structure.

aftershaft is as long as the main feather, and the feathers appear double, but in most birds it is considerably smaller; and in a great many species, and in the flight and tail-feathers of all, it is lacking altogether. There is some reason for believing that the main feather represents a development from the upper half of the reptilian scale and that the aftershaft represents the lower half, but the feathers of modern birds show great variation as to its presence or absence, even on different parts of the same bird. When present it certainly aids in keeping the bird warm by supplying a double insulation, a function that is more often supplied by down feathers growing about the bases of the contours.

Let us now place a small portion of the web of the feather under a lens and see of what it is composed. What at first looks like a con-

tinuous leaflike surface we find is very easily broken up into a series
of plates, arranged on either side of the main shaft, set at a slight
angle, and more or less overlapping at their edges. These are called
barbs and, if they are again examined with a lens, it will be seen
that they are not exactly plates, for their apparent breadth is due
to innumerable little branches set close together, on each side of the
barb, known separately as *barbules*. These barbules overlap, and
when examined under a high power of the microscope are seen to
have their overlapping edges furnished with two types of projections
called *barbicels* and *hamuli* or *hooklets*. These microscopic projections, when present, furnish the interlocking device which gives the
contour and flight feathers their consistency and stiffness. Without
them the feather would appear downy, as is usually the case in that
portion of the feather that is covered by the overlapping of other
feathers.

We have now described the parts of the complete feather. We will
not at this time go deeper into the structure of the parts, the deposition of pigments and other methods of producing their many hues,
but merely call attention to some of the commoner modifications of
feather structure that anyone interested can find in the plumage of
almost every bird that falls into his hands.

We have been describing a typical contour feather. In some the
downy portion is reduced to a minimum, the aftershaft is wanting,
and the barbicels and hamuli are greatly developed. Such are the
tail-feathers and flight-quills of most birds. In others the shaft may
be greatly drawn out, barbs and barbules absent for most of its
extent and present only at the tip, as in the ornamental plumes
of some of the Birds of Paradise and some of the Hummingbirds;
or the barbs may be well developed throughout and the barbules
largely wanting, producing the filmy plumes of the Egrets.

More or less completely investing the body beneath the contour
feathers are a series of *down-feathers* or *plumulæ*. The typical down-
feathers lack the rhachis of the contour feathers, the barbs branching
directly from the calamus, and they lack entirely the barbicels and
hamuli so that they have no stiffness and are altogether downy.
Young birds in their first or natal plumage have nothing but down
feathers, and the amount of down varies with the different species.
Young Kingfishers and young Flickers have no natal covering whatsoever; most ordinary birds have a sparse covering on the top of the

head and back; the down of young Cuckoos is quite hairlike; while the down of young Hawks and Owls almost completely covers the head and body. The downy covering is carried to the extreme in gallinaceous birds, waterfowl, shore birds, marsh birds, and others which have precocial young able to run about as soon as hatched. The natal down is not strictly the same as that of adult birds, for it really represents the incoming juvenal feathers and is pushed out on the tips of these feathers as shown in the accompanying photographs of the Marsh Hawk (Fig. 136). The structure, however, is essentially the same, a rhachis being absent and the barbules relatively few in number and without the interlocking devices.

Fig. 136. Young Marsh Hawk (left) with natal down being pushed out by incoming juvenile feather. Right, below shows the continuation of the shaft from natal down to juvenile feather. Right above, the same magnified.

In some birds, feathers are found intermediate between the down and the contour feathers, and they are called 'semiplumes.' The rhachis is present and the barbs and barbules in full number, but the barbicels and hamuli are lacking. These feathers are ordinarily completely covered by the contour feathers and serve the same purpose as the down in preventing radiation and keeping the bird warm.

In a few birds there are some specialized down feathers growing in large patches on the breast or over the hips or in smaller groups scattered through the plumage. These *powder-down feathers* are conspicuous in the Herons but very small in the Parrots. The feathers in these powder-down patches grow continuously and the tips of the barbs and barbicels are continually breaking off in the form of a fine powder which sifts over the rest of the plumage as a soft whitish bloom transforming the coal-black feathers on the back of a Swallow-tailed Kite into a soft gray, the feathers of a male Marsh Hawk into a pale gray, and giving a peculiar filmy appearance to the feathers of the Herons. This bloom easily brushes off and is entirely lost in most museum specimens.

Another type of modified feather is that known as the *filoplume* or thread feather which has an almost invisible rhachis and only a slight tuft of barbs at the tip. They are scattered more or less throughout the plumage of some birds and seem to increase in number with age. They are quite conspicuous in an old fowl after it has been plucked and before it has been singed. Their function is not well understood. The bristles covering the nostrils of Crows and Jays and at the angles of the mouth of Whip-poor-wills, Flycatchers, and other birds are likewise modied feathers of a somewhat different type from the filoplumes.

Feather Arrangements

A discussion of feathers is not complete without a word about their arrangement on the bird's body. The general impression given by a bird's plump, well-rounded appearance is that the feathers are borne all over the bird's head and body, but even the most casual examination will show that this is not the case. Instead they grow in certain well-defined areas or lines called *feather tracts* or *pterylæ*, and the spaces between them that are more or less bare except for a little down are called *apteria* (singular *apterium*). The exact extent

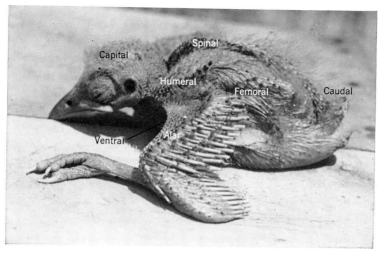

FIG. 137. Young Crow showing feather tracts.

of these feather-tracts varies considerably with the different species of birds, but their number and position are remarkably constant. It is probable that the original birds had feathers rather evenly distributed over their bodies, and a very few, like the Ostriches and

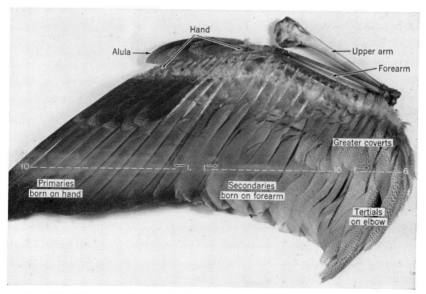

FIG. 138. Wing of a Canvasback showing arrangement of flight feathers.

Penguins that do not fold their wings compactly as do most birds, still retain this characteristic. All others, however, have developed the bare spaces to accommodate the folded wings and have lost their feathers wherever they would impede the action of the wings or legs, relying upon the extent of the adjacent feathers to cover these bare areas. The feather-tracts and apteria are best observed on young birds before the incoming feathers have broken from their sheaths, and the preceding photograph of a young Crow shows well the general arrangement. The *capital tract* covers the top and sides of the head more or less completely. The *spinal tract* extends from the head to the tail but may be variously branched or interrupted. The *caudal tract* includes the tail-feathers and their coverts, usually of the same number as the tail feathers but sometimes more and sometimes less. The *humeral tract* lies across the upper arm and forms the so-called scapulars. The *femoral tract* lies across the thigh and gives protection to the side of the body. The *ventral tract* starts on the neck and divides to pass down each side of the breast, leaving bare spaces of varying size beneath each wing and on the middle of the breast. The *alar tract* covers the wing in a very definite manner and has been more intensively studied than any of the others, so that names have been given to the different rows of feathers, and the constancy of the number and the position of the feathers in the different species of birds has been recognized. The *crural tract*, covering the outside of the leg, is concealed in the photograph of the young Crow.

The main flight-feathers are of two groups, the *primaries* and the *secondaries*. The former are borne on the modified hand of the bird, the latter on the forearm, as illustrated in the accompanying photograph of the wing of a Canvasback from which the skin and most of the small feathers have been removed (Fig. 138). The innermost of the secondary group of feathers borne on the 'elbow' are often elongated and spoken of as *tertiaries* or *tertials*. At the base of each of the flight-feathers there grows a smaller feather called a *greater covert*. Each greater covert, similarly, has a *middle covert* and each middle covert a *lesser covert*. There are always several rows of lesser coverts, and the various rows of coverts overlap like the shingles on a barn. The thumb, which is more or less free in birds, bears a few feathers which together are spoken of as the *alula* or false wing.

The definiteness of the arrangement of a bird's feathers and the importance of the feather-tracts, and more particularly the apteria, can best be appreciated by one who attempts to mount a bird so as to make it look 'natural.' A successful taxidermist knows well the anatomy of the bird and makes a special study of the 'pterylosis,' or feather-arrangement, of the various species which he attempts to mount. One of the greatest helps to quick and accurate field observation of birds is a knowledge of feather arrangement.

STRUCTURE AND HABIT

Discussing the bird as a flying machine, we have endeavored to point out how all birds are intrinsically alike in their general structure because of the physical requirements of flight. It remains for us, now, to call attention to the differences in the structure of birds arising from their varied habits, especially those of procuring their food. Whether the differences in the form of bills and feet that are found among birds are due to their different methods of securing their food, or whether it is the other way around, and their method of feeding is due to the differences in the structure of these parts is a disputed point which we will not try to settle here. Suffice it to say that the majority of scientists today believe that modifications of the individual bird which are the direct result of its environment are not inherited, but that the process of Natural Selection or the Survival of the Fittest serves to weed out those birds which do not show adaptations to their mode of living, and the result is the same. That is to say, the differences in the form of bill, and feet, and wings that we are familiar with today are the sum total of a great many little and big variations that have been preserved through the course of evolution because they were adapted or well suited to the mode of life of the bird. That a beautiful adaptation between a bird's structure and its mode of life does exist, there can be no doubt, and one of the most interesting studies in ornithology is the endeavor to learn the reason for each little peculiarity of structure that we find in our familiar birds.

The changes or adaptations that have occurred in the evolution of birds have been for the most part gradual. This is evidenced by the fact that today the birds that have arisen from common ancestors are still, broadly speaking, more like each other than they are like other birds, in spite of their diversity of habits. Were it not so it would be impossible to group birds into Orders and Families. The fact that some birds have been more plastic than others in their adaptations and have developed parallel with unrelated birds of similar habits, caused many of the difficulties in the earlier schemes of classification. Thus the Hawks and Owls are really very distantly related, the Owls belonging near the Nighthawks and Whip-poor-wills, but because of the Owls' carnivorous habits, they look superficially like the Hawks and were put with them for the sake of convenience in the first editions of the A. O. U. Check List of N. A. birds. Herons, Kingfishers, and Loons, likewise, have bills that are much alike, adapted to spearing fish, but in other respects they are very different and no one would think of calling them closely related.

A good example of divergent evolution, on the other hand, occurs among the Gulls, Terns, and Skimmers, which are really closely related as shown by their anatomical structure but which have bills which are extremely different in form, probably because of their different feeding habits. Shrikes, Grosbeaks, and Warblers, belonging to the Order of Perching Birds, likewise are similar in all their structures except their bills, and it is natural to suppose that they had a common ancestor and that their variously shaped bills have arisen as adaptations to particular feeding habits. But, as before intimated, it may be that the history of these birds was the other way around, and that these diverse bills have persisted from the thousands of possible variations of their ancestors because the individuals were able to adapt their habits to fit their modified structures. Indeed there is much evidence to support the belief that both factors have been important in the course of evolution.

Irrespective of how the changes have come about, let us consider some of the structures or implements of birds in relation to the birds' methods of life. Let us suggest in a few paragraphs a field that promises rich rewards to the careful observer.

THE IMPLEMENTS OF BIRDS

When one passes through the halls of any of our large museums and inspects the collections of mounted birds from all over the world, one is impressed by the great variety of form and color. Almost every imaginable combination of colors is found represented in the plumage of some bird, and the many modifications of size and shape are such as to leave one confused by the heterogeneous assemblage. One is almost led to believe that Nature has given loose rein to her imagination and allowed her most fantastic dreams to take the form of birds. Yet we are constrained to believe that there is a reason for everything, that no structure exists unless perfectly adapted to the function which it has to perform. The varied colors of birds we will consider later; in these paragraphs we will consider some of the modifications of bill and feet, the implements of birds.

The long legs, slender neck, and the great bent bill of the Flamingo, we are told, are eminently adapted to its peculiar method of feeding on the minute mollusc life of the tropical mud-flats where it lives. The tremendous bills of the South American Toucans and African Hornbills serve as arms for reaching far out to the smaller branches for the fruits upon which these ungainly creatures feed. But let us consider some of the commoner North American birds with reference to their food and see if there are similar reasons for their variety of form.

The Hawks, with their strong, hooked bills, sharp talons, and powerful wings fitted for the pursuit of small birds and mammals, we have already mentioned, and have noted that the type of bill and foot are so necessary to birds having a carnivorous diet, that the Owls, though unrelated, have developed similar structures. One group of the common perching birds, the Shrikes, have taken up a carnivorous diet and have likewise developed hawklike bills, although their feet are of the ordinary perching type and are not used to assist them in securing their prey. The Vultures, on the other hand, which have degenerated from a predaceous habit to a diet of carrion, while retaining the hooked bill for rending flesh, have lost the powerful talons and the accompanying strength of limb through disuse so that now they even spring from the ground with difficulty.

But, if one examines more closely such a group of birds as the Hawks, all having the same type of food, one discovers differences of form of body and wings according to their method of securing their prey, as already pointed out. There are, for example, those like the Red-shouldered and Red-tailed species, which find their quarry while soaring high in the air with their keen eyes fixed upon the ground. These have broad, rounded wings, fanlike tails, and rather heavy bodies. Others, like the Marsh Hawk, beat back and forth close to the ground, seldom if ever soaring, and these have long narrow wings and slender bodies. Still others like the Cooper's and Sharp-shinned species, remain perched on some outpost awaiting the approach of their quarry and then dart out after it, and these have short, rounded wings for sudden bursts of speed.

Another group of animal feeders are those which feed upon fish, frogs, and crayfish. Practically all have long, pointed, javelin-like bills for spearing their prey, but their various methods of catching the fish have brought about modifications of their other structures. The Herons and Cranes, which catch their fish by stalking them in shallow water, have long, slender legs for wading and long toes for distributing their weight and keeping them from sinking into the soft mud. The Kingfishers, on the other hand, which secure their fish by plunging from above, have little use for their legs and these, following nature's economy, have degenerated. The Terns, likewise, with similar habits, have weak legs, although the toes are webbed for swimming. The Gulls, which have become scavengers and seldom plunge for their food, have developed somewhat hooked bills for rending the flesh of the larger dead fish upon which they feed.

Another fish-eating bird, and one that plunges for its quarry, is the Osprey or Fish Hawk. This bird still retains the sharp, hooked bill characteristic of its family and so, instead of spearing its fish as does the Kingfisher, it catches them in its strong, sharp, talons and the soles of its feet are armed with sharp horny tubercles to cut through the slime covering the fish and keep it from slipping from its grasp. When the Osprey rises from the water with its prey and flies to some high tree to devour it, it has merely to continue holding it in its talons in order to tear it to pieces with its strong bill. But when the Tern or the Kingfisher rises from the water, the small fish is transfixed by the partially opened bill of the bird. (All of the fish which I have examined that have been speared by Terns or Kingfishers have shown the two holes made by both mandibles.) Just how the bill is extricated is a mystery to me unless it is done under the water before the bird rises. Perhaps some observer, who has been more fontunate than I, can explain it.

Others of the fish-eating birds, such as the Loons and Grebes, are expert divers and pursue the fish beneath the water. They have powerful legs with strong webbed or lobed toes, the legs being situated far back like the propeller of a boat so that, although most graceful on the water, they are extremely awkward and almost helpless on land.

The group of insect-eating birds is large and varied, for there are many kinds of insects and many ways of securing them. Some insects live in the soft mud about the shores and marshes, and for these the birds must probe; some live among the leaves and harder soil of the forest floor, and for these the birds must scratch. Others live within the trunks and branches of trees, and to secure these the birds must be proficient carpenters supplied with chisels for gouging. Still other insects spend most of their time darting hither and thither in the sunlight and these must be caught on the wing. Lastly, there are those insects that hide in the grass or among the leaves of shrubs and trees, and these must be searched out with keen eyes. And so, among birds, we have probers in the Snipe and Woodcock, scratchers in the Grouse and Quail, borers in the Woodpeckers, flight-feeders in the Swallows, Swifts and Nighthawks, and gleaners in the Blackbirds, Thrushes, Vireos, and Warblers. In each group of birds we find those modifications of bill, feet, wings, tail, tongue, and eyes which best fit the birds for securing the insects in their particular way.

Among the vegetable feeders the largest number live upon seeds and are of rather generalized structure except for their bills which are heavy and conical like those of the well-known Sparrows and carried to the extreme in the Grosbeaks. There are a few birds like our Hummingbirds, the tropical Honey Creepers, and the African Sunbirds which take a large part of their sustenance from the nectar of flowers. These birds have slender, probe-like bills and more or less tubular tongues modified so as to be best suited for sucking the nectar from the various-shaped corollas of the flowers. Among the three-hundred-odd species of Hummingbirds we find almost every conceivable variation in the shape of the bill, from those like Docimastes, with probes nearly three inches long for sucking the nectar from large tubular flowers, to those of the tiny Rhamphomicron, with a bill scarcely half an inch in length, so short that the Hummer alights on the base of the flower and pierces the nectary in an unlawful way. A few Hummingbirds have curved bills, one almost sickle-shaped, and others slightly upturned, and all are adapted for feeding on particular flowers.

Other vegetable feeders are found among the waterfowl, a considerable part of the food of many species consisting of the leaves, stems, or roots of aquatic plants. Their broad, flat, fluted bills and their curiously fringed tongues are excellently adapted for sifting their food from the silt and water, and their bills are so sensitive that they can locate their food no matter how roily the water or how dark the night. One group of Ducks called the Diving Ducks find their food in deep water and it is interesting to observe that in those species like the Canvasback and Scaup Ducks which dive without using their wings, the feet are placed far back toward the tail and are relatively very large. In species like the Oldsquaw and the Scoters that use their wings under the water and in all of the Dabbling Ducks, like the Mallard, and Pintail, and Teal, the feet are relatively much smaller. The Diving Ducks, likewise, have much shorter necks and stockier bodies than the Dabbling Ducks, another adaptation to their mode of life.

Finally, there are birds which feed almost entirely upon fruits, and a few, the Sapsuckers, which derive most of their nourishment from the sap of trees. This they secure by drilling a series of small holes through the bark and establishing regular 'sugar bushes,' visiting the different trees as often as the sap collects. Occasionally, it is reported, the sap ferments and the unsophisticated Sapsuckers are treated to a beverage which rapidly causes them to act in a questionable manner. Indeed one has been reported to have become so confused that it mistook a man's leg for the limb of a tree, and very often they fly into windows, or dash themselves against the sides of houses, or fly erratically through the trees as though they did not see very distinctly. Whether this is due to fermented sap or to some other cause, has never been definitely settled and there is still plenty of opportunity for experiment and observation to establish the truth. The Sapsuckers are degenerate Woodpeckers, and although they still retain the characteristic bill, feet, and stiff tails, their tongues, instead of being greatly protrusible, spearlike, and armed with barbs as in the true Woodpeckers, have become split and brushlike for better gathering the sap.

Were we to consider fully the food of all species of birds, we would discover that there is scarcely an animal or vegetable substance that does not furnish the food of some group of birds. Between the Loons and Grebes that find their food at the bottom of the lakes, and the Swallows that dart over the trees, there are birds, probing in the soil, scratching its surface, turning over fallen leaves, gleaning through the grass and herbage, searching the leaves and twigs of shrubs, chiselling in the trunks of trees, and climbing about the branches; and each bird has some adaptations, some modifications, some implements that are fitted to its own peculiar food and method of securing it.

12

Plumage Coloration and Plumage Change

The Coloration of Birds:

If you have followed the hoarse song of the Scarlet Tanager and found him perched on some dead branch ablaze in the sunlight; if you have noted the emerald back and the ruby throat of the Hummingbird as he flashed through your garden; or if you have seen the Indigo Bunting change from pale to deepest blue and then to black, as you moved around him, you must certainly have begun

FIG. 139. A White Red-shouldered Hawk (albinism).

to wonder at the marvels of bird coloration. Then, if you have tramped the woods and heard the Grouse rumble from the roadside and the Woodcock go whistling from under your feet, or if you have tried in vain to locate the Vireo singing in the tree-top you must have been impressed by that law of Nature that causes her children to be clothed so differently. For the Grouse and Woodcock and the Vireo in their haunts are as invisible to the untrained eye as though they were but a part of the twigs and leaves that surround them, while the Tanagers and Hummingbirds hold the eyes of even the least observant. What, then, are the laws determining that one bird shall be clad like the sun and his neighbor like the soil? What is the reason for this brilliancy, on the one hand, and how is the concealment, on the other, brought about? Certainly there is enough of interest in the coloration of birds to make it worth our while to analyze the problem in some detail.

Let us begin by considering the actual colors which make up the birds' coloration, for they are very different in their origin as well as in their general effect. One who ordinarily thinks of the colors of animals as produced by pigments or color-granules deposited within the skin or hair will be surprised by the small percentage of the colors of birds' feathers that are produced in this way. In ordinary birds in fact, there are thought to be but three pigments in any of the feathers: reds, yellows, and browns. A green pigment occurs in the African Plantain-eaters and a few other birds but in other birds the green is due to a yellow or brown pigment overlaid with a structure that refracts the light. Blue and all the metallic colors are due entirely to this process of refraction, the exposed portion of the feather being coated with a transparent colorless layer of extreme thinness (8-1000th of an inch) which breaks up the rays of light. A Scarlet Tanager is red in any light because the red is a pigment, but an Indigo Bunting or a Bluebird is blue only by reflected light, when refraction occurs. Thus, when a Bluebird gets wet or when it is perched between one and the sun, it will appear only black or brownish. This fact adds to the difficulty of bird-study, if also to the interest, for everyone has had the experience, occasionally, of being unable to distinguish the colors of a bird even though at close range. It doubtless also accounts for many of the strange descriptions of birds that one receives from inexperienced observers.

Some authorities claim that a black pigment is also to be found in the feathers of birds, but when the brown pigment is very dense it appears black, and it seems impossible to distinguish between the two. Occasionally an excess of this brown or black pigment develops in the feathers of an individual which will make it appear much darker than the other members of the same species. This is called *melanism* (from the Greek *melas,* meaning black) and apparently it can sometimes be brought about by subjecting moulting birds to extreme humidity.* In nature, regions of extreme humidity usually produce darker races of birds than arid regions. Thus, the Sooty Song Sparrow of the Pacific Coast is so much darker than the Desert Song Sparrow of Arizona that one would not hesitate to call them distinct species were it not for the fact that their color patterns are identical. The dark and light phases of the Rough-legged and Swainson's Hawks are other examples of *melanism,* but even more

Fig. 140. A Cory's Least Bittern (erythrism).

familiar is the case of the black and gray squirrels, examples of each occurring in a single litter of young without reference to sex or vigor. In this case humidity can play no part, though it is said that the black phase was formerly more abundant when the country was heavily forested, and it is still the dominant form where the primeval timber exists, while the gray phase is the abundant form of the wood-lot and open country.

The opposite of *melanism* is *albinism* (from the Latin *albus,* meaning white). It is caused by an absence or degeneration of the pigment. Pure albinos are snow-white, having no pigment whatsoever

* See C. W. Beebe. Geographic Variations in Birds, with Especial Reference to the Effects of Humidity, Zoologica I, pp. 1-41.

and the eyes are red owing to the blood showing through the unpigmented iris. They are apparently much more frequent with domestic animals than in the wild state, as in the familiar white mice, rats, and rabbits, but they are likely to occur at any time with any species. The brown pigment seems the most likely to disappear, pure albinos of birds having red or yellow in their plumage being extremely rare. Partial albinos are much more frequent with all species, and mottled Robins and Sparrows or birds with white feathers in unusual places are not at all infrequent. Usually this partial albinism is symmetrical on each side of the bird but is not always so. The exact cause of albinism is not known though it is thought to be a form of physical weakness due to inbreeding or to some other cause.

More unusual than albinism is what is called *dichromatism* (from the Greek di + khromatikos, meaning two-colored) or the occurrence in a species of two color phases irrespective of age, sex, or season. The familiar Screech Owl affords us a good example where extremes of red and gray individuals occur as well as intermediates. These may be, and often are, individuals from the same nest, and they may be all males or all females. It is apparently due to an excess of red or brown pigment and may represent but a step toward melanism. *Dichromatism* likewise occurs with certain other Owls, and with certain Hawks, as well as with some species of Herons. The case of the rare Cory's Least Bittern (Fig. 140) is one of the most interesting as scientists are not entirely agreed as to whether it represents a distinct species on the verge of extinction or whether it is but a dark phase of the common Least Bittern. Its color pattern is apparently identical with that of the common Least Bittern but all of the buffs have been replaced by chestnut.

But to return to the gorgeous Tanagers and the inconspicuous Grouse, surely there is some reason for the difference in coloration which study might lead us to understand. In thinking over the birds with which we are familiar we soon discover that brilliant colors, in almost every species, are restricted wholly to the males, and a moment's reflection suggests to us that the law of 'The Survival of the Fittest' would soon weed out any bright-colored females, should they arise, by drawing attention to their nests and inviting the destruction of their offspring. The very exceptions to the rule further substantiate it, for when bright colors are normal to the female, as in the Kingfisher and Red-headed Woodpecker, nature protects the offspring by causing the eggs to be laid in holes in trees or in tunnels in the bank where the female is entirely hidden from sight while incubating.

In the few cases where the female is brighter than the male, as in the Phalaropes, the male incubates the eggs and cares for the young.

Another method of protecting conspicuously colored birds is by endowing them with extreme wariness and it is seldom that any of them will allow as close an approach as do their dull-colored mates or relatives. They seem to realize that they are conspicuous and rely upon their alertness to escape. Moreover, is it not of direct benefit to the species that there should be a conspicuous decoy to lure away from the vicinity of the nest any enemy that passes that way so that should the male be seen and captured, the offspring might still persist?

Brilliancy of plumage probably originates, we are told, because of an excess of strength and bodily vigor, and this fact undoubtedly tends to perpetuate and increase the brilliancy, when ever the bright colors are not directly disadvantageous to the species, because the vigorous bird is most likely to secure the best mate and have the strongest offspring. It may well be asked, then, why the males of all species are not conspicuously colored and able to rely upon their wits to escape their enemies. But think for a moment of the environments which birds are called upon to fill. In the tree tops and the great open spaces where enemies cannot lurk unseen, we find the conspicuous Tanagers, Trogons, and Honey Creepers, the Gulls, Terns, Herons, and Flamingoes. On the other hand, in the thickets and dense coverts near the ground where enemies can approach closely or lie concealed, we find our most protectively colored Grouse, Woodcocks, Sparrows, etc. Thus it is clear why the gaudy Tanager is confined to the tree tops and why the streaked Sparrow must simulate its dry grass haunts if it would persist. Birds dwelling within reach of skulking enemies seldom wear brilliant colors or bear feathers that are continuously conspicuous. They are protectively colored and often fit into their environment to such an extent as to be practically invisible. The ways in which this concealment is brought about are varied and interesting, so much so, in fact, that we will devote the second part of this chapter to the discussion and will now pass on to a few other matters regarding the coloration of birds.

In discussing brilliant colors we should remember that very few birds wear the bright colors throughout the year, the Kingfisher, the Cardinal, and the Red-headed Woodpecker being notable exceptions. The vast majority shed their bright colors after the breeding season and do not don them again until the following spring. With many of the Ducks, however, this change from a brilliant to an obscure plumage in the male occurs as early as June or July and by the time most birds are ready to take on their obscure plumage in August and September, they are ready to assume their brilliant feathers once more. After the breeding season all birds moult every feather on the body, including the wings. In the spring moult of the Tanagers and Indigo Bunting and others, in order to replace the bright feathers, the change is incomplete as the old feathers of the wings and tail are retained.

It is interesting to examine the young of these birds in which the male is brighter than the female, for almost invariably they resemble the female, or when there is a seasonal difference in the males, the male in winter plumage. It is a well-known fact that the young of animals often summarize in their development the steps through which their ancestors have passed in the course of their evolution. The plumage of the young birds, therefore, or the winter plumages of the males may often show relationships that one could never guess by examining the breeding plumages. Thus, the immature and winter plumages of the Blackpoll and Bay-breasted Warblers are almost indistinguishable, although the adults are very different in the spring. The spotted breasts of young Robins and Bluebirds indicate their relationship to the Thrushes, and the streaked breasts of the young Chipping and Field Sparrows show the typical Sparrow coloration from which the adults have departed. With a very few species, the young in their juvenal plumage are just as bright as the males or even brighter. Young Kingfishers, for example, can scarcely be distinguished from the adults except by the rufous feathers in the band across the breast, and young Downy and Hairy Woodpeckers tend to have the whole top of the head reddish rather than a mere crescent of red on the nape.

To simplify the relationship of brilliant plumage to age, sex and season, the following table of bird coloration is offered:

I. Birds never brilliant in any plumage.
>   Male, female, and young; winter and summer almost identical.
>> Examples: Song, Vesper and Fox Sparrows.

II Adult birds brilliant in some plumages but not all.
>   A. Males alone brilliant and during breeding season only;
>   females and immatures always dull.
>> 1. Dull winter plumage worn from October until April.
>>> Examples: Goldfinch, Indigo Bunting, Scarlet
>>> Tanager.
>> 2. Dull winter plumage worn from July to October
>> (Eclipse Plumage).
>>> Examples: Most Ducks such as Wood Duck, Mal-
>>> lards, Pintail, Canvasback, Scaup, etc.
>   B. Males and Females both brilliant during the breeding
>   season only. Immatures and adults in winter, dull.
>> 1. Males and females approximately alike.
>>> Examples: Black-bellied and Golden Plover.
>> 2. Males somewhat brighter than females.
>>> Examples: Turnstone and Red-backed Sandpiper.
>> 3. Females brighter than the males.
>>> Examples: All of the Phalaropes.
>   C. Males alone brilliant throughout the year; immatures like
>   the females.
>> Examples: Cardinals, Ring-necked Pheasants.

III. Male and Female brilliant at all seasons.
>> 1. Juvenal plumage dull, adults equally brilliant.
>>> Examples: Red-headed Woodpecker, Robin.
>> 2. Juvenal plumage as brilliant as that of adults.
>>> Examples: Kingfisher, Chickadee, Shrike.

Concealing Coloration of Birds

There is one principle underlying the coloration of all protectively
marked birds which does more than anything else toward rendering
them inconspicuous, and that is the principle of "counter-shading,"
as it was named by its discoverer, the artist-naturalist, Abbott
Thayer. It has long been known to artists that to make objects appear
solid and conspicuous on the canvas, one must paint in their shadows, but it remained for Thayer to apply the reverse of this prac-

tice, and to point out the way to make solid objects appear flat and inconspicuous is to paint out their shadows. He applied this principle to the coloration of animals and recognized that protective coloration is brought about largely by the lightest colors being placed on the throat and belly, which parts are thrown into the deepest shadow, and the darkest colors being placed on the top of the head and back, which receive the greatest light. Between the back and the belly there is a gradual change to lighter, exactly counter-matching

FIG. 141. Mimicry in the Screech Owl; simulating bark (left), dead leaves (right).

the amount of shadow, so that the apparent solidity of the bird is thus destroyed or 'painted out.'

This principle was admirably illustrated by the late bird artist, Louis Agassiz Fuertes, with the bird models shown in Fig. 142. Two blocks of wood were cut out in the general form of a bird and colored uniformly dark. He placed them out of doors on a gravel walk in good light and then, with his brush, proceeded to paint out the shadows on one of them by adding touches of white paint so as to balance the shadows exactly, with the result that, to the amazement of onlookers, this one gradually disappeared from view.

The principle of 'counter-shading,' like many other great discoveries, is very simple. The human eye, and probably all eyes, judge the solidity of an object by the shadows which it casts, and an object which throws no shadows upon its underparts has no solidity. Through 'counter-shading,' then, the bird loses its solidity, appears flat, and being so, it falls off into the background and becomes a part of it. If, in addition, its color pattern is similar to its haunts, it becomes practically invisible. And so we find that the Grouse and the Woodcock, living on the forest floor, have a color pattern of spots and patches of light and dark brown; the Sparrows and Meadow-larks of the fields are streaked with buff and rufous, like the dead grasses; Owls are irregularly marked like the rough bark of trees, and Sandpipers and Plovers are specked like the sand of the seashore or streaked like the drift.

One might expect that the white underparts of birds would render them conspicuous even though the birds did appear flat. On the contrary white serves largely as a mirror and reflects to the eye the color that is about it. One can easily demonstrate this by a series of cards white beneath and colored above held at a reflecting angle one above another. The white bottoms will all appear the color of the card just below. Thus the white belly of a Killdeer may appear brown or green to the observer's eye depending on whether it is standing on the mud or the grass.

It is not difficult to demonstrate that white may appear even darker than black and vice versa when reflecting light at different angles. Fuertes, the distinguished bird artist, devised the simple piece of apparatus shown in the accompanying photograph, Fig. 143, which demonstrates that white may appear blacker than black or black whiter than white. The two cards, appropriately marked when viewed in a vertical position appear as black and white are supposed to, the white card marked with black letters and the black with white. When they are turned, however, so that the black reflects the sky and the white reflects the ground, the illusion is complete. Thus in nature the snow-white breast of a bird may reflect green grass or brown leaves and it may appear just as dark as the bird's back.

With insects the simulation of color pattern is often carried to the extreme. There are butterflies and moths whose markings imitate exactly the dead leaf or the bark upon which they rest. Furthermore the shape of the wing is often modified to make the simulation

FIG. 142. Counter-shading—a demonstration. Below—solid-colored and counter shaded models of a sandpiper. Above left—same models upside down. Above right—a white card behind the two models. Models by L. A. Fuertes.

more complete. 'Dead leaf' butterflies, walking sticks, and measuring worms, are familiar examples of insects in which the shape has been modified as well as the color, and this device of nature for giving protection has been called "mimicry." If we define mimicry as the simulation of shape, as well as color, of animals to their environment, we will find it of rather rare occurrence among birds and never as perfect as with insects. The Screech Owl, with its feathers drawn close and its ear-tufts erect, however, certainly 'mimics' a broken piece of bark or dead leaves, and the Nighthawk, sitting lengthwise

FIG. 143. Black may be whiter than white.

on a limb, simulates the broken stub of a branch in shape as well as color. The Bittern, standing among the dead cat-tails, with its bill pointing toward the zenith, and the Least Bittern on its nest in the pose shown in the photograph (Fig. 144), are, likewise, exam-

Fig. 144. Mimicry in the Least Bittern, pose, pattern, and color.

ples of mimicry, for they resemble in shape, as well as in color, a projecting snag or a broken reed.

In the plumages of certain birds that are normally very difficult to see when at rest, we find a very different color pattern which seems at variance with all that has been said. Instead of there being a gradual transition from the dark to the light areas, there is a

FIG. 145. Importance of color pattern. 1. Common Snipe with two young (upper), 2. Ruffed Grouse (middle), 3. Woodcock (lower).

sudden, abrupt change, often heightened by a black border. On the head of the Wood Duck (color plate) for example, the white of the throat extends up on the cheeks in the form of crescents. These, together with the white stripes through the crest and the black-and-white bars on the sides, would seem to make it most conspicuous. Similarly the Killdeer (Fig. 146) has its brown head separated from its similarly colored back by a conspicuous white ring, and its snowy breast is crossed by two coal black bands. In spite of these marks, one finds that both the Wood Duck and the Killdeer in their natural environments, are very inconspicuous, and we are led to believe that these "ruptive marks," as they are called, serve apparently to split up the bird into several pieces, destroy its continuity of form, and thereby conceal it by making it unbirdlike. Those who followed the development of 'camouflage' in World War I will recognize in counter-shading and ruptive marks two of the principles that were utilized as much as any to conceal battleships, large guns, ammunition trains, and even small buildings.

One other class of markings we might consider here since they are similar to the ruptive marks in being themselves extremely noticeable. I refer to the so-called 'flash colors' or 'banner marks.' The white tail of the deer and the cottontail, which are raised and made as conspicuous as possible when the animal is fleeing; the white outer-tail feathers of the Junco and the Meadowlark, the white

patch on the rump of the Flicker, and the striking black-and-white wings of the Willet, all fall into this class. These marks were at one time supposed to serve as signals to the young or to others of the species to keep the flock together, but Dr. C. Hart Merriam has suggested a still better use for them by explaining how they may serve to give protection from their enemies. When the animal or bird is fleeing, the eye of the enemy naturally fastens upon the

FIG. 146. Ruptive marks of a Killdeer and young.

very conspicuous flash color and when the Meadowlark, for instance, drops into the grass, or the Flicker claps up against the side of the tree, the banner mark suddenly disappears. But the eye of the enemy, through the persistence of vision, follows on in the same direction in which the bird was going before realizing that it has stopped and, in the interval elapsing, the bird slinks off a few feet farther or slips around to the other side of the tree and is nowhere to be seen. The Willet, upon alighting, often lifts its conspicuously marked wings high over its back as if to attract attention to the very spot where it has alighted, but always, upon closing them, it runs along the beach a few feet so that the eye of an enemy can search in vain for the conspicuous quarry that it marked so carefully a moment before.

These then are the five main principles underlying the conceal-

Fig. 147. Flash colors of a Willet. Above—Willets flying. Below—Willet near nest.

ing coloration of birds. Some authorities have gone so far as to claim
that all birds are protectively colored, but the majority feel that the
colors of some birds cannot be explained by any of the foregoing
principles, that they may even be conspicuously marked. A Crow
on the snow or against the sky, or anywhere except in a coal-hole,
is bound to be visible from any angle. But the Crow has been endowed with an intelligence and a wariness which need no concealing
coloration to supplement them. Dr. Chapman has suggested that one
can usually tell from the actions of the birds whether they consider
themselves conspicuous or not, for the protectively colored species
always permit of a close approach while those that are conspicuously
marked fly at the first intimation of danger and never rely upon concealment even when wounded.

How Birds Change Their Plumage

No phenomenon of nature is more striking to the observant
watcher as he enters the September woods than the change that has
been wrought in the realm of birds. The hundreds of voices that
claimed his attention during the spring and summer are now hushed
and he hears only the occasional notes of a Red-eyed Vireo or a
Wood Pewee. So quiet are the tree-tops and so silent the forest floor
that he is almost ready to believe that the birds are gone, but, as he
follows the border of the woods farther, he suddenly finds himself
in the midst of a flock of birds even more numerous than the hosts
of spring. They are scratching in the leaves, shaking the bushes and
weeds, and chippering in the tree-tops in such manner as to announce their presence beyond any doubt, although they are difficult
or even impossible to see.

In the fall the birds are no longer scattered evenly through the
woods and fields but have gathered in flocks, sometimes many species
together, and are moving slowly southward. Where food is abundant
they stop for some time, but they shun all places where food and
water are scarce. In spite of their numbers, however, they are difficult
to see among the autumn greens and browns, for the familiar liveries
of spring have been discarded for suitable travelling attire. Little
change has come over the Sparrows and Vireos, whose dull plumages
serve for both summer and winter, but the bright Tanagers, Bun-

tings and Warblers have now assumed the modest dress of the females and even the Robin has his red breast tinged with gray.

Fall is a time when careless observers become hopelessly confused and lose interest in bird-study, but it is the time of all times when the keen observer revels in a wealth of unusual plumages and rare records. Those of us whose opportunity it is to teach others and to lead children or beginners through the woods and fields in search of birds find ourselves confronted with innumerable difficulties. The lack of song, the dull colors, the secretive ways of the birds, the luxuriance of the weeds and the denseness of the foliage of the trees that discourage the single observer, are almost unsurmountable barriers to a class or group. We are led to rejoice when the frosts and winds make the woods more penetrable, though they likewise thin out the ranks of the birds.

Lucky are the ones who live near ponds or bodies of water that attract the shore and wading birds for they alone present the unobstructed vision that one is accustomed to in the early spring and longs for all the fall. The Sandpipers and Plovers, the Herons and Bitterns, and sometimes the Rails and even the Ducks present opportunities for study such as one enjoys with the most birds in the spring. Those who have no shores to visit, however, must content themselves with isolated observations and make intensive studies of such birds as can be found. Perhaps it is just as well for us that nature takes this way of directing our attention to some of her less striking phenomena, for were we forever surrounded by pleasing songs and brilliant plumages, we might overlook entirely the changes that are so imperative in renewing the worn, frayed plumage. But when our attention is called to it, we find in the molting of birds a lesson that is as interesting as it is vital, a lesson that can be demonstrated as beautifully with the Sparrow in the street as it can by the rarest and most secretive Warbler.

August is the month of molting, the season when birds change their faded worn plumage for fresh feathers often of a different color. Some birds do not complete molting until September is far advanced while others, particularly among the Waterfowl, begin molting in June and by September have passed through two molts, having taken on a dull plumage and discarded it again. With most birds, however, September finds them in their full winter plumage.

The change has been such a gradual one that, although every feather has been shed and replaced, it has scarcely been noticed unless there has been a change of color as well. Beginning always at a definite feather, usually the innermost primary wing-feather, the molt proceeds with regular sequence until all the feathers are replaced. The second feather is not lost until the first is partially grown, and before the third and fourth are lost, the first is practically matured. The same is true of the tail feathers, so that a bird is never normally without its locomotor organs and steering gear. An exception to this is found in the Ducks, Rails, and Diving Birds which are not dependent upon their wings to escape their enemies and which, there-

Fig. 148. Moulting House Sparrow showing progress of the moult in different parts of the body and wing. New feathers are darker.

fore, can safely molt all of their primaries at the same time and be temporarily deprived of the power of flight (Fig. 151). On the bird's body, likewise, the molt proceeds gradually from a certain point, only a few feathers being lost at a time. The half-naked Chickens seen in many farmyards are cases of arrested feather development which does not occur in nature except in cases of disease.

As was pointed out in the last chapter, feathers are not worn indiscriminately over a bird's body but along definite lines called feather tracts. Between the feather tracts, which are apparently regular in every species of bird, there are extensive bare areas which are dependent upon the overlapping of the feathers of adjacent tracts for protection. In the young of most birds, until the feathers are ma-

COURTSHIP OF BIRDS

Mallard "Grunt-Whistle"

Prairie Chicken Booming

Ruffed Grouse Drumming

COURTSHIP OF BIRDS

Song Sparrow Singing

Song Sparrow Fights Mirror

Willow Ptarmigan Fights Mirror

COURTSHIP OF BIRDS

Trumpeter Swans Courting

Ruffed Grouse Displaying

COURTSHIP OF BIRDS

Cowbird Display

Wild Turkey Displays

Sharp-tailed Grouse Challenge

Sharp-tailed Grouse Dance

tured, the feather tracts (pterylæ) and the naked spaces (apteria) are very conspicuous. The sickly Chickens appear naked not because the bare spaces are any larger, but because they are entirely exposed by the scarcity of feathers in each tract.

Most birds molt only once a year, but it would obviously be impossible for a bird that changes to a dull coat after the nesting season to assume its brilliant breeding plumage without another molt in the spring. Thus we find, in the case of such brilliantly colored birds as the Scarlet Tanager, Goldfinch and Indigo Bunting, that the males undergo a spring or 'pre-nuptial' molt as well as a fall or 'post-nuptial' change of plumage. The prenuptial molt, however, is usually incomplete, for the wings and tail feathers, which are dull even in brightly colored birds, are usually made to serve both plumages.

In some birds where there is a conspicuous change in color from the winter to the breeding plumage, it is accomplished in another way known as 'feather wear.' This is possible because each feather

FIG. 149. Wings of House Sparrows showing progress of molt.

is tipped or edged with a color different from the main portion of the plume. The feather tips give the general color to the winter plumage, but as they wear off, the color of the breeding plumage is exposed. Browns, yellows, and grays occur most frequently as color-tips, with blacks, browns, or reds beneath. The Robin's breast becomes redder with the advance of spring because the gray tips of the feathers wear off. The black spot on the throat of the male House Sparrow (Fig. 152) and that on the breast of the Meadowlark treble in size for the same reason. The Redwinged Blackbird loses his reddish-brown cast and becomes intensely black, while the Snow Bunting wears away the rusty color from its head and breast and shows snowy white for the summer.

In birds like the Purple Finch and Indigo Bunting, in which there are no apparent gray tips to the feathers and which still seem to become more intensely colored as the season advances, the feather wear is of a different sort. It was formerly believed that the feathers became repigmented from the blood of the bird but today that is considered impossible, because once the feather is mature, it is a dead structure, physiologically disconnected from the body and serv-

Fig. 150. Male House Sparrow (winter, left and summer, right) showing the effect of feather wear

ing only in a mechanical way for flight and protection. To understand what actually happens in the case of these birds, it is necessary to know something of the structure of the feather under the lens as shown in the last chapter.

All feathers are composed of a mid-vein or shaft and the web. If the web is examined carefully it will be seen to be composed of a series of fibers called 'barbs' attached on each side of the shaft. Each barb, similarly, bears two rows of barbules. When the barbules are examined under the microscope, they are found to bear a number of minute recurved hooklets which fasten into the hooklets of adjacent barbules and give to the feather its firmness, being best devel-

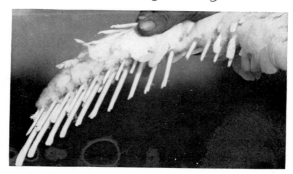

FIG. 151. Moulting wing of a Whistling Swan (all flight feathers and coverts lost at once).

oped in the flight feathers, which require the greatest strength. Some feathers, and the innermost parts of most feathers, lack this device and are, therefore, always soft and fluffy, giving little resistance to the passage of air through them. Now in the case of the Purple Finch and Indigo Bunting, the red and blue colors are located mostly in the barbs, while the barbules and hooklets are dusky. With the wearing away of the barbules and hooks on the body feathers, the

FIG. 152. Moulting Spotted Salamander and its cast skin.

barbs become more conspicuous and the color of the bird becomes apparently more intense.

That molting is not confined to birds is well recognized and its homology to the 'shedding of the skin' in reptiles and amphibians is conceded. Of course, the snake or amphibian does not actually shed its skin but merely the hard outer cuticle. This cuticle, as in the case of the birds' feathers when fully formed, is a dead structure and it is inelastic. Consequently, as the snake or frog or salamander grows, this 'shell' becomes too small for it and must be replaced by a larger one. The more food one of these cold-blooded animals consumes, the more rapidly it grows and the more often it has to molt. It is not seriously discommoded by the process, however, except for a short time when the loosened cuticle over the eye becomes opaque and renders it nearly blind. When this occurs the animal rubs its nose against a stone, splitting the hard cuticle and then gradually wiggles itself free, leaving the skin entire, a sort of a ghost of its former self.

With birds the molting is a more serious matter. It requires far more energy to grow a new set of feathers than merely to form a new cuticle, in fact, so much so that most of the other activities must stop and the bird's entire strength be given to molting. As a result, song ceases, fighting and display are never indulged in, and nesting responsibilites are completed and out of the way. The birds retire to the thickets and move about only in search of food. It is a period of sickness or indisposition and the birds largely shun each other's company. During the molting time many birds practically disappear and are nowhere to be seen for several weeks. The Redwinged Blackbirds, for example, are very abundant in every little marsh until the last of August. Each evening they can be seen flying in large flocks to roost in the marshes and each morning leaving again to feed on the upland fields. The sexes separate in flocks by themselves and show little interest in each other. Suddenly the male birds disappear, shortly the females and immatures follow, and there ensues a period of several weeks when no Blackbirds are seen either morning or evening, nor are they to be seen during the day about the marshes. In a few weeks they appear again and this time in even larger numbers than before, for they have been joined by migrating birds from the North. In former years it was supposed that the early disappearance was caused by the resident birds leaving for the South and that the reappearance of Blackbirds announced the arrival of birds from the North, but the unaccountable part of the story was that although the August birds were supposed to be leaving for the South they never arrived. Instead the Blackbirds in the South likewise disappeared. The mystery of their disappearance, however, can easily be explained by anyone who will venture out into the heart of the larger marshes during the first of September, for there he will find, after sufficient search, large flocks of short-winged, short-tailed Blackbirds skulking about the more open areas and hesitating to fly far. For it is at this period that they are just completing their molts by the replacement of the outer primaries, the loss of which in shortening the wing, makes flight difficult and the long flights to the uplands practically impossible. Hence they are seldom seen and it might easily be concluded that they had left for other parts.

Thus it is with other birds also. They cease singing and go into hiding until the molting is practically completed, but it is not long before they regain their former vitality and some even revive their full springtime songs. The majority, however, prefer to rest after their strenuous labors, filling their crops with fruits and seeds and laying up a store of fat that will serve them in the long journeys that they are about to undertake.

In studying the fall plumage of birds it is always interesting to compare them with their spring plumages and try to determine what changes have taken place through the molt and what further changes will be necessary to bring the birds once more into their breeding plumage. Just as the streaked breasts of young Chipping Sparrows and the spotted breasts of young Robins show their family relationships, so the fall plumages of many birds are indicative of their relationships. Every bird has some interesting phase to its plumage-change and so, no matter how scarce birds may seem, one can always find something interesting to watch or toward which to direct his observations.

13

Birds in Their Relation to Man

Useful Birds

In the heart of Salt Lake City there stands a granite column surmounted by a great sphere upon which are alighting two Gulls of gilded bronze. The square pedestal bears plaques in high relief commemorating an incident in 1848 when the early settlers were saved from starvation by great flocks of Gulls which devoured the 'crickets' that threatened to destroy their crops. The monument is surrounded by a pool of water where song birds come to drink and bathe, and it is dedicated to useful birds.

So far as I know this monument is unique, yet, in a larger sense, the whole verdant world is a monument to the thousands of insectivorous birds without whose help the preservation of vegetation would be impossible. The Mormons looked upon the advent of the Gulls as a heaven-sent miracle, and this monument will carry the message down through the ages. Yet the world is full of such miracles and history is replete with instances that must pass unsung. Every spring the miracle of unfolding life overshadows the miracle of the returning birds which unwittingly preserve for us the opening leaves and the sprouting seed wherever found. So accustomed are we to the services of birds that we take them for granted. We are oblivious to the fact that birds must eat to live until they descend upon our corn or our cherries. Their misdeeds we proclaim from the housetops, their services go unnoticed.

To most of us the economic value of birds is such an old story that we are surprised when we meet anyone who has not heard it. There is so much of interest and beauty in the bird itself that those who know and appreciate birds most are sometimes forgetful of their less fortunate brothers whose knowledge of birds extends not much beyond the symbolic Eagles on our currency.

Whole books have been written and for years the United States Government maintained a Division of Food Habits Research in its Bureau of Biological Survey which filled our ornithological literature with valuable treatises on this subject, so that it would be foolish to attempt here more than a bare outline, a chassis to which the reader may add such body and accessories as best suit the ornithological roads he has to traverse.

Fig. 153. Yellow-billed Cuckoo with tent caterpillar.

With the spread Eagle, then, as our symbol, we will divide all birds into five groups: first and foremost of which are those birds which serve man by destroying obnoxious insects; second, the birds which serve man by destroying the seeds of weeds; third, the birds which destroy small rodents; fourth, the scavengers; and fifth, those birds which serve best as game. Let us begin with the insect destroyers.

Entomologists are agreed that there is a loss to agriculture in the United States of over a billion dollars every year through the ravages of insect pests. They are further agreed that were it not for its natural enemies, almost any insect would in a short space of time inherit the earth. Indeed if so tiny an insect as the plant louse, weighing only the millionth part of an ounce, should be allowed to reproduce unchecked; and should its offspring all find sufficient food to reach maturity and in turn to bring forth their young throughout the year, it would in a single season result in so vast a body of insects that their combined weight would be greater than that of all the people in the United States. And there are nearly a million different kinds of insects, each striving to do this very thing. Little hope would there be for mankind were it not for the natural enemies of insects, chief among which are the birds. From the grubs that burrow in the soil and cut off the roots of plants to the moths that flutter above the tree-tops, there are thousands of different kinds of insects insidiously working and threatening to destroy the grass at our feet, the plants in our gardens, the crops in the field, the fruit trees in the orchard, the very forests themselves. But for each type of insect nature has devised corresponding types of birds to feed upon them and to help keep them within bounds. The Snipe and the Woodcock probe in the loose soil, the Larks and the Sparrows scratch among the dead leaves and grasses, the Warblers and Vireos and Wrens scrutinize the foliage, the Nuthatches and Creepers search the bark, the Woodpeckers drill into the trees for borers, and the Swallows and Flycatchers guard the air itself. Where insectivorous birds are plentiful it is a lucky insect that escapes, but where birds are scarce it is a lucky plant that completes its life cycle.

The amount of insect food required by birds, particularly young birds growing feathers, is nearly as remarkable as the reproductive capacity of the insects themselves. Anyone who will watch for a few hours a nestful of young Robins or other birds being fed by their parents, or who will attempt to raise a young Crow, will be duly impressed by the quantities of food consumed. A few years ago I was interested in the growth of a young Black Tern which we raised to maturity. Dr. M. D. Pirnie kept an accurate record of the weight of the young bird and the amount of food which he fed it, and one day, when it weighed only 31 grams, it consumed 48 grams of earthworms.

And this bird was no exception to the rule, for repeated experiments with many kinds of birds have shown that they require at least half their weight of food each day merely to maintain life, and if they are to develop normally, as much again.

Of course, birds are not the only enemies of insects, for parasites and disease and predaceous insects all play their part in maintaining the balance of nature, and the birds merely step in where the others leave off.

Before passing on to the next group of birds it might not be amiss to list the families of birds that are more or less dependent upon insects for their existence. Among the water-birds there are many which we would ordinarily classify among the 'fish and frog eaters' which feed upon aquatic insects when these are more easily secured than fish, or even upon land insects such as grasshoppers and caterpillars. Thus many insects are found in the food of the Grebes and the Ducks, while some of the Gulls and Terns are notorious insect destroyers. Many of the Herons and Bitterns and Ibises forsake the water during outbreaks of grasshoppers, and the majority of the marsh-birds and the

FIG. 154. Downy Woodpecker working on bark beetles.

shore-birds get a large part of their food from aquatic insects and insect larvæ.

Of the land-birds, the young of the Gallinaceous birds live largely on insects, as do the adults to a certain extent; some of the Hawks and Owls are insectivorous, all of the Cuckoos, the Woodpeckers, the Nighthawks, the Swifts, and the Hummingbirds to a certain extent. The twenty-five families of perching birds found in North

America are all more or less insectivorous with the exception of the members of the Lark and the Sparrow families that live primarily upon seeds, except during the breeding season, and certain of the Crows and Blackbirds that are rather omnivorous, taking insects only when they are more easily secured than anything else. Of

Fig. 155. Bobolink with cutworms and grasshopper.

course, many of the truly insectivorous birds among the Flycatchers, Tanagers, Vireos, Waxwings, Thrushes, etc., are fond of fruits and I have seen even the tiny Hummingbird gathering fragments of ripe mulberries for its young.

Fig. 156. Meadowlark with white grubs.

The second group of birds useful to man are the seed eaters —the weed destroyers. As already intimated, this group is much smaller in variety of species, but they often make up in numbers what they lack in variety. Birds in this group belong primarily to the Sparrow family, the true Larks, or the Doves. The majority feed their young upon insects, but the Doves and the Goldfinches seem to be able to get along on seeds alone.

The actual value to man of the seed-eaters is much less than that of the insect-eaters for obvious reasons, but the great numbers of weed seeds consumed by these birds should always be borne in mind. Professor F. E. Beal, in studying the food of the Tree Sparrow in the State of Iowa, estimated that this species alone, during the few months of its stay, consumed over 875 tons of weed seed each season.

The third group of birds consists of the carnivorous Hawks, Owls,

FIG. 157. Long-eared Owl's nest and young with meadow mice in storage.

and Shrikes that get a large part of their food from small mammals and assist man in his struggle to produce food, by destroying small rodents. Mice, rats, gophers, prairie dogs, and ground squirrels are at times fearfully destructive and we are dependent upon some natural method of control throughout most of their range. During severe winters when the snows lie deep on the ground, the meadow mice sometimes girdle thousands of fruit trees and their damage to grains and other crops, even in normal years, cannot be estimated. So great is their reproductive capacity, we are told by Mr. Vernon Bailey, that should they have abundant food and protection so that all of their offspring live and breed, it would be possible within a single year to have a million offspring resulting from each pair. Plagues of mice do frequently occur and the only Pied Pipers that we can depend upon are the Hawks and Owls, each one of which requires the equivalent of three mice a day in order to live. It is a short-sighted policy, therefore, that puts bounties upon their heads even though some of the species may be destructive to poultry and game birds.

Owls normally swallow their prey entire or in very large pieces with no effort at removing fur or feathers. The stomach digests out what is good and rolls the bones and fur and feathers into pellets which are then ejected from the mouth. Large numbers of these pellets often accumulate beneath an Owl roost and one can easily discover what they have been feeding upon by examining these pellets. I recommend their examination as one of the most con-

Fig. 158. Birds as scavengers—Black Vultures on dead donkey.

clusive ways of demonstrating the value of these much-maligned birds.

The fourth group of birds is composed of those that render efficient service to mankind as scavengers. In the South, the Black and Turkey Vultures clean up all carrion left exposed, from mouse to mule, and in the North, the Crows and the Herring Gulls perform the same service, particularly about harbors and shores where the dead fish might otherwise pollute the air and water and make life unbearable. The Vultures are sometimes blamed for the transfer of certain cattle diseases from one pasture to another and it is possible, on the wide ranges where dead cattle are never buried, that the Vultures may be one of the means of transmission, though no definite proof has been delivered, and the flies, which frequent the living as well as the dead, seem much more likely carriers.

The fifth group of birds which serve man are the game birds. Every year in New York State alone nearly a million persons take out hunting licenses and the actual money value of the game secured is estimated at over $10,000,000, and yet New York State is not one of the leading game producing states. According to figures recently published, the number of persons who took out hunting licenses in

1959 in the United States was approximately 18 million, indicating to us, whether we ourselves are hunters or not, that the game birds of the country are an important asset.

There was a time when any bird big enough to eat was considered a game bird and thousands of Robins and Meadowlarks and Flickers were exposed for sale. Today we rightfully restrict the numbers of

FIG. 159. Birds as scavengers—Gulls over city garbage dump.

game birds to those which serve man best in that capacity, and those species which serve better as destroyers of insects or weed seeds have been removed from the game list. The Robin, the Meadowlark, the Killdeer and the numerous little Sandpipers that trot along our shores now have the protection which they deserve though they were once classified as game.

The ideal game bird is one which, so far as its food habits go, is neutral, neither beneficial nor destructive, or one which is actually destructive if it becomes too numerous; a bird that is prolific, wary, and under normal conditions so well able to care for itself that it requires skill to secure it. Such are the Ducks and Geese; such are the Pheasants, the Turkeys, the Grouse and the Quail, though the last named is so beneficial in its food habits that in some states it has been removed from the game list. Its reproductive capacity is such, however, that when given complete protection, it is said to multiply so rapidly as to overstock the coverts and cause epidemics. The Woodcock and the Snipe are satisfactory game birds so far as their economic status is concerned, but they are not very prolific. The Yellowlegs that until recently were found on the game list are even less satisfactory as game birds, for they are not only not prolific but likewise not wary and are easily killed. The Rails are unsatisfactory for the same reason—that it takes so little skill to secure them. So long, however, as the sportsmen are content to confine their activities to the legitimate game birds, we should recognize their economic right to them, and their responsibility in conserving them.

After we have divided all birds into these five groups according to their use, we find that there are a few left over. These are mostly fish-eating birds like the Auks, the Murres, the Cormorants, the Gannets, the Pelicans, and most of the Gulls and Terns, the Herons and the Kingfishers. Ordinarily the food of these birds is of negative importance—they do neither good nor harm. Their great value is in the charm and interest which they lend often to unattractive places, and, if the dollar sign must be attached to their wings, it will be on the basis that thousands of nature lovers the country over value them as they do the mountains and the forests, as national monuments, to be handed down from generation to generation.

DESTRUCTIVE BIRDS

In the broad open meadow of bird-protection there grows a weed. It has deep roots, and as often as it is cut down it springs up again, blossoms, and scatters its seed, to the confusion of those who know not its existence, and to the dismay of those who thought it dead. It is impossible to uproot it, for it is as much a part of the meadow as the clover and the timothy. It is impracticable to conceal it, for it is widespread and conspicuous to every passer-by. The name of the weed is 'destructive bird,' and it appears in many forms. Sometimes it is a Hawk or an Owl; again it is a Heron or a Kingfisher; at times it seems to be a Crow or a Pheasant or a Blackbird; or it may be only a Robin, a Warbler or a 'Jenny Wren.' Whatever its form, it flares by the roadside and demands to be explained.

Before the seed of bird-protection was planted in the broad open field, the flowers of this weed were the only ones the general public could recognize, and it is little wonder that scant attention was given to the meadow and that it has taken so many years to make its real beauty and worth apparent to the multitude. But in our enthusiasm over the value and the beauty of the meadow, let us not forget that the weed still exists and that there are still those who cannot see

Fig. 160. Kingfisher with small sucker, a fish of no commercial value.

the meadow because of the weed. Let us recognize frankly its existence, let us admire whatever of beauty and interest there is in it, but let us not hinder its control when that is necessary for successful agriculture.

We may be interested most in the protection of all forms of wild life and the perpetuation of all species, valuable or otherwise, for the inspiration of naturalists yet unborn. But in our zeal for protection let us hold truth above all else, for it is upon truth that the strength of our whole protective policy rests. Let us neither deny nor attempt to conceal the fact that a number of birds are quite destructive to man's interests, and let us place our trust in the exhaustive scientific investigations of these species made by ornithologists of unquestioned ability and integrity, and stand by the recommendations based upon their studies. The majority of us do not have time to make these studies; our intensive observations are limited ordinarily to rather restricted areas, and our opinions, which are usually based on our own observations, are often biased by local conditions. If the Screech Owls eat my songbirds and the Sparrow Hawks steal my young Pheasants, if the Crows take my Duck's eggs and the Kingfishers catch my trout, and the Blackbirds ruin my corn; if the Robins filch my cherries and the Wrens drive off my Bluebirds, I am likely to develop prejudices that will affect my opinions of these birds throughout the land. It may be difficult for me to realize that my bailiwick is a mere atom on the face of this green land, and that my observations are confined to but a few days and, at best, to but a few of the activities of these species. I may be in a good position to judge what should be done to these birds on my own premises, but I might be quite unfair to my friends' birds in some other state. The man, on the other hand, who has no song-birds he calls his own, who raises no Pheasants, nor Ducks, who has no fish-pond nor garden nor fruit trees, and does not go to the trouble of building bird houses for the Bluebirds, but takes his joy out of following the migrating birds with his field glass to learn their songs and identification marks; though he may know every bird that visits the land, in every plumage that it assumes, and be able to recognize every sound that it makes, he is in no position to judge the economic status of the different species until he has made that study his life-work. So let each of us continue to record as faithfully as he can his own observations on the activities of each species in the locality with which he is familiar, and then let us together call upon the economic ornithologist to summarize all that is known and make recommendations accordingly. It is only in this way that we can present a united front to those forces that are forever threatening the bulwark of bird-protection and that are ever looking for a weakening of the ranks through which to scatter the seeds of discord.

When the ornithologists of North America first came together in 1885 and formed the American Ornithologists' Union, one of their first activities was the formation of a committee to investigate the English Sparrow. Introduced into New York City in 1851 and 1852, it had already spread throughout the Eastern States and was regarded as a menace to our native birds. At that time there was no governmental agency to carry on such investigations, and what was more natural than that the ornithologists should select from their own ranks men trained in such observation to secure all the available information and make recommendations as to the proper procedure in disposing of this apparently undesirable immigrant. The work of this committee soon outgrew the available funds; a memorial was presented to Congress and there was established in the Department of Agriculture a Division that in the ensuing years developed into the Biological Survey and later the U.S. Fish and Wildlife Service as we know it today.

The Fish and Wildlife Service has always numbered on its staff leading ornithologists of the country, and some of their earliest and most important and really illuminating work has been the investigation of the true economic status of birds of doubtful value. The results of these investigations have been published in the form of Bulletins, and the information is available to everyone who is interested. Some of the Bulletins are now out of print, but all of them can be found in the Year Books of the Department of Agriculture which are in every public library, and all the earlier reports were summarized in a very useful book by Julius Henderson called "The Practical Value of Birds." The Hawks and Owls, the Crows and Jays, the Blackbirds, the Sparrows, the Herons, the Sapsuckers, the fruit-eating birds, together with many others, have been studied impartially and judgment rendered as free from prejudice as it is possible for scientists to be.

Based upon the findings of the Fish and Wildlife Service the National Audubon Society has drawn up a model law giving protection to all birds except those species which studies have shown to be prejudicial to man's interest, and this law has been adopted by most states of the Union. The law of New York State, for example, proclaims that "Wild birds other than the English Sparrow, Starling, Crow, Grackle and Kingfisher shall not be taken or possessed at any time, dead or alive, except under the authority of a certificate issued under the authority of this article." The birds listed are those which the Fish and Wildlife Service have put on the doubtful list or which have been found to be more destructive than beneficial. Other birds which are occasionally destructive, either at certain times of the year, or in certain localities, have been found to more than make up for their destructiveness by the good which they do at other times and in most localities. To provide protection to fruit-growers or fish-culturists or others who may suffer from the destructiveness of any species of birds that are normally beneficial but which because of peculiar local conditions have become a great nuisance, there is another paragraph in the Conservation Law of New York State which provides that "In the event that any species of birds protected by law shall at any time, in any locality, become destructive of private or public property, the Commission shall have power in its discretion to direct any game protector, or issue a permit to any citizen of the state to take such species of birds and dispose of

Fig. 161. Screech Owl has captured a Redstart for its young. Owls also eat many mice and June beetles and other destructive insects.

the same in such manner as the Commission may provide." Similarly, there is in the laws of most states provision for the protection of all valuable birds and also protection for the citizens from the depredations of any of the birds protected.

The lack of protection given to any bird would not be so important in itself were it not for the psychological fact that by making it one of the exceptions to the general rule, public attention is directed toward it, and general condemnation heaped upon it by vast numbers of people who would not know the bird if they saw it. The result is that the bird's sins are multiplied in the public mind until the weight of them seems impossible for some individuals to bear and a movement is started to exterminate the species. Ammunition dealers and gun clubs often fan the flames until legislatures are prevailed upon to offer bounties for their capture, or gunners organize 'vermin shoots' in the name of public service. Crows and Hawks are usually the victims of such mob violence and public animosity is aroused against them by lurid propaganda.

That Crows are sometimes very destructive there can be little doubt, though extensive studies of their food habits show also much in their favor. It is most certain, too, that some of the Hawks are deserving of punishment, and even the severest control measures may be necessary about poultry farms and game-preserves. Propaganda designed to stimulate active antagonism to these birds on the part of the general public and killing campaigns by gunners are,

Fig. 162. Duck Hawk with leg of fowl.

however, very short-sighted and should be actively discouraged by all nature-lovers. The harm that they do is not measured in the number of Crows and Hawks killed. We might even agree that reducing the numbers of some of these destructive species is beneficial, but the sending of numbers of men and boys into the woods and fields bent on destruction, stimulated only by a desire for vengeance upon a supposed enemy, undoes years of constructive work by bird protectionists. After all, game-laws and bird-protective laws mean little without public sentiment behind them, and the greatest work that the bird study movement has done has been the fostering of a real interest in birds and all outdoors, so that the youth of the country go forth into the woods asking themselves not, "What can we kill?" but "What can we see?"

The sportsman with his dog and his gun in zealous pursuit of Grouse or Pheasant or Waterfowl is not inspired with a spirit of vengeance. He is primarily an observer of all wild life, matching his wits and his skill against those of his chosen quarry. But fill him with insidious propaganda about the destructiveness of the so-called 'vermin' to his chosen sport, tell him that were it not for the Crows and the Hawks and the Owls, he would always return with a full bag, and his whole attitude changes. He is no longer the interested observer of wild life, he thinks himself a modern crusader, a full-fledged officer of the great outdoor law, newly appointed to pass upon the virtue of every living creature which he meets, and it will live or it will die as he decrees.

A few sportsmen have conceived the idea of luring Hawks and Crows before their guns by using a stuffed Owl with head and wings that will move at the pull of a string. Those that happen to be located along the migratory flight-lines of the Hawks manage to kill a considerable number during a few weeks of the spring and fall. It is claimed that, because of their activities, certain species of Hawks have become quite scarce along the Atlantic coast. Where this sport has been commercialized by the offering of bounties, there is little question that it will have a baneful influence on some of our most interesting, even though destructive, forms of wild life, and all nature-lovers should use their influence to have any such bounty laws repealed.

Commercialization of wild life has always been the means of its extermination. The history of the United States is replete with examples of extinction or near extinction of valuable forms of wild life by the placing of a price upon their heads. The Passenger Pigeon that formerly occurred in this country in countless thousands was entirely exterminated by the market hunters. The Egrets of our Southern States, the Terns of our Atlantic coast and the many brightly colored song-birds would have followed the Passenger Pigeon, through the activities of the feather trade, had it not been for the National Association of Audubon Societies and the creation of a public sentiment against the wearing of the plumes of wild birds. The Heath Hen is gone. The Prairie Chickens, the Sharp-tailed Grouse, the Ruffed Grouse and the many species of shore birds and water-fowl that were formerly sold in the markets may never recover from the effects of commercialization.

The placing of bounties on the heads of destructive birds would, probably, not result in as thorough an extermination as was accomplished in the case of the Passenger Pigeon, but it would be frightfully expensive to the tax-payers of the country and would probably result in so thorough an upsetting of the balance of nature that we might never recover from it. Mice and rats and ground squirrels and gophers would multiply unchecked. Weak and diseased birds would live on to start epidemics among their species, our whole scheme of nature might become disorganized. Better by far that these species be controlled where they are being destructive and be permitted to perform their natural function elsewhere.

We must, then, as naturalists and nature-lovers, discourage all killing, especially by children, for it psychological effect, if for no other, and actively combat all bounty systems and organized slaughter of any kind. At the same time, let us recognize the rights of farmers and sportsmen to protect their interests on their own farms or preserves and not strive for such comprehensive protection as might hinder them in the defense of their property. And, above all, when the economic status of any species is called into question, if it has not already been studied in detail, let us ask for a competent investigation by the Fish and Wildlife Service or by the State Ornithologist and stand by the recommendations of the investigator, whether they agree with our preconceived notions or not.

THE BALANCE OF NATURE AND THE CONSERVATION OF WILD LIFE

Some years ago a very keen naturalist of the U.S. Biological Survey, Vernon Bailey, made an intensive study of meadow mice.* In order to determine their rate of increase, he kept a pair in captivity and by supplying them with proper foods, exercise, etc., he was able to get them to breed in a normal manner. His original pair averaged five young to the litter and had seventeen litters within the year. The young of this pair began breeding when they were only forty-six days old, so that had they all lived and bred, and had Mr. Bailey had facilities to raise all of the offspring, at the end of the year, he tells us, he would have had over a million mice resulting from the original pair.

* Journal of Agricultural Research, Vol. XXVII, No. 8, p. 523, Feb. 23, 1924.

Think of the possibilities! A pair of mice gets into a granary or a pair of rats into the cellar where food is abundant. Is it any wonder that we are occasionally over-run with them? The miracle is that we are not continually besieged and run off the earth.

A single plant-louse may have as many as 100 young in a season. Her young mature so rapidly that there may be thirteen generations each year. The offspring of the twelfth brood alone, should they all live and breed, would, according to the late E. H. Forbush, former State Ornithologist of Massachusetts, number over ten sextillion, or, as he very graphically has illuminated it: the twelfth generation alone would form a procession, with ten to the inch, that would reach all the way around the earth, and from the earth to the sun, and from the sun on out into space to a point so inconceivably remote that light from it, traveling at 186,000 miles a second, would not reach the earth in 2,500 years.

A single daisy plant or a wild mustard bears sufficient seed to completely smother the surface of the earth in a few years, if they all lived and reproduced. Why is it then that we are not completely annihilated? How comes it that there is still room on the earth for us, and for fragile anemones, when every one of the thousands of species of plants and animals and insects has the power to overrun the entire earth within a few years if its offspring should all live?

The answer comes in what Darwin called "The struggle for existence and the survival of the fittest" resulting in "The balance of nature." Predatory animals, scarcity of food, storms, floods, fires, parasites, and disease all join hands to keep down any undue increase. The more abundant the mice or the insects become, the more numerous become their natural enemies and down goes the balance again. Before man enters the picture the natural agencies of destruction and the reproductive capacity of the organism balance on the fulcrum of the natural law which is "The survival of the fittest." It must always be so, for if the balance is upset, the organism either becomes extinct or it becomes a great pest.

Thus it was when the white man first came to this country. All nature looked serene, but down underneath there was going on continually that everlasting struggle between forest and prairie, between oak tree and pine, between burdock and blue grass, between the mountain lion and the deer, the fox and the mouse, the Hawk and the Sparrow. Every bird, animal, and flower was loaded down with natural enemies to the limit of its endurance. Nature was in balance. Then man stepped in with his ax and at one stroke he decided the age-long struggle between oak and pine, and at the same time he decided a thousand lesser battles in favor of one or another species and mostly in favor of himself. Some there were which he freed from bondage and immediately they increased without end and became weeds; others there were that could not stand the added burdens forced upon them and they sank gradually into oblivion. Man upset the balance that had existed for thousands of years. The weight of all the human agencies of destruction was too much for the reproductive capacity of wild life to bear up, and wherever man trod, the balance was ruthlessly upset. First came lumbering and then agriculture, with restriction of wild land. With it came the forest fires and the drainage of the marshes and the pollution of the streams. Then came an ever-increasing host of hunters and fishermen with improved guns and ammunition—with good roads and with cheap automobiles to speed them to the uttermost haunts of the wild things. And wild life broke under the strain—first the large game and then the lesser beasts and fowls—until we were threatened not only with the extinction of the bison and the elk and the antelope and the bear, but the Turkey, the Heath Hen, and the Wild Pigeon. The two last named, together with certain other species, are now gone for all time.

Is it any wonder that thinking men have risen to the necessity for concerted action to prevent such catastrophes, that restrictive laws have been passed and a campaign of publicity and general education started, and that certain remedies have been piled on the scales in an attempt to offset the human agencies of destruction? Laws are passed and wardens appointed to enforce them; a great campaign of reforestation is well under way; the state establishes fish hatcheries and game farms to replenish the streams and the coverts, and requires a license fee from all sportsmen to support them; game is imported from foreign countries and an effort is made to improve the streams and coverts by planting foods and shelters and by controlling some of the natural agencies of destruction; and, last but not least, comes the establishment of sanctuaries or refuges where wild life shall be inviolate. Let us hope that the doctor has not been summoned too late—that the balance may yet be restored. But it is not as simple as it used to be. The modern balance of nature presents a different picture.

In order to have a firmer fulcrum for the modern balance, the rock of legislation was added to its base. But even this is not as simple as it should be, for in order to secure sane and just legislation it is necessary to have a public awakening that the legislators may know who are back of them. Organization is necessary. The interested citizens band together into clubs and encourage their children to join junior organizations. The local clubs band together into state societies and again into National organizations—public interest is aroused and public opinion formed.

But to keep the 'Remedies' and the 'Human Agencies of Destruction' in balance in this great land of ours is no small job. It requires a balance upon the original balance with a nicety of adjustment that seems impossible to achieve. Our new fulcrum becomes 'Knowledge'—knowledge of all the facts connected with lives of our wild folk, our forests, our shrubs, and even our wild flowers—knowledge of the best means of applying the various remedies and of all the inter-relations that are likely to be upset. And so we have knowledge assisted by our educational institutions, the schools and universities, by the public museums, by State Conservation Commissions, by the U.S. Fish and Wildlife Service, by the U.S. Forest Service, and by the great body of interested citizens whose place in the picture is to keep the lid on the pot of remedies to prevent graft or spoliation. At the other side of the balance we see the pot of 'Human Agencies of Destruction' boiling and stewing and threatening to erupt because the lid is 'Public Indifference' which in itself does more for the destruction of wild life than any other agency.

The balance of nature is not as simple as it used to be in this country and it is much more easily upset than in the days of our forefathers, so that it behooves those of us who are interested in the preservation of birds or other forms of wild life to be ever on the alert. A little indifference on our part and a hundred new forms of destruction will originate; a little lack of interest in any of the remedies that have been so laboriously secured and they will slip from the balance. The various governmental agencies and educational institutions that are striving to keep the balance delicately adjusted need our unqualified support. The local bird club or Junior

Audubon Society may not seem very important to one who does not understand the architecture of the present-day balance of nature, but rest assured it is one of those important stones of the foundation or fulcrum without which the whole structure might topple.

BIRD SANCTUARIES, PUBLIC SHOOTING-GROUNDS, AND THE UTILIZATION OF NON-AGRICULTURAL LANDS

Since earliest Egyptian times there have existed places in which the hunted could take refuge without fear of pursuit. Then it was a niche or a seat in a temple, or perhaps the whole courtyard where fugitives could escape the vengeance of pursuers for a short time by taking advantage of the universal belief in the 'contagion of holiness.' These places were called 'sanctuaries,' or sacred places, and it was deemed sacrilegious to remove even a criminal who gained access to such a place. In varying degrees this right of sanctuary has been recognized by different nations and different creeds to the present time, but always with the idea of staying the hand of vengeance and saving human life.

In recent years the thought has developed that not only are human beings entitled to such places of refuge but that all hunted creatures should have places of safety into which they can flee to ward off complete annihilation. And these, too, have been called "sanctuaries" and their numbers are increasing every year. Some comprise only a few acres, designed to give protection to a few local birds; others comprise thousands of square miles and are destined to save wide-ranging, large game animals and migratory birds. The whole idea is an expression of our realization that the destruction of wild life has proceeded to a point where drastic action is necessary to preserve it from otherwise inevitable extinction.

Man's action in creating these sanctuaries is not altogether altruistic nor should it be. The naturalist wants a place where he can study wild life in a natural, undisturbed state; the sportsman wants to create reservoirs of game to overflow into his depleted coverts; and the economist desires to perpetuate every natural resource that may redound to the common good of all. Nor should there be any conflict between the various interests working for the conservation of wild life, though they go about it differently and from different motives. The naturalist should be encouraged in his efforts to conserve all kinds of wild life, whether or not certain species are of any practical importance, and the sportsman should not be hindered in harvesting a legitimate surplus of the recognized game species. If, by the combined efforts of both, our farm lands can be made more productive, or our waste lands made to yield an income, the economist will rejoice and lend his willing assistance to the promotion of the cause.

So much has been written on the subject of bird-sanctuaries and game-refuges, and so many sanctuaries have already been created through various agencies, that it might be thought that there is little left to be said or done. On the contrary, scarcely has a beginning been made, and the sanctuaries that are numbered by the hundreds today will be numbered by the thousands before this generation has passed. And we should welcome every agency that provides new means for their establishment. The present sanctuaries have been created principally upon public lands or lands donated for that purpose to the state or to some responsible organization, such as the National Audubon Society or the Federation of New England Bird Clubs. The laws of the United States and of Canada make it comparatively simple for the chief executives to establish Federal bird- and game-refuges on non-agricultural public lands, and by 1924, forty such had been set aside in Canada and over seventy in the United States.* The majority of States and the Canadian provinces, likewise, have made provision for the establishment of sanctuaries on state and provincial lands, or lands donated for that purpose. The purchase of lands by the State or the Federal Government for the explicit purpose of establishing such refuges begun in 1924 by the purchase of the Upper Mississippi Wild Life Refuge, however, was a relatively new idea but one fraught with such great possibilities that by 1953 we had established in the United States and Alaska 274 refuges totalling 17,414,461 acres. The provision that the funds accruing from the sale of "Duck Stamps" required of all duck hunters shall be spent in part for the improvement of waste, wet lands is a very wise provision which has the approval of all conservationists.

It is hardly to be expected that public funds should be expended for any venture unless the community as a whole is to benefit from

* For a history of the establishment of the Federal reservations, see "The Bird Study Book" by Dr. T. G. Pearson and "Wild Life Refuges" by Ira N. Gabrielson, 1943. The Macmillan Co.

it. The ordinary bird-sanctuary probably benefits farmers and prop-erty-owners in the immediate vicinity much more than those at a distance, and, no doubt, some of these would not admit they were being benefited at all. When, however, the sanctuary idea is com-bined with other civic improvements, such as reforestation and public recreation, and makes good use of lands that have ceased to be of real agricultural value, there can be little question that the purchase of private lands by the State, Provincial, or Federal Govern-ment from public funds is entirely legitimate.

According to W. B. Greeley, Chief of the U.S. Forest Service,* there exists in the United States, chiefly in the East, some 81,000,000 acres of land which was originally in forest, but which has been so denuded and burnt over as to be absolutely unproductive. Ten times the area of New York State has been cut over and still lies untilled, and not far from one-fourth of the soil of the entire United States is unfit for any practicable crop except timber. The census shows that twenty states have lost in cultivated land, and New Eng-land now has less farm-land by 13 per cent than at the time of the Civil War. What were once thriving lumber towns are now deserted villages, and the nearby land that is of agricultural value has become pauperized for want of a market. Every year sees hundreds of farms abandoned throughout the East while thousands of others are run at an economic loss.

The Federal Government is stepping in, purchasing and reforest-ing lands at the headwaters of navigable streams. The various State and Provincial governments are following suit, and private initiative follows on a still smaller scale, until the total of some 36,000 acres of land is being planted annually. But this is a mere drop in the bucket compared with the 10,000,000 acres that is being cut over each year. Tree-growth is so slow and the average citizen so lacking in vision that the whole movement falters for want of public in-terest and the resulting funds. There are millions of acres of idle land, and yet a timber-famine stares us in the face.

Every year in this country over fourteen million citizens shoulder their guns and tramp the fields and marshes in search of game. Ninety per cent of the hunting is done on the lands of others who permit of the trespass largely because of the theory prevalent with us

* 'Idle Land and Costly Timber.' Farmers' Bulletin No. 1417. U.S. Department of Agriculture.

that the game does not belong to the land-owner who feeds it but to the first one to reduce it to actual possession. But soon this conception of 'free shooting' will change; the farmer will no longer permit the city-dweller to tramp his fields and climb his fences. And what will the hunter do then for his recreation? The desire to hunt will not cease—far from it. The sportsmen will band together and voluntarily tax themselves to purchase hunting privileges of the land-owners or to purchase idle lands upon which they may hunt. Indeed, the time has already arrived and they have done so in several states. Some years ago, New York State passed a measure creating a 'Conservation Fund' to be derived from the sale of hunting and fishing licenses, the moneys from which to be spent for the improvement of hunting and fishing in that state, and one of the specified methods of so doing was the purchase of land for game-refuges and public shooting-grounds. A number of other states have created similar funds which can be drawn upon for this purpose, and a like bill was finally passed in Congress for the establishment of Federal refuges throughout the country for migratory game-birds. Here, then, is a third use for idle lands.

But sportsmen and foresters and naturalists and bird-lovers are not the only ones who love the life in the open. With the development of the motor-car there has come a great gypsy public demanding the right to live out-of-doors and a place so to live, and they have forced through state legislatures huge appropriations and bond issues for the establishment of numerous state parks and public recreation-grounds. It is altogether fitting and proper that they should have their desire, for the outdoor life makes better citizens of them. This gives us a fourth use for idle lands—bird-sanctuaries, public forests, game-refuges and public shooting-grounds, and the public parks and recreation grounds. How well do these interests harmonize?

At first thought one would say that a public shooting-ground might well conflict with a bird sanctuary. With the strictest definition of the word sanctuary, doubtless it would, for all creatures cannot receive equal sanctuary if it is desired to increase the number of one or more kinds above the normal. But those who have had any experience in the practical management of bird-sanctuaries or game-refuges are agreed that they are futile unless a constant effort is made to reduce the number of predaceous species. Otherwise, while it is a sanctuary from man and a paradise for the Hawk and the Owl and the fox and the weasel, it becomes a death trap for the defenseless song-bird. It is questionable whether the term sanctuary could be honestly applied to it. A well-managed public shooting-ground should have maintained upon it much more game than is normal to the region, and the number should not vary materially from year to year. If, for some reason, the game supply fails one year in a public shooting-ground, the area can immediately be closed to hunting until the numbers recuperate. There can be little doubt that the song and insectivorous birds will benefit by the warden service supplied, and by the planting of food-bearing shrubs and trees, a requisite part of the procedure in every well-managed game-refuge.

The modern conception of a public shooting-ground is one based on the Pennsylvania system wherein each public shooting-ground contains within it a considerable refuge or sanctuary, enclosed by a single wire, where no hunting is allowed and into which all game may flee when pursued. During the hunting season, no one unaccompanied by the warden, is permitted to enter with or without a gun. Indeed, such a game-refuge is much more of a sanctuary than many of the established bird-sanctuaries where visitors are frequent. There is, therefore, no real conflict between the bird-sanctuary and the public shooting-ground nor between any of the interests working for the conservation of wild life and the utilization of waste land. The problem resolves itself into one of procedure, with all hands willing to push if the wheels begin to spin.

The question naturally arises, where are these combinations of bird-sanctuary, public shooting-ground, public forest, and recreation grounds to be located and how are they to be developed and maintained? In 1922, the state of Michigan commenced what has been called a "Land-economic Survey" of the various counties of the State, with a view to taking an inventory of the natural resources of the State, determining once and for all the best uses for the land. Similar surveys have been started in New York and other states, particularly of what have been called 'marginal farm lands'—farms that have been abandoned or that are being worked at a possible economic loss. It is obviously undesirable to remove from agriculture any land that can be profitably worked so long as there is plenty that cannot be worked, and that is crying to be reforested.

Such an economic survey, then, should precede the establishment of refuges so as to determine what lands are available, what their real value is, and the probable cost of purchase. The economic survey should be followed by a biological survey to determine the flora and fauna of the region, the amount of land already in forest, the amount of brush-land, open pasture, cultivated fields, and marshes. If there are lakes or streams within the proposed area, they should be included in the survey, and the existing population of fish, birds, game, and predaceous species should be estimated, together with the amount of available food-plants or food-organisms. This is necessary before any rational policy of control can be instituted. The biological survey should be accompanied by a forest survey, to determine the planting and cutting policy best adapted to produce an ultimate income to the state from timber production, while at the same time increasing the water-storage, and improving the coverts and the streams for game and for fish. In determining the planting policy, especial attention should be given to the needs of birds and game, because extensive coniferous plantings, with their scarcity of food-plants and lack of sunlight, are veritable deserts for most species, and afford only protection. When laid out in smaller units, however, with brush-land and swales and some open land intervening, where food-plants are grown, they are conducive to a maximum production of bird-life and game. The number of birds will increase with the circumference of such areas rather than with their diameter, so that the greater the number and the smaller the area of each, the greater will be the resulting bird and game population. The forest survey should determine the smallest unit suitable to a good working policy within the proposed area, and this would undoubtedly vary with local conditions.

When these surveys have been completed, the state will be in a position to purchase intelligently the tracts of land that will serve best the varied interests involved, and to proceed with a rational policy of development that will result in real recreation grounds for the sportsman and for the nature-lover, and, at the same time, provide for a timber supply in the future and protection for the water-sheds. From 1,000 to 3,000 acres of each tract will be inclosed by a single strand of wire, with signs at frequent intervals proclaiming it a sanctuary and prohibiting entrance of any kind during the hunting season. Four times the area of this sanctuary, and surrounding it, will be the public shooting-ground where law-abiding citizens may go for two or three months during the fall and early winter with their guns and reap the surplus of certain game species that overflow from the sanctuary. At other times of the year this area also will be a sanctuary under the protection of a warden whose business will be to see that no shooting occurs except that which he does himself to lessen the number of predaceous species which might otherwise increase to the destruction of the major aim of the sanctuary.

At the present time such sanctuaries as these are dependent for their financial support upon funds derived from taxation of the sportsmen alone, and, doubtless, this is more or less just so long as they reap the major benefits from them. Before they have existed many years, however, it will probably be apparent that many other citizens are deriving much pleasure and profit from them, and that the state as a whole has been greatly improved by their establishment. When that time comes, doubtless the public treasury will come to their support with appropriations or bond issues, and it will not be many generations before all of the idle lands have reverted to the state, making a vast chain of sanctuaries and shooting-grounds and public forests and public recreation-grounds such as the world has never known, and birds and game will be more plentiful than when Columbus discovered this fair country.

Part II—Methods of Bird Study

14

Bird Walks, Bird Calendars
and Bird Banding

On Christmas Day, or during the week thereafter, hundreds of observers take to the woods and fields in search of birds. From Nova Scotia to British Columbia and from Florida to California, groups of bird-watchers start out with field-glasses in hand to make an annual bird census. First suggested by Dr. Chapman in 1900, the Christmas Bird Census has come to international fame, and the pages of the April issue of the *Audubon Field Notes,* where the various lists are reported, are eagerly scanned by bird-watchers the world over. Reports from the West Indies, South America, and Europe often arrive in time to be printed. Even in far-off Australia there are interested bird students in the field who enjoy exchanging their lists and their observations with others on this side of the globe.

The bird-walk has become a delightful and wholesome practice, giving enjoyment to the most experienced ornithologists as well as those learning their first birds. At the same time, it helps to assemble records of considerable scientific value. The Christmas Bird Census, for several reasons, produces records of greater accuracy and, therefore, of greater scientific value than similar records made at other times of the year, but for the enjoyment of the observer, a census taken during the spring migration, among the nesting birds of summer, or with the drab birds of fall is even more interesting. Indeed, competition among observers during the spring, to secure long lists of birds on a single walk, often ranges high, and the bird-walks become correspondingly exciting. For the compilation of a local list of birds to show which species occur in a given region, where and when they are found, such records are invaluable. Summaries of several years' observations at a given place are often printed in *The Auk,* a journal with which all serious bird students should become acquainted. Bird students should likewise become familiar with the *Wilson Bulletin* and those of the West with *The Condor*.

School teachers who start their bird-study with the Christmas or New Year's bird walk derive sufficient impetus from it to assure the interest of their pupils for the rest of the year. Of course, this is the period of school vacation, but for just that reason the children are freer to spend more time in the field. A school or class competition can be inaugurated to find the most winter birds, either in a single day or during the entire vacation. The combined lists of all will then form the start for a school bird calendar.

For the benefit of any who cannot get out into the woods and fields themselves, or for those who wish to refresh their memories or those of their children on the winter birds and where to look for them, the author will outline the bird-walk which he, himself, takes each Christmas or New Year's Day. The birds which he sees in central New York will not be exactly the same as those which his friends in the South or West will see; there will even be some differences in the Middle West, but the winter birds are remarkably uniform throughout the northern states, varying chiefly in relative abundance.

A Christmas Walk With Birds

It is a gray morning, the day after Christmas. Ever so lightly the feathery snow crystals drift downward and falter as they meet the branches of the mulberry tree by the window. But it is cold; they do not cling to the branches, but sift down to join their fellows in a quilt inches deep on the lawn and on the feeding-shelf at the window. The birds' 'Christmas tree' is well laden, but a rift in the smooth snow blanket covering the shelf shows where an early Junco has been scratching for the seeds that he has learned to expect so regularly.

We hasten to sweep away the snow and scatter fresh 'chick-feed' for the Juncos and Tree Sparrows and sunflower seeds for the Chickadees and Nuthatches. We brush off the suet holder on the upright stub at one end of the shelf, only to find that it must be replenished for the hungry Woodpeckers. We get a doughnut from the pantry and hunt for an old pancake to put out for the Blue Jays. Our bird walks always begin at home and the more birds we can see while at breakfast, the longer our list will be, and this is the day for the Christmas Bird Census. The celebrations for the kiddies the day before prevented our going on Christmas Day, and we have set aside the 26th for a good old-fashioned hike across the fields and through the woods.

What an ideal day we have for a walk! The snow stops falling and the air clears until the distant hills are once more visible. Fortunately, clouds still veil the sun and we will not have the discomfort of its bright light reflected from the snow to our eyes. Were we hunting spring birds, we would have started soon after daylight, but the winter birds do not become active until the sun is well above the horizon and then they remain active throughout the day.

Before breakfast is over, our bird-list is well started. The Chickadees announce the arrival of the first troop by their tinkling conversational notes and a scolding *chick-a-dee-dee*. The *yank-yank* of a Nuthatch tells us that he is close by, and the sharp Robin-like call of a Hairy Woodpecker proclaims that he will have his breakfast of suet before the Downy this morning. Soon our window cafeteria is in full swing, and we can scarcely keep the children at the table, so anxious are they to climb to the broad window-sill and look into the beady black eyes of the hungry birds. The sunflower seeds seem to be the first choice of the Chickadees, and although there are plenty scattered over the shelf, and there are a dozen Chickadees and Nuthatches about, it is seldom that more than one comes to the shelf at a time. Sometimes a Chickadee hops to the edge of the shelf with a seed in his bill and, after tucking it under both feet, proceeds to hammer it open. At such times others will sneak in behind him and carry off the seeds, but more often they wait and each takes his turn. The Nuthatches are thrifty and believe in laying up a store against the time when the cafeteria proprietors may close the doors, and so, grasping two or three seeds at once, they fly to the elm and tuck them into the crevices of the bark. At first, when they are hungry, they hammer them open, but soon they are content merely to carry and hide them away. Last spring one of the seeds that had been hidden in the bark during the winter germinated and produced quite a little plant before it died from lack of nourishment. The little Chickadees are also provident, and they find the tiniest crevices in twigs and weed-stems in which to hide their seeds after having removed the shell.

Next comes the old Hairy Woodpecker. With a swoop he lands on the far side of the suet stub, and, with a flirt of his head, looks first to one side and then to the other. If anything alarms him, he clings, immovable as though frozen, to the bark, but if all is safe, he edges around the stub with short hops until his full profile is visible to us. Then, after another pause, he climbs jerkily up to the suet which we have arranged on the window side of the stub. There is no difficulty in distinguishing the Hairy from the Downy at this distance, for the pure white outer tail-feathers are quite distinct and his larger size is very appreciable. Later on we may have some trouble when we see the bird at a distance too great to see the tail feathers or to judge the size. Just to remind us of the great difference in size along comes the Downy and alights on the opposite side of the stub, and when we have them both together we wonder why anyone ever confuses them.

Next comes the Tree Sparrow, and he settles down in one spot on the shelf and proceeds to gorge himself on the cracked corn and millet. Even the children know it is a Tree Sparrow for, as it faces the window, the single dark spot on its plain fluffy breast shows very distinctly. The *chimp-chimp* of a Song Sparrow in the hedge and the distant *jay-jay* of a Blue Jay tell us that other visitors will soon be coming, but it is high time we started on our walk.

We plan our course so as to cover as diverse types of country as possible, following up the ravine until we come to the open fields, then along hedge-rows and past the old orchard to the sugar-bush, through the sugar-bush to the hemlock woods, and then down to the frozen swamp and the lake-shore. The crisp air adds zest to our steps, and we are glad that there are no birds to stop us until we get warmed up. It seems that all the birds of the ravine have gathered about our feeding-station, for we hear not another sound until we surmount the hill and come to the open fields. Then a rolling twitter overhead attracts our attention and we see a little cloud of Snow Buntings swirling over, their white breasts and broad white patches in their wings giving them the appearance of a veritable snow-flurry. The illusion is heightened when, with a broad sweep, they wheel and settle down on an adjacent field where we can see other dark-colored birds feeding among the weeds that project above the snow. There were several darker birds among the Buntings and we hasten on in the hope of discovering some of the rare Lapland Longspurs that sometimes stray into our part of the country with the Buntings. We are met with disappointment, however, for when we sneak up behind the old rail-fence and get our glasses on the flock, we discover that they are Horned Larks. The Prairie Horned Lark is the common one with us, though occasionally the 'Northern Horned Lark' visits us in winter, and so we scan the flock very carefully to see if some of the birds are not yellower above and behind the eye. There is much difference in the amount of yellow on the throats of the birds we are watching but this is apparently indicative only of age or sex. They are all gray above and behind the eye, and we have to be content to add but two species to our list. The Snow Buntings, likewise, show considerable variation in the amount of brown on their heads and backs, though none of them is as distinctly black and white as all will be in the spring when the brown veiling of the feathers wears off. They are rather erratic in their movements and suddenly, without the slightest warning, as though by some innate understanding, the whole flock of Buntings and Larks frisks off, mingling their twitters and sharp *tse-tse* notes.

We continue down the fence-row and soon hear the convivial notes of a flock of Tree Sparrows feeding about the weeds and briars at the edge of a little run. They are always cheerful, and even on this winter morning indulge in little snatches of canary-like song expressive of their good will, though far from the varied strains that they will take back to Hudson's Bay with them next April. On the opposite side of the little gully are some alders, and just as we discover a flock of small, dark-colored birds feeding on the catkins, they are off with an excited chatter that pronounces them Redpolls. Why they should be so wild at this time of the year when they are so tame in the spring, I have yet to discover, and my fondest hopes of discovering Greater Redpolls or Hoary Redpolls among them are always shattered by having them depart thus wildly before I can get a good look at them. We write down just plain 'Redpoll' and continue to think that some looked larger and some much lighter colored than the rest and wonder if after all, all three kinds were not represented in the flock.

Now we come to the old orchard. A few frozen apples still cling to the trees, and we hope to find a flock of Cedar Waxwings or at least a few Starlings but luck is not with us. Even the hollow tree that has always sheltered a Screech Owl stands empty. A sharp call from a thick patch of sumac at one side of the orchard, however, gives us a start. It has such a familiar sound, yet one that we have not heard for so long that at first we do not recognize our old friend 'Cock Robin.' All his relatives left over a month ago, but this daring bird had apparently determined to brave the winter and eke out his living from the sumac bobs, the frozen apples, and the blue berries of the red cedars which cover a sheltered hillside just beyond. His red breast is veiled by the gray tips of the feathers, and he is by no means the tame, confiding, and conspicuous bird that frequents our lawns during spring and summer. Indeed, we get but a glimpse of him as he darts off through the thicket; he is wilder than the Redpolls.

The hillside covered with junipers yields us nothing new, though it is crossed and recrossed by the tracks of a cock Pheasant and at least two females. Molly Cottontail has apparently played tag here with several of her friends, though most of the tracks are concealed by the snow of the early morning. So, we continue to the woods beyond and soon are scanning the trunks of the maples for the owner of the shrill sibilant voice that we heard as we climbed the fence. It sounded like a Brown Creeper but since Golden-crowned Kinglets and even Chickadees have notes which are quite similar, we search until we find our bird. At last we see what looks like a flake of bark flip off from the trunk of a big maple, 30 feet from the ground, and sail down to the base of an adjacent tree, and we know that we have found the Creeper. Upward he goes on his never-ending search for insects, spiralling around the trunk and never stopping. We station ourselves near a large tree in the direction in which he seems to be trending, and, sure enough, after spiralling nearly to the top of his tree, he glides down to the base of the tree where we are standing, barely missing us in passing. Either he has become near-sighted from 'keeping his nose to the grindstone' or else he is lacking in fear or common sense, for he pays not the slightest attention to us but continues on his twisting course almost within arm's length. He is not alone, we soon realize, for we hear the notes of three or four others which seem to be following through the woods in the same general direction. Apparently they are tagging a little flock of Nuthatches and Chickadees and Downy Woodpeckers that have already passed by and whose notes we can hear in the direction in which the Creepers are moving. They are traveling toward a stand of hemlock, a likely place for other birds, so we follow also.

Beneath the hemlocks the snow is covered with small cones from the branches above. Squirrels or birds have been having quite a repast, but apparently, all is quiet now. We search the branches in vain and are about to decide that the red squirrels are responsible for the cones when a cheeping sound at the far side of the grove attracts our attention. We hasten to that side just in time to see a flock of a dozen or more dark Sparrow-like birds hastily leaving the higher branches. They swing together into a compact flock,

FIG. 163. White-winged Crossbill.

making a clicking sound as they go, and seem to be bound for distant parts, when, suddenly, they swing on the arc of a big circle and back into the same tree almost as suddenly as they left. Now we get a good look at them as they crawl along the branches and we discover that they are White-winged Crossbills. Most of them are greenish females or immature birds but several are dull red males. We watch them as they snip off the small cones; and then, holding them upside down beneath their feet, insert their curiously crossed bills, now opened, and with their tongues scoop out the seeds that lie in the axils of the scales. At times they are silent but again they indulge in excited chippering or in plaintive cheeps. They seem not the least bit afraid of us but all of a sudden they are off, like the Redpolls.

When the Crossbills depart from the hemlocks we search carefully for Pine Grosbeaks or Siskins but without avail. We do find, however, a sleepy old Screech Owl roosting close against the trunk of one of the hemlocks where a branch had been broken off. He might easily have escaped detection, so closely did the pattern of his breast simulate the bark, and doubtless he would have, if he had been a gray Owl instead of a red one, but in his case, though pattern and shape were obliterative, his color exposed him. We delivered a lecture to him upon the subject of protective coloration, and expect, that, hereafter, he will roost only among red oak leaves.

At the edge of the hemlock grove, among the young trees, we next

come upon some tracks in the snow which remind us of the Pheasant
tracks we discovered earlier among the cedars. The feet that made
them, however, were evidently considerably smaller, the toes broader,
and there is an almost continuous line between the tracks made by
dragging the toes. They are not Crow tracks, because there is scarcely
a mark left by the hind toe and the front toes are set at too wide
an angle. So we decide they must have been made by a Ruffed
Grouse, and proceed to follow them. The tracks lead us in and out
among the young hemlocks, across a patch of alders, to an old root
fence along the edge of the woods. Here is a tangle of wild grape-
vines with many of the dried grapes still clinging, and here, judging
from the tracks, the old Grouse has spent some time feeding. There
are many old tracks still visible under the freshly fallen snow, indicating that this is probably a favorite resort, and there are several
depressions in the snow close under the roots of the fence where
he has probably roosted at various times. Finally we find some very
fresh tracks leading back into the alders towards an upturned tree.
The tracks are farther apart as though the bird had been running,
and we decide that he had been feeding when we approached and,
upon seeing us, had run back into the alders to escape detection.
Now we keep our eyes focused far ahead in the hope of seeing
him running but while we are stepping over the fallen log, we are
startled by a roar of wings from behind the upturned roots of the
tree and know that our bird is off. So well does he know our position,
however, and so accurately does he direct his flight that he keeps
the roots in the line of our vision until he is far out of range of any
possible gun. We catch not a glimpse of him until he is disappearing
over the top of a young hemlock in the distance. Where Grouse are
not hunted, they become extremely tame, as also when they are kept
in captivity. But a wise old bird, that has been through one hunting
season, has learned many tricks for rendering himself invisible and
will defy even the most stealthy observer to get a close view of him.

We are not the only ones startled by the flushing of the Grouse.
A scolding *chimp-chimp,* like a wooden-voiced Song Sparrow, tells
us that a little Winter Wren was not expecting all that noise in his
quiet domain and is expressing his disapproval. Mouselike he creeps
up toward the top of the upturned roots, his little tail standing
straight in the air, but, upon getting a good look at us, he buzzes

over to a nearby brush-pile into which he disappears with vehement scolding.

As we are pushing our way through the alders, trying not to slip into any of the soft spots that seem to be scattered about in the most unexpected places, we hear a chattering and warbling ahead from a fairly large flock of birds. Some of the chattering notes are almost like those of the Winter Wren, only more metallic. These, we discover, are made by Purple Finches which, with a number of Goldfinches, are feeding upon catkins of the alders. Most of the Purple Finches are in the streaked plumage of the female or immature but even these occasionally indulge in a low warble, like that of the brilliantly colored males, and all of them, when excited, give the chattering notes that first attracted our attention. One familiar only with the summer Goldfinches would never recognize the dull gray little birds among the Purple Finches as his friends, even though there is a tinge of yellow to the males. Their sweet, canary-like call-notes, however, are the same, though when on the wing, their *per-chic-o-ree* note is seldom heard and their undulating flight is less conspicuous than during the summer. So, also, the warbling of the Purple Finches is inconspicuous and merely suggestive of their loud springtime outbursts.

Our walk through the rest of the maple and beech woods is rather uneventful, and we direct our steps toward the marsh and woodland at the head of the lake where we are pretty sure to find one or more 'summer birds' trying to spend the winter with their hardier cousins. This year it is a Catbird that is eking out its existence from the abundant wild grapes. Last year it was a Northern Yellow-throat, and at other times it has been a Long-billed Marsh Wren, a White-crowned Sparrow, or a Hermit Thrush. Flickers, Red-bellied Woodpeckers, Swamp Sparrows, or other birds, unusual for this locality in winter, are also likely to be found so that we always approach this area with great expectancy. Tree Sparrows are abundant and there are a number of Song Sparrows with them. We find more Chickadees and Nuthatches and Downy and Hairy Woodpeckers than in all of the other places combined, and the snow is crossed and recrossed in every direction with the tracks of Pheasants. Sitting on the tip-top of a locust tree along the road we espy a bird about the size of a Robin. He sits a little less erect, however, as though he were facing into a stiff breeze. His markings do not show well against the sky and, as we are trying to make sure of our identification, he bursts into a strange song. Songs from birds during the winter are very unusual, and this song has such a spring-like quality that, even were we not looking for birds, it would arrest our attention. At first it sounds like a Catbird, then a Robin, and then strangely different from both, though with much the same quality. We can hardly believe that it is a Northern Shrike, but such it proves to be. Later we see the same bird hovering over a willow bush in which several Chickadees are scolding and hopping about. Apparently they are too active for him; he cannot corner them in his customary way and he gives up the attempt.

Now we follow some weasel tracks out into the cat-tails at the head of the lake where the walking is rather difficult owing to the thick growth. We are rewarded for our efforts by flushing a big yellow-brown Owl from a log on which he had been roosting and, on pushing farther into the marsh, flush several others from the ground or matted rushes where they have been spending the day. We know that nothing but Short-eared Owls would be found in such a place, and though we cannot make out the ears, even when we steal up within close range of a bird that has alighted on a pile of drift on the lake shore, there is nothing else for it to be. We gather up some of the pellets disgorged by one of the Owls on what seemed to be a favorite roosting log, to determine what the birds have been feeding upon and, though we examine many of them, we can find nothing but the bones and fur of meadow mice and those of an occasional shrew. The numerous tracks and burrows of mice in the snow show perhaps what has attracted the Owls to this spot, for their wanderings seem to be controlled largely by the abundance of mice which constitute their chief article of diet. It is a pity that so many of them are sacrificed as targets for gunners when they are among our most necessary birds.

Following these Owls has brought us to the lake shore where we will complete our Christmas list with a good variety of waterbirds, perhaps the most interesting of all. The lake is frozen for several hundred yards from shore, but, beyond the edge of the ice, there are hundreds of Ducks. Now is the time when binoculars, or even telescopes, are a great convenience, though, if we walk down the west shore of the lake beyond the edge of the ice, we can get fairly close to some of the flocks that are feeding. After the hunting season closes and they lose some of their timidity, we will be able to get quite close to many of them which now are wild.

Scarcely do we show ourselves in the open before some stocky dark colored Ducks that were swimming close to the edge of the ice take fright and rise with a splash and pattering feet, leaving quite a wake on the quiet surface of the lake. They are Golden-eyes, or Whistlers, and we can hear the music of their wings even at the distance of several hundred yards. They are not as dark as they at first seemed for, as they fly away from us, the large white patches in their wings are very conspicuous, and when they turn, their snowy white breasts flash. A whole flock of them flying directly away remind me of nothing so much as a spray of cineraria flowers, for their centers are dark bordered by the clear white patches in their wings, and tipped again with black. In rising the effect is heightened by the shape of the flock which never stretches out but lifts in a cluster. On the water the immature birds and the females with their brown heads and gray breasts and flanks appear very dark, but the old males, with their snowy breasts, and white flank feathers concealing the black of the wings, may appear even whiter than the Canvasbacks. Once on the wing, a flock of Whistlers usually scatters and travels in very loose formation. Each bird seems to have an idea of his own as to just where he is going and how fast he wants to travel. It is interesting to watch them veer off from a flock of decoys that happen to be in their line of flight, with as much as to say, "You can't fool us," when other Ducks, under the same circumstances, would turn directly to the decoys, even if they didn't alight right among them. A single Whistler can be distinguished by the trained eye as far as it can be seen against the sky by its blocky head, heavy body, and well-developed tail. The little Buffleheads are built on much the same lines but they usually travel much closer to the water where they appear much blacker owing to their nearly uniform dark wings.

The other Ducks that were feeding along the edge of the ice merely swim out toward the center of the lake as we approach, with the exception of one wary old Black Duck that jumps up even farther away than the Whistlers, rising straight into the air, so differently from any of the diving Ducks. The satiny white lining of his wings shows conspicuously against his dark body as he fans the air, and makes his identification easy, though a female Mallard might show the same against her yellow-brown or gray-brown body. The other Ducks are Greater Scaups, Canvasbacks, and Redheads, and when we climb the bank on the west shore of the lake to the porch of a summer cottage and look down upon them, we have little difficulty in distinguishing them. From the side, the white flanks of the male Scaups make them appear almost as white as the Canvasbacks, but from above their darker backs quickly dispel the illusion. There are numerous flocks scattered over the lake, some with as many as 500 to 1,000 birds and others with but few. Some of the flocks are mixed while others are purely of one species. Especially is this true of the Redheads which seem to be clannish, and, whether on the water or in the air keep in close, soldierly ranks. Canvasbacks and Scaups mix more often, but one frequently sees a Canvasback leave a flock of Scaups to join a flock of his own kind. With all three of these commonest species, the males are greatly in excess of the females, though this is rather difficult to explain. Some duck-hunters think that the females are more delicate and therefore go farther south for the winter, but inquiry among my southern friends has as yet failed to reveal a place where the females are greatly in excess of the males. On an average, the males on Cayuga Lake exceed the females at the rate of four or five to one, and in many of the flocks of Canvasbacks there must be twenty males to one female.

It is interesting to watch the flocks of Ducks come flying down the lake to join their brothers on the water. With a little experience one can identify most of them by the shape of the flock: the Whistlers by their very open formation; the Redheads by their dense ranks, usually flying rather close to the water; the Scaups by their irregular form—rather open flocks and seldom in lines; the Canvasbacks, most majestic of all, flying in lines or V's like Geese, usually high in the air but rising and falling as they advance. One never tires of watching them circle, set their wings, bank, and drop with a splash beside their fellows. One likes to scan the various flocks with his glasses searching for stragglers of other species and he may often have the pleasure of discovering a group of Scoters, Buffleheads, Hooded Mergansers, or Ring-necked Ducks. Some winters one will find Mallards, Pintails, Baldpates, or others of the 'dabbling ducks' that must rely largely upon food brought up from the depths by the divers. Indeed it is a regular trick of the Baldpates to steal from the Redheads. Some winters a few Coots, Pied-billed Grebes and Loons remain, and always there are numerous American Mergansers and Horned Grebes, that one can count on finding. Overhead many Herring Gulls and the smaller Ring-billed Gulls sail gracefully in their search for dead fish or descend in numbers over a flock of feeding Mergansers to torment them until they drop their catches. Occasionally one may find a Bald Eagle sailing over the lake, like the Gulls, or descending to the ice to feed on a dying Duck. Always the lake holds thrills and is a fitting close to a day's hunt for birds.

Returning home through the woods we come upon a flock of Crows gathered about a water-hole, and we are reminded that they are the first we have seen that day. Toward evening we will see long lines of them filing toward their roost in a pine grove a few miles up the lake and, had we been out earlier in the morning, we would have seen them dispersing to their feeding-grounds, but, curiously enough, it is possible to tramp for hours in winter through Crow-infested country without seeing a single Crow, when, if one had walked in a different direction, he might have seen hundreds, yes, thousands.

Keeping Track of the Birds

It is not surprising that bird migration has fascinated mankind, that governments employ scientists to study it, and that thousands of people, scientists and laymen, spend much time following the birds in an effort to learn their secret. The sport of bird-study never grows old; it never grows monotonous; and grown-ups join with the children in the competition to see the first Robin, the first Bluebird, and the first of each species in its turn. The return of the birds in the spring takes thousands into the woods and fields to enjoy nature and affords to many the inspiration for keeping a journal of passing events. The accurate recording of one's observations is something to be greatly encouraged, and many a fine habit in man and woman develops from such a practice started in school. The majority of school children will doubtless never continue their studies of birds far enough to add much of value to the volumes of ornithological knowledge, but this is no reason why they should not receive the benefits to be derived from learning to observe accurately. They should, therefore, be encouraged in every way to follow the return of the birds from day to day and to record their observations on some form of a bird-calendar. Incidentally, the teacher or the parent will find that the keeping of a bird-calendar is one of the simplest and most profitable ways of stimulating bird-study, and it is the object of these paragraphs to suggest methods for its use.

There is a feeling among some people that mere interest in birds is sufficient to lead a child to all the benefits that can be derived from their study. While it is true that the child's interest is the primary and essential thing to awaken him and open the door to a great storehouse of pleasure and resource, this interest can be well utilized by his teacher to inculcate the most fundamental of all teachings, *accuracy of observation*. It is not sufficient that the child's eyes be opened; it is necessary that they be trained to see. The man who sees accurately understands what he sees, and makes a success of life instead of a failure. A judicious use of a bird-calendar, with emphasis laid upon the accuracy of the records, will not only arouse interest in bird-study and maintain it, but also will give to the children a most vital training. It is a matter of common knowledge that the active imagination of a child will lead him to see almost anything that he is expected to see or wishes to see without any intentional dishonesty on his part. As a result, he often reports impossible observations of birds out of season or birds not found in the locality, and, unless the teacher is circumspect, these observations are given equal value on the bird-calendar with more commonplace but correct observations. It should not be necessary for a teacher to know all of the birds himself or the proper time of arrival of all of them before starting a bird-calendar in his school. What is important is that he should cultivate an attitude of accuracy himself and impress the children with the need of it. Many a fine bird-calendar has fallen short of its full usefulness because the teacher has not dared to question the children's observations and has allowed inaccurate reports, knowingly or unintentionally, to appear upon it.

There are available, for most localities, local lists of the birds known to be found in that part of the country. Many of these local lists give the average date of arrival of each bird. If a teacher can refer to such a list he can quickly tell whether a child's record is improbable and question him accordingly. The training which a child receives in this way may do more good than the calendar itself, for not only will it impress him with the value of careful observation, but it will also impress him with one of the greatest marvels of migration, the accuracy of the spring arrival of each species of bird year after year.

DIRECTIONS FOR KEEPING A BIRD CALENDAR

For the use of individuals wishing to keep a full record of their observations throughout the season and from year to year, the method employed by Dr. Frank Chapman and described on page 10 of his "Handbook of Birds of Eastern North America" cannot be improved upon. At Cornell University, in addition to keeping individual records of this kind, we maintained for years a 'Bird-Chart,' which was essentially the same as a roll-book spread out, upon which the observations of all who coöperated were recorded. It was made of profile paper and covered a wall-board about 9 feet long and 4 feet wide. At the left were three vertical columns for the names of the birds, the names of the discoverers, and the localities where the birds were first seen. The remainder of the chart was divided into squares so that there were 365 of them following the name of each bird to receive the daily records. For convenience the chart was ruled into weekly columns and a rider was used bearing the names of the birds to facilitate the entry of records. The chart was long enough vertically to receive the names of about 200 birds which was the average number reported each year. The chart system, which was started nearly fifty years ago by Dr. A. H. Wright, has always stimulated a great deal of interest among students, and has resulted in a great deal of valuable information, which is of easy reference. For ordinary school-room use, however, such a chart is too cumbersome and is much more elaborate than necessary, but the main features of it should be retained. In fact during recent years the Cornell Chart has been abbreviated and there is no longer a column for each day of the year.

There are three main types of calendars that have proved successful for school use, that the author is familiar with, and there may be others equally good which he has not seen. In all three there are at least four vertical columns: the first for the name of the bird; the second for the name of the discoverer; the third for the place where it was seen; and the fourth for the date when it was first seen. In order to verify the first record, it is well to keep the second record also, so that if too great discrepancy occur between the first record and the average date of arrival, the second date can be retained instead. The calendar would be of still greater value if a record were made when the bird became common, when it began to nest, and when it was last seen, but, for most school calendars, the first four or five items are sufficient.

The three types of calendars differ primarily in their decorations: Some teachers prefer to have but a single competition in the drawing-class to select the design for the calendar, and this usually results in one with the birds at the top of a sheet and all of the observations beneath. Other teachers find time for considerable drawing and try to have each bird that is seen illustrated. Often the child who sees the bird is permitted to make the illustration, which is then cut out and pasted in the margin opposite its name. This requires a very large card, and often several of them. The method which seems most attractive to the writer is to have a separate sheet for each bird upon which the observations for several years can be kept. As often as a new bird is studied and drawn, the best drawing should be saved for the bird-calendar. Perhaps but few of the birds are illustrated the first year, but those that are, serve as inspiration to the next year's class to surpass them. As soon as a bird is reported, its card should be brought forth, the date, authority, and locality added, and then it should be hung up in a conspicuous place. Perhaps the class will try to improve upon the picture, and the competition which results will stimulate the drawing lesson, while the presence of the names of the boys and girls in the last year's class who observed the bird the previous year, will stimulate them to better observation out-of-doors.

Whichever type of calendar is employed, it should always be borne in mind that quality is better than quantity, and that accuracy is of prime importance. The calendar should be started before the birds begin to come back in the spring, so that it will include the winter residents. The nearer the first of January it is begun the better, though it may be started at any time. The children must learn to recognize that certain birds are with us throughout the year (permanent residents), others merely spend the winter in the locality and nest farther north (winter residents), while the majority spend the winter farther south and either nest with us during the summer (summer residents), or pass through on their way to a more northern nesting ground (transient visitants). The last two groups are the ones that make the keeping of a bird calendar so interesting, because of the accuracy of their arrival in the spring, but the first two must not be forgotten.

Bird Banding

Bird banding as a method of bird study is comparatively recent in the history of ornithology but it has made rapid strides during the past 25 years and is already giving us definite information on points in the migration and life history of birds that were previously not discoverable.

Between 1710 and 1898 there are recorded a few sporadic attempts to mark birds to learn of their travels, but nothing of importance was started until 1899 when Herr Chr. C. Mortensen, of Viborg, Denmark, commenced systematically to mark Storks, Teal, Starlings and a few birds-of-prey. He received so many interesting returns from his banded birds that it stimulated others both in Europe and America to follow in his foot-steps and by 1914 there were nearly 20 different projects started in Europe and in this country. The American Bird-banding Association had been formed previously by Dr. Leon J. Cole and had been functioning for five years. This association, sponsored after 1911 by the Linnean Society of New York, supplied the bands and fostered the project until 1920 when it was taken over by the Biological Survey at Washington and greatly enlarged.

Fig. 164. Banded Chickadee.

The first bands bore the words, "Notify *The Auk,* N.Y.," or "Notify Am. Museum, N.Y.," and were, of course, serially numbered. The recent bands have "Write F. and W. Serv. Wash. D.C. U.S.A. By 1958 11,000,000 birds had been banded, with more than 800,000 "returns." Collaborators are scattered all over the United States and Canada and the number of returns and the value of the returns increase daily.

In the first years of bird banding most of the energy was expended in banding fledglings with which there is such a high rate of mortality that the returns were relatively few. Between 1914 and 1920, however, Mr. S. Prentiss Baldwin, of Cleveland, Ohio, and Thomasville, Georgia, achieved such success in trapping and banding adult birds, and obtained so many interesting returns, that it not only gave great impetus to the banding work but changed the project largely to his methods. Thus today, except for colonial nesting Herons and Sea Birds, most of the banding is done at feeding stations.

The trapping for banding in no way interferes with the feeding station, and it certainly adds a great deal of interest and value to it. New baits and new traps are continually being devised in an effort to increase the number of kinds of birds that can be banded and one's ingenuity is ever taxed to the utmost. One should not consider this method of bird study, however, unless he is prepared to use the utmost care in identifying his birds, in keeping his records, and in watching his traps. It cannot be entered upon without first securing a trapping permit from the Fish and Wildlife Service and one from the State Conservation Department, and such permits are granted only if one's knowledge of birds and dependability in keeping records have been vouched for by several ornithologists. Applications should be addressed to the Bird-Banding Division of the Fish and Wildlife Service, which has headquarters at the Patuxent Research Refuge in Laurel, Maryland. Once the permit has been granted, bands and the proper forms for keeping records and reporting the banding results will be furnished the bander without charge.

Four Bird-Banding Associations, Northeastern, Eastern, Inland and Western, publish bulletins which contain many useful articles for the novice or experienced bander. The quarterly journal, *Bird-Banding,* contains longer articles which are usually based upon facts obtained by banding birds, and also has very complete reviews of domestic and foreign ornithological articles.

A collaborator supplies his own traps which he can make or purchase from any of the dealers that advertise in the Bulletins of the Bird-Banding Associations. Some traps are automatic, working on the principle of a funnel through which the birds find their way to the feed with little difficulty, but are unable to find their way out. Others work on the principle of a falling door and may be automatic, the bird releasing the door when it alights on a perch or tread within the trap, or the door can be released by a string at the option of the operator. Some traps are designed for the ground, others for shelves, still others for tree trunks and some for the water.

For years the author looked forward each year to the season for trapping ducks, especially the Canvasbacks and Scaups as it is one of the most exciting sports imaginable. An enclosure of two-inch poultry netting about 12 feet in diameter is built along the lake shore where the ducks have been lured by cracked corn in about two feet of water. Pieces of old water piping are used for posts to support the wire and are easily driven into the stony bottom of the lake.

FIG. 165. Scaups entering a trap preparatory to banding.

The poultry wire reaches from the bottom to about two feet above the surface of the water but the enclosure is not roofed over when Diving Ducks are to be trapped. It is much more important to see that there are no holes at the bottom for when the trap is sprung the ducks all dive and hunt for a way to get out at the bottom instead of trying to fly over the top. Two posts at a little less than four feet apart form the gateway and the door made of gas piping four feet square and covered with the poultry netting lies on the bottom with a wire or rope extending from its outer edge to a blind on the shore.

The ducks at first show little fear of the trap and the main object is to catch as many as possible each time it is sprung. After it has been sprung a few times, however, they learn to dive on the outside, pass through the gateway under water, get the corn and pass out again without ever showing themselves in the trap. It then becomes largely guess work as to how many are feeding inside the trap, and there is great uncertainty about springing it. One has to estimate the number that are left outside, the amount of churning going on inside, and try to spring the trap at just the psychological moment when there are the most inside. If one waits too long most of the ducks will get all they want to eat and leave; if he springs it too soon, he will get too few for his effort. Since there is a constant parade of ducks entering and leaving under water where they cannot be seen, I leave the reader to imagine the tenseness of the situation when the trap is sprung. Ordinarily it is sprung but twice a day, early in the morning, and again towards evening, and during the rest of the day the ducks can feed as they please though never should enough grain be left inside so that they will not be hungry in the evening.

One not located so that he can trap wild ducks can still derive a great deal of healthful recreation out of trapping and banding small birds for the principle is the same, and when the returns begin to come in, there will be all the excitement of an election.

One might expect that the trapping and handling of the birds would so frighten them that they would leave the vicinity and never venture near the traps again. On the contrary many of them form the trap habit and will be seen going into it even when it is not baited, and they may be taken several times a day. Even the wary ducks have been retaken within two hours of the time they were banded and released.

In recent years the Fish and Wildlife Service personnel have been using Japanese mist nets to catch and band insectivorous birds whose habits do not lend themselves to ordinary trapping. It takes a good deal of experience to use them without injuring some of the birds and they are not recommended for ordinary banding.

15

Attracting Birds

Feeding the Winter Birds

In many places where the birds have been fed for years and have learned to hunt about windows and doorsteps, they find food wherever it is put out for them in a very short time. In other places where winter feeding has not been practiced, the birds have to be taught to come to windows, and it may be some time before they find the food. These directions are intended primarily for those who live where winter feeding has not become the custom, or where there is not yet much local interest in birds.

What Food to Use

To begin with, the birds which ordinarily come to feeding stations fall into two groups: those that feed normally

Fig. 166. Face to face with a friendly Chickadee—the author's daughter.

upon insects, and those that feed normally upon seeds. The insectivorous birds include the Woodpeckers, Nuthatches, Chickadees, Kinglets, Creepers, and Jays. These birds, in addition to feeding upon insects, feed during the winter upon all fatty substances, and it is for this reason that it is easy to supply them with food. Beef suet, meat scraps, all kinds of nuts, raw peanuts or peanut butter, sunflower seed, pancakes, and doughnuts seem to contain the necessary substances and are much relished by them. The granivorous birds, found in northern United States during winter, are mostly members of the Sparrow family, and those that come most commonly to window feeding-stations are Juncos, Tree Sparrows, Song Sparrows,

Purple Finches, and Evening Grosbeaks. All kinds of seeds are suitable for them, and many stores offer seed mixtures especially for the birds.

When nothing else is available, cracked grain, commonly called 'chick-feed,' is the most convenient and the cheapest. Weed seed collected by the children, sweepings from the barn floor, screenings from the mill, and bread crumbs are all equally satisfactory. Some people like to make up special foods that all birds will eat. Nut fragments from processing plants* poured into melted suet until it is crumbly is perhaps the best. A cake made up from the follow-

FIG. 167. Brown Creeper visits suet protected by wire screening. The squirrels cannot carry it all off but it is still available to the birds.

ing formula is likewise very satisfactory:

Heat: 1½ qts water, 1 cup suet, 1 cup sugar. Add: 1 pint cold water, 2 cups corn meal, ½ cup flour. Boil.

If you have not already begun feeding the winter birds when you read these lines, begin now. The best time to begin, however, is in the fall before the birds have formed the fixed habits which later on take them over approximately the same course every day. Early in the season they learn which trees are infested with insects and which ones are barren of food and ordinarily they fly from one good tree to the next, skipping the barren trees. If one happens to select trees barren of insect life for the suet, the birds may not find it for a long time. On the other hand if one watches the birds before placing the suet and selects trees through which they regularly pass, it makes little difference how late in the season he begins.

* Like "Pecano," available at Albany, Georgia.

How to Begin

The best way to begin is to select the window or spot in the yard where one wishes the birds to come and, from this as a center, as nearly as possible in the four directions, fasten pieces of suet in the branches of the trees to a distance of several hundred feet. If a bird comes anywhere in the vicinity it is then apt to find one of these pieces of suet and will sooner or later find its way to the desired

Fig. 168. A successful feeding station at Herbert Stoddard's home in Georgia, with winter Goldfinches and Myrtle Warblers.

spot. When one bird has found the suet at the window, it will not be necessary to keep up the supply in the other places, for birds are continually watching each other as well as hunting for food and are quick to follow the one that has found a good feeding place. In the beginning it will be more satisfactory to tie the suet to the most conspicuous branches available, but at a permanent feeding station, likely to be visited by Crows and squirrels that will try to carry off all the suet in one piece, it is best to put it behind a piece of wire netting or to ram it into a hole bored in a tree or a post erected for that purpose.

If there are weed patches or shrubbery near, where the seed-eating birds regularly feed, one should encourage them to return to that place by scattering more seed, but if there are none, as is often the case, one can rely upon the Chickadees and Nuthatches and House Sparrows to show them the way, and can begin by putting seed directly on his feeding-shelf. There is scarcely any locality where flocks of House Sparrows will not almost immediately find the seed and consume it about as fast as it is put out. One should not be discouraged, however, for they ordinarily act as decoys and by their chirping announce to the passing native birds the presence of the food. After the native birds have found the food, it is time to outwit the Sparrows with anti-Sparrow devices.

The Permanent Feeding Station

The type of permanent feeding station to be used must be determined by local conditions. If there is a window available, with a tree somewhere near it, by all means use some sort of a feeding-shelf or box at the window. The advantages of having the birds at such close range more than outweighs the occasional distractions that may occur in the schoolroom or elsewhere at unsuitable moments. Many teachers tell me that discipline becomes much easier after the birds have been attracted to the window, because the children are more willing to give strict attention to their studies when they are told that they will be allowed to watch the birds for a few minutes upon completing their lesson.

One need but nail a cleat along the outside of the window-ledge to keep the food from blowing off, and fasten a branch to the window casing to which suet can be tied. It is better to use some sort of a shelf, however, that will give a little more room for the birds, so that more than one can feed at a time. Our native birds like lots of 'elbow room' while feeding.

The chief trouble with an open shelf at the window is that during snow-storms, when food is most needed by the birds, it is covered up. Some sort of a covered shelf is therefore better. A very convenient window feeding-box can be made from a "soap-box" or box of similar size, one end of which is nailed to the window casing so that the open side faces south. If what is then the back is replaced by a pane of glass, so that it is well lighted within, the birds will not hesitate to enter and will be able to get the food even during the worst storms. No matter what sort of a window-shelf is used, it is always well to fasten a branch—and preferably an evergreen branch or small tree—to one side of it. Sometimes a number of branches can be used effectively to break the force of the wind and at the same time to decorate the shelf. The more the feeding station, wherever it is, looks like a little corner of the woods, the better the birds will like it.

When the windows open on a court or narrow street or some place where, obviously, birds could not be attracted to the windows, one may have to be satisfied with feeding the birds some place in the yard, around the flag-pole, or on a post erected for the purpose. In such places the weather-vane feeders and other more elaborate de-

FIG. 169. Evening Grosbeaks at a window sill shelf. Photo by D. G. Allen.

vices that are advertised are very satisfactory. A very simple and satisfactory shelf, however, can be made by any child out of the top of a barrel. The hoops are used to make a framework over part of the shelf, and this framework is covered with cloth or woven with evergreen twigs to keep out the snow. This sort of a feeding-station could be put up in any place where one wishes to feed the birds.

In front of one of the windows at the Laboratory of Ornithology at Cornell we have what we call our "Early American Feeder," built like one corner of a rail fence with an upturned old pine stub added. Several basins made of copper screening with good drainage are added in appropriate places as food shelves so that many birds and squirrels feed at the same time.

One of the most attractive feeding stations I have seen is the one in front of the picture window at the home of Herbert Stoddard near Thomasville, Georgia, where he has recorded 65 different kinds of birds utilizing his Pecano mixture. (See Fig. 168). An additional

Fig. 170. The "Early American Feeder" (fence-rails and pine stump) at the Cornell Laboratory of Ornithology, with Evening Grosbeaks. Photo by D. G. Allen.

hollow log shelf on the window sill is sometimes covered with 40 or 50 Goldfinches and Myrtle Warblers and there is a constant parade of other species at this and the other devices for holding the food in front of the window.

ANTI-SPARROW AND SQUIRREL DEVICES

If one is plagued with House Sparrows at his window feeder they may be discouraged by having the front half of the shelf arranged so that it will teeter when the bird alights on it. The front half of the floor is held with leather hinges and supported at the corners by rubber bands or light springs. When a bird enters the box this board teeters much as though the entire box were about to tip over. The wary House Sparrows have learned to be suspicious of such devices, and, though whole flocks of them perch on top of the box and peer over the edge at the food within, not one dares, at first, to enter. After other birds have been feeding for several weeks, a few Sparrows may learn to enter without causing the board to teeter, but the slightest tap on the window sends them away in fright.

Where squirrels become obnoxious it may still be possible to feed the birds by building an anti-squirrel feeder but it taxes one's ingenuity. It is especially needed on automatic feeders where a week's supply of expensive sunflower seed is offered. The best arrangement I have seen is a feeder on a pipe with a loose metal cone at the top below the feeder around which the squirrels cannot climb.

Bird-Houses

The making of bird-houses is an old, old story, but, like many other classic tales, it will bear re-telling. The original idea was simple enough, but of recent years it has been encumbered by so many suggestions that people hesitate to undertake what is really an easy task, for the more simple the box, the more natural will it appear and the more attractive will it be to the birds. The fanciful doll-houses, with several compartments, chimneys, frescoes and verandas, while occasionally used by House Sparrows or Purple Martins, are usually very ineffective, and, of course, entirely out of place. The more the bird-house resembles the old hollow limb in the orchard or the hole in the fence-post, the more pleasing to the eye of the bird it will be.

There are over 30 species of birds in the United States and Canada which utilize holes in trees for nesting, including many of the most useful. The borer-destroying Woodpeckers, the larvæ-destroying Nuthatches, the insect-egg-destroying Chickadees, the mosquito-destroying Tree Swallows—all build in holes in trees and may be attracted to nesting-boxes. In these days of scientific forestry, when every dead tree is condemned and when every dead branch is lopped off by the 'tree doctor,' their natural nesting-sites are rapidly disappearing and their numbers must necessarily decrease unless they are provided with artificial nesting-places. It is a wise timber-owner who puts up at least one nesting-box in the place of every dead tree which he removes. The Chickadees and Woodpeckers that are with us in winter, and the Wrens and Bluebirds that return in the spring, will move on unless they find plenty of nesting-sites.

FIG. 171. Bird house—it rents for a song.

Of the hole-nesting birds, a comparatively small proportion have yet learned to accept the artificial nesting-site, only nine species taking them regularly in Eastern United States and nineteen more utilizing them occasionally. It is to be expected, however, that eventually all the species will learn to adapt themselves, and, perhaps, even others will so modify their present nesting habits as to accept the artificial structures. This proved to be the case in the well-known experiments of von Berlepsch in Germany, where out of 1000 nesting-boxes placed on his estate, birds gradually were induced to occupy over 900.

The species which regularly use nesting-boxes in this country are as follows: House Sparrow, Starling, House Wren, Bewick's Wren, Bluebird, Chickadee, Purple Martin, Tree Swallow, Violet-green Swallow, Flicker and House Finch.

The species which occasionally use nesting-boxes are as follows: White-breasted and Red-breasted Nuthatches, Tufted Titmouse, Carolina Wren, Crested Flycatcher, Prothonotary Warbler Screech, Saw-whet and Barn Owls, Sparrow Hawk, Wood Duck and Dipper. The species using covered shelves or shelters open at the sides, are the Robin, Phœbe, and Barn Swallow.

MATERIALS

The best materials to select in building bird-houses are weathered boards, rustic cedar or redwood slabs of wood with the bark adhering, or asphaltum roofing-paper. Smoothly planed boards and paint should be avoided except on such houses as are intended more for ornament than use. Gourds, when obtainable, can be made very acceptable by cutting a hole of the proper size in one side, cleaning them out and drilling a small hole in the bottom to drain off any rain that may beat in. Tin cans may be used but are usually unsightly

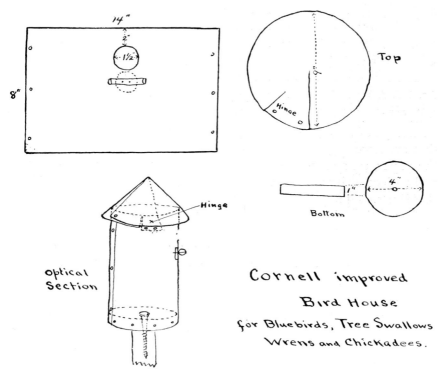

Fig. 172. Diagram for a simple bird house to be made from roofing paper.

and become excessively hot in the sun, unless covered with bark. One end should be replaced by a block of wood and the opening of the proper size should be made toward one edge of this or in one side of the can. Green bark of chestnut or other trees can sometimes be obtained and nailed into the form of a hollow cylinder, but such boxes are usually not durable. A hollow limb, a deserted Wood-pecker's nest, or a block of wood hollowed out in the form of a Woodpecker's nest are all good devices, but usually it is easier to cut

Fig. 173. A House Wren at the paper house.

rough boards into proper lengths and nail them together securely in the form of a small box. Sometimes boxes of the proper size, such as chalk-boxes or starch-boxes, can be found ready made and require only some reinforcements.

If one plans to make a great many of standard size, heavy asphaltum roofing-paper lends itself most readily at a minimum of expense. A working drawing of the Cornell improved bird-house for birds up to the size of Bluebirds is given in Fig. 172. These can be made in numbers for a maximum of 20 cents each, and have the advantage of being as easily made by girls as by boys. The only tools that are necessary are a pair of heavy scissors or a knife for cutting the paper, an awl for punching holes for the rivets, a tack-hammer and a piece of iron pipe or a window-weight against which to flatten the rivets. The *split* rivets used to fasten the edges together can be purchased at any hardware store. If a great many boxes are to be built, it is wise to have a short piece of 1½-inch pipe sharpened to serve as a punch for cutting the holes, but otherwise this can be done with the knife. The blocks of wood, 4 inches in diameter, can be cut from a log of that size or made in numbers in the manual training department or the local carpenter shop on the jig-saw.

The first exercise should be to draw the pattern, cut it out, and pin it together. The best pattern should then be taken to mark the roofing paper. In putting together the patterns, one soon learns

Fig. 174. Young House Wrens in an old chalk-box house.

the order in which the various steps should be taken. Thus the perch and the roof must be fastened to the piece forming the sides before it is fastened into cylinder form. The circular piece cut out for the opening may be used to reinforce the front on the inside where the perch is nailed in place. The very last step is the nailing of the completed house to its base, which, it is well, to have previously fastened by screws or face-plate to the top of the post or pipe where the bird-house is to be permanently placed. It will be seen, therefore, that this house is intended only for use on top of a post, which incidentally provides greater safety for the birds.

MEASUREMENTS

Whatever material is used, the exact size of the box is not of great importance except that it should not be so large as to waste material,

FIG. 175. Some correctly built bird houses.

nor yet so small as to give insufficient room for the nest. A box should never be smaller than 3½x3½x6 inches inside measurements, and it is better to make it somewhat larger, even for Wrens. In making bird-houses for the first time, it would be well to make them of medium size so that they will be acceptable to the greatest variety of birds. In this way the chances of attracting them are increased. Such a box would measure about 4x4x9 inches inside with the long axis vertical. If special effort is to be made to attract Flickers, Screech Owls, or Sparrow Hawks, boxes 6½x6½x24 inches should be made. If Purple Martins are desired, a house of from ten to thirty compartments should be constructed, with each compartment 6 to 8 inches square. Rows of gourds tied to cross-pieces raised on poles will likewise attract Martins and are extensively used in the South. If one wishes to build a large Martin-House, explicit directions and working drawings can be obtained from a pamphlet entitled 'Bird-Houses and How to Build Them,' published by the U.S. Department of Agriculture. All other bird-houses should be built with only one compartment.

OPENINGS

The *size* and *position* of the opening are much more important than the exact size of the box. A round hole is best, and, except in Martin-houses, should be cut above the middle line on one side and preferably about 2 inches from the top. All hole-nesting birds,

FIG. 176. Much used colonial Martin houses—the only bird house nesters that prefer to nest in colonies. All other bird houses should be single compartments.

except the Martins, wish to be out of sight of the entrance while incubating. There should never be more than one entrance to the box, but if the box is very tightly built, a ¼-inch hole may be drilled just beneath the roof for ventilation and another through the floor for drainage. These are unnecessary however, and in natural nesting cavities, of course, never occur. If there are not many House Sparrows or Starlings about, it is best to make the openings in all the boxes, except those for the largest birds, 1½ inches in diameter. This will admit birds up to the size of the Bluebird and the Tree Swallow, and is not large enough to be objectionable to the Wrens and the Chickadees. If Sparrows are numerous, one can keep them out of the boxes and still admit the smaller species by making the opening 1¼ inches in diameter. One can keep out the Sparrows until the Bluebirds arrive by having a removable piece with a small opening fastened over the 1½-inch hole. When the Bluebirds are seen trying to get in, this piece can be removed, and then the Bluebird will have an even chance with the Sparrows.

If one wishes to build houses for particular birds, the following table of proper diameters for the opening, will be found useful:

(*a*) 1⅛ inches: House Wren, Bewick's Wren, Carolina Wren, Chickadee.

(*b*) 1¼ inches: White-breasted Nuthatch, Tufted Titmouse.

(*c*) 1½ to 1⅝ inches: Bluebird, Crested Flycatcher, Tree Swallow, Violet-green Swallow.

(*d*) 2½ inches: Flicker, Saw-whet Owl, Purple Martin.

(*e*) 3 inches: Screech Owl, Sparrow Hawk.

(*f*) 4½ inches: Barn Owl, Wood Duck.

Nesting Material

No nesting material in the form of straws, feathers, or sticks should be placed in the box, though if they are placed abundantly in the vicinity they may encourage nesting. If a prospective tenant finds nesting material in the box, he will usually consider it already occupied and move on. In Flicker boxes, however, there should be placed in the bottom a couple of inches of ground cork or coarse sawdust, mixed with a little earth, because Woodpeckers build no nests and must have something to keep the eggs from rolling about. A layer of sawdust will do not harm in any other box but is not necessary.

Placing the Box

Quite as important as the proper construction of the bird-house is the selection of its location. It is possible to put up ten or fifteen boxes and have nothing but House Sparrows nesting in them, but, if properly placed, they would be occupied by Wrens, Chickadees, Swallows, or Bluebirds. If several boxes are put up, they should be at least 25 feet apart and, preferably, farther, or constant fighting will usually result until one of the tenants is evicted. If one examines the natural nesting-places of any of these hole-nesting birds, he will find that, with few exceptions, they are in open places in bright sunlight or light shade, and seldom among thick branches of a tree or in dense shade. The best place for the box, therefore, is on a pole, 5 to 15 feet from the ground, in an open space or at the edge of trees facing the open. An iron pipe, an inch or more in diameter, and 8 feet long, driven into the ground 2 feet, makes an ideal location for a box, as it likewise gives protection from cats and squirrels. It is for this reason that the Cornell bird-house is designed to be put up in no other way. A post on the porch or the unshaded side of the house will also serve if the box is turned to face outward. The trunk of a large tree, several feet below the first branches, a telegraph pole, or a high fence-post are other places which will prove suitable, although perhaps not quite so satisfactory as the separate post. An excellent place for the large Flicker or Sparrow Hawk box is the top of a dead tree, particularly if the smaller branches are cut away from around the box. Occasionally a Wren or a Nuthatch will use a box placed in the shade among the branches of a tree, but such places, while appealing strongly to most people as highly desirable, should be shunned. House Sparrows are the only birds that will regularly use boxes so placed.

CARE OF THE BOX

If a box is well made, once in position, it need never be removed, though it will probably last longer if taken inside during the winter. Frail or fancy boxes should be taken in each fall and replaced in March. Cleaning a box is not necessary under ordinary circumstances, as the birds will do their own renovating, but it is well to have the top or one side hinged, so that one can inspect the inside if necessary, to throw out the nests of the Sparrows, or squirrels, or mice, or hornets that sometimes usurp the box before the birds arrive. Aside from this there is little need of care, and at the end of the season the old nests can be thrown out or left in, it making little difference to the birds when they return the following spring. The lice which often infest the nests of Wrens are harmless and die soon after the young leave. If anything is to be done, the nests should be sprinkled with insect powder while still occupied.

TIME TO PUT UP BOXES

The boxes should be in place as early in the spring as possible, especially those intended for Nuthatches and Chickadees that are with us throughout the winter. Although they do not begin nesting until April, Chickadees often commence excavating their nesting cavities in February. Boxes put up after March 1, and even as late as May 1, are often occupied the same year, but the chances are much better if they are put up early. Anyone planning a bird-house competition in the schools should start in winter, so that the boxes will be ready by April 1.

PLANTING TO ATTRACT BIRDS

Equally important with winter feeding and placing of nesting boxes, if one wishes birds about his home, or in a bird sanctuary, is

FIG. 177. Waxwing on mulberry branch, a fruit much used by birds and with a long season.

the planting of food-bearing shrubs, vines and trees, and the arrangement of the shrubbery so as to give the greatest number of available nesting places.

Scattered trees and clumps of bushes with open spaces between are much more attractive to nesting birds than the same area completely overgrown to even the most atractive vegetation. Most birds must have sunlight and they nest about the periphery of tangled vegetation rather than in the center of it The principles of landscaping ordinarily employed, therefore, make for a greater number of birds than the complete covering of an area with shrubs and trees. Where such areas already exist, the number of nesting birds will be increased if broad paths are cut and planted to grass or at least kept open. The two types of woodland where birds are most scarce are parks completely planted to trees with the underbrush all cut out and the trees themselves pruned high, and secondly solid stands of coniferous trees. Ordinary city parks and areas reforested in the usual way with a solid growth of pine or spruce provide very little food and relatively few nesting sites and are almost devoid of nesting birds. The addition of the proper shrubbery to the park and the planting of food bearing trees along wide fire lanes in the reforested areas might convert them into most desirable bird sanctuaries. The planting of millet, buckwheat and sunflowers in the plowed portion of the fire lanes and the selection of the proper flowers for the park gardens will likewise increase bird life.

Fig. 178. Plant sunflowers for Goldfinches and Chickadees.

In deciding upon a planting program to make an area attractive to birds, due care should be given to the selection of such a variety of trees and shrubs and to the fruiting season of each, that food will become available throughout the year. A fine crop of Mountain Ash berries will bring in flocks of Waxwings during the winter and early spring, but it will provide nothing for the summer birds—not even nesting sites of value. The addition of a few mulberry trees, dogwood bushes, wild cherries, viburnums, and barberries, on the other hand, would provide an almost continuous supply of bird food throughout the year. The Mulberries would begin to ripen in June and the barberries would carry their berries until the following May, with the others filling in the interval between. A list of the more desirable species suitable for planting in bird refuges follows, those starred providing nesting sites as well as fruit for certain birds. The period during which the fruit is available to birds follows each.

FRUIT-BEARING TREES, SHRUBS AND VINES ATTRACTIVE TO BIRDS

*Five-leaved Ivy or Virginia Creeper, August-February
  Boston Ivy, September-March
  Red and Black Choke-berries, July-June
*Spicebush, July-November
*Japanese Barberry (The fruits are eaten mostly during the spring when
        other fruits are scarce) July-June
*Common Barberry, July-June
  Black or Cherry Birch, September-April
  Yellow Birch, September-April
  White Birch, September-April
  Red Birch, June-September
  Hackberry, January-December
*Dogwoods, June-March
  White-flowering Dogwood, August-January
  Autumn Olive, August-January
  Cornelian Cherry, July-November
*American Hawthorns, October-April. (Preference should be given those
        varieties that hold their fruit like the Washington Thorn)
*English Hawthorn, August-March
  Weigelia or Diervilla, November-March
  Oleaster or Wild Olive, September-April
  Japanese Oleaster, July-September
  Wintergreen, January-December
  Black Huckleberry, July-October
  Shrubby St. John's-wort, November-April

*Common Juniper, January-December
*Irish Juniper, same
*Red Cedar, same
 American and European Larches, October-April (The tiny bagworms
     that infest these trees are fed upon extensively by Siskins and Red-
     polls)
*Common Privet, July-April
*Riegel's Privet, same
*Tartarian Honeysuckle, September-May
 Fly Honeysuckle, March-June
*Wild Grapes, August-June
 Partridge Berry, January-December
 Mulberry (One of the best bird foods), May-August
*Bayberry, or Candle Berry, July-June (especially for Myrtle Warblers)
 Sour Gum or Tupelo, July-October
 Mahaleb Cherry (the best of the wild cherry bird foods), June-July
 Wild Red or Bird Cherry, June-November
 Sand Cherry, June-August
 Wild Black Cherry, July-November
*Flowering Crab, September-June
*Buckthorn, August-April
 Sumacs, January-December
*Blackberries and Raspberries, June-October
*Black Elderberry, July-October
 Red Elderberry, June-August
 Sassafras, July-October
 Buffalo Berry, June-October
*Green Brier, August-June
 Nightshade or Bittersweet, July-April (eaten by few birds)
 Mountain Ash, August-April
*Multiflora Rose, September-May

This list is not at all complete but gives a sufficient variety to enable one to select bird foods for almost any type of planting desired.

BIRD BATHS AND DRINKING FOUNTAINS

Another method of making one's garden more attractive to birds
is by maintaining a constant supply of fresh water for them. Of
course, if there is a stream close by, this is not necessary and an

artificial bath may not be well patronized. In most places, however, unless water is available, the birds will desert the garden in summer for more favored spots, for they must have water. Dripping water is more attractive than quiet water and a fine spray is perhaps preferred to anything else. In a formal garden the bird bath may become

a highly decorative feature built in the form of an ornamental fountain, or it may be a part of the rock garden, or may be merely a shallow pan on the lawn where the water is refreshed as needed. Most birds like to bathe as well as to drink so no matter what the form of the bird fountain, there should be some place where the water is very shallow and where the bottom is not slippery. Care should be taken, also, to protect

Fig. 179. Bird bath in the rock garden.

the bath from cats, for birds in soaking plumage are almost helpless.

Nesting Materials

Still another way of making one's grounds attractive to birds is by

Fig. 180. Wool gathering—a Yellow Warbler takes cotton for its nest.

supplying them with nesting materials during May and June. Short pieces of white or gray string or yarn, horse-hair stuffing from some old upholstery, or pieces of cotton are materials which Orioles, Chipping and Song Sparrows, Yellow Warblers, Redstarts, Goldfinches and Indigo Buntings appreciate. If the season is very dry and it is possible to keep one corner of the garden very wet so that Robins, Phœbes and Barn Swallows can get mud for their nests, they may stay and nest in your

garden instead of going elsewhere. The cotton and strings should be tied loosely to a conspicuous branch, the top of a bush or similar place or they may be strewn on one corner of the lawn or placed in a loosely knitted bag and hung from a branch or placed in a wire mesh container like suet. No nesting material, however, should ever be placed inside a bird-house.

16

Birds' Nests—How to Find and Identify Them

It is easy to understand the small boy's desire to make a 'collection' of birds' eggs, and the impulse that leads more advanced students into the study of oölogy. It is little wonder that oölogists are willing to risk their lives in the quest for rare or beautiful sets of eggs. We have come to condemn the practice, but can still understand the instinct that impels some collectors to take every egg they find, particularly if it is of some rare species on the verge of extinction. It is perfectly right that every accredited museum should possess the nest and several sets of eggs of each species of bird, just as they should have mounted specimens of the birds themselves, but large private collections that are used to satisfy only the cravings of the individual are a prodigal waste and should be prohibited.

FIG. 181. A Ruby-throated Hummingbird and its nest.

We look forward to the day when the camera will entirely replace the egg-box, and when color-prints or transparencies will replace the rows of egg-shells in the private collection. As a youth the author collected birds' eggs as ardently as spare time would permit, and continued the practice until he was given his first camera and came to realize what a wealth of opportunities he had been wasting—opportunities for making worth-while observations of the birds, and of their home-life, opportunities for making a collection of photographs

309

that would show not only the beautiful eggs that thrilled him, but the nest as well, and its setting. By leaving the eggs in the nest he was able to get photographs of the old birds and of the young and of many interesting habits of both old and young. As long as he was satisfied with the discovery of the nests and the transfer of the eggs to his collection, whole chapters in the life-story of each bird were as unknown to him as though they never existed. As long as he was satisfied with a mere collection of eggs he could show his discoveries to but a few friends, while now that he has been converted to the camera he can share them with everyone, and, through the medium of the printed page and the half-tone reproduction, his 'collection' is gradually being shown to all who are interested without its losing any of its original charm to himself.

During these many years of egg-collecting and then photographing the author naturally developed a 'knack' for finding birds' nests which seems not to be understood by some of his friends who have been at it for less time. It is partially 'knack' and partially method. The latter can be put down in black and white; the former is difficult to express. If by publishing the method which he employs in finding birds' nests he should encourage the collecting of eggs, he would be greatly disappointed. If, on the other hand, it makes the problem of the photographer and student of home-life easier, he will feel amply repaid. Certain it is that if one would study the home-life of birds he must first know how to find their nests. There are a number of good books, like Chapman's 'Handbook of Birds of Eastern North America,' which give descriptions of each bird's nest and the situation usually selected by the bird, but even with this information before him it is no easy matter to find the nest of any particular bird.

Now let us assume that we want to find the nests of all the birds living on a certain tract of land of perhaps 50 acres. The tract contains woods and fields and swamp and shore, with a great variety of bird-life. There are two general methods of procedure, both of which will have to be employed; one by watching and listening and the other by hunting. If the task were allotted to the author he would begin by finding out just what birds were present in the area. He would get up at daybreak the first morning and listen and he would mark down on a rough map of the place just where each bird was singing. It is a matter of common knowledge now that when the

nesting season arrives each male bird selects the area which he con-
siders suitable for nesting and proceeds to defend it from trespassing
by others of his kind. Except when feeding, he spends most of his
time in this area and announces his presence by singing. He continues to do this ordinarily until he has found a mate, the nest has
been built, and the eggs hatched. Then his ardor cools. It is not
difficult then, after one or two mornings of early rising, to learn
just what birds are nesting in the area and the territory defended
by each and thereby the approximate nesting-place.

If one is averse to early rising, or cannot get to the spot before
some of the birds have stopped singing or moved off to their feeding-
ground (which is sometimes removed from the nesting area) he can
secure much the same information by concealing himself at different
points in the area and 'squeaking.' The 'squeak,' which is an imitation of the call of a young bird or an old bird in distress, is quite
easily mastered by gently pressing the back of the hand or the
crooked index finger against the moistened lips and kissing force-
fully. It requires a little practice to produce just the right inflection
which will bring up all of the birds that are nesting in the vicinity,
but even a crude call will bring up the Robins and Catbirds and
their distress notes will in turn bring up the other birds. Some of
them will appear with food in their bills and these should be carefully watched as they will return promptly to their nests. The
others should also be marked and the general direction of their
coming and going noted. If one cannot master the gentle art of
'squeaking,' he can purchase a bird caller from the local novelty
store.

With the knowledge of what kinds of birds are nesting in the
area, one should familiarize himself with the probable nesting-sites
as given by Chapman's Handbook, if he is not already familiar with
them, and then begin the real work of finding the nests. It is important first to spend some time sitting still and watching, and then begin actively to hunt through all the likely places. One usually has to
do enough hunting anyway so it is well to begin by watching. If the
birds are carrying food to their young it will not take long to find
the nest, though the birds will not ordinarily go to it if they realize
that they are being watched. As long as they give alarm-calls (and
these are easily recognized as such) they are not likely to go to their
nests. One should, therefore, withdraw or conceal himself until their

alarm passes, being careful, however, never to lose sight of the bird, especially if it has food in its bill, for it is remarkable how rapidly a bird can disappear, feed its young, and reappear with an empty bill. If the birds are not carrying food, it will, ordinarily, take a little longer to find the nest, for the trips of the male bird to bring food to the female or to inquire after her well-being are less frequent than to the young. If the female is incubating, however, he is sure, in nearly all species, to go to her sooner or later, or else she will come to him. In the latter case it is merely a matter of watching her until she returns to the nest. It is needless to say that a pair of field glasses or binoculars are indispensable for this sort of work, for one must be able to see whether the bird is carrying food or merely swallowing all it catches, and when it disappears into a thick clump that may or may not be its nest, one needs to be able to determine this at a distance, for to show oneself may spoil the best chance of finding the nest.

The author recalls his first hunt for the nest of the Black-throated Green Warbler. I had been watching the male bird for about a half hour when suddenly the female appeared. She was promptly pursued by the male through the tree tops and I had difficulty in following them. Very soon, however, the male returned to his singing, and I paid no more attention to it but devoted myself to the female. After ten or fifteen minutes of feeding she flew to a hemlock where I thought I could see a thick spot toward the tip of one of the branches. According to Chapman this was the proper sort of a place for the Black-throated Green to nest, and I approached it with confidence only to be disillusioned. The male, seeing me, gave an alarm call, the female disappeared, and I was as far from finding the nest as when I started. Had I remained in hiding and examined the spot with glasses, the female would have been seen to pass right by it and to the top of a birch sapling about 25 feet away where later the nest was found. By showing myself too soon I wasted at least an hour.

The first nest of any species is always the most difficult to find because one works more or less blindly. After having watched a bird about its nest long enough to find it one becomes familiar with the bird's different calls and mannerisms so that the next time he is able to interpret what he sees and make short-cuts to the next nest. Recently, in Florida, for example, the author spent a half day finding a Black-necked Stilt's nest in a large flooded field but, having found it, he found five more in half an hour. The difficulty in the first place lay in the fact that as soon as he appeared the females would run considerable distances from the nests toward him and behave in a most misleading manner long before he reached the vicinity of the nests. By sneaking up within range of eight-power binoculars without the males being aware of my presence, I could mark the females on their nests and then it was plain sailing. And thus it is with many species. Nests are difficult to find until you know how.

One who is interested in finding birds' nests never hears an alarm-note without investigating the cause, never sees a bird with nesting material or food in its bill without remaining immovable until he marks where it goes with it. The location of a bird's song is as important as the song itself, and when he hears it from approximately the same place on successive days he gradually marks out the territory to which he can safely confine his hunting or watching.

When it comes to actually hunting for the nests there are a number of little tricks that make their discovery less difficult. In the matter of equipment a stout cane or staff is nearly as important as a pair of field-glasses; it is so convenient for rapping on trees, 'tickling' the underbrush, or parting the dense marsh vegetation. The author always cuts a small sapling about 5 feet long, whenever he starts out on a nest-hunting expedition and it becomes one of his best friends. In its use one soon learns to be discreet. A loud rap will startle a Crow or a Hawk from its nest, or a Woodpecker from its burrow, but the same blow may cause an Owl or a Chickadee to sit still closer. A scratching sound, on the other hand, may cause these last named to stick their heads out and save us many an unnecessary climb to determine whether or not the hole in question is tenanted.

In his youth the author spent many fruitless hours scrambling through dense thickets and tangles until he learned that the birds did not like to go to the center of these thick places any better than he did, and chose the circumference for their nesting-places. Indeed, the number of available nesting-places varies with the circumference of the thickets rather than the total area, and a field that is dotted with clumps of thorn bushes or shrubbery will contain many more birds' nests than the same size field completely covered with the same bushes. There are two methods of finding nests in such places: one is to shake or brush the shrubbery with one's staff, at the same time listening and looking for any movement suggestive of a bird leaving its nest; the other is to put one's head inside the canopy of leaves and scrutinize the inside of the hollow sphere of foliage. No matter how carefully concealed a nest may be from the outside, it is usually conspicuous from the inside. If one uses a staff he should shake the shrubbery several times and then remain quiet for a moment. Then, if he has frightened the bird from its nest and failed to notice it, he will probably hear its alarm-call. If one is hunting in snake-infested country, the use of the staff serves to frighten any snakes that might be resting in the bushes. It is rather disconcerting to put one's head inside of a thick bush and come face to face with a moccasin or even a harmless black snake. It is much better to awaken him with the staff and give him a chance to get away.

In hunting for nests of the field birds, like Bobolinks or Meadowlarks or Grasshopper Sparrows, a heavy rope 25 to 50 feet long is convenient. If the bird is incubating or brooding it will seldom let the rope pass over it without flushing, and two persons with the rope between them can cover a field in a short time. One must watch the rope carefully, however, for many of the birds will run some distance before flying and the nests are then difficult to find.

Field birds nest rather indiscriminately over the entire field but marsh birds, like the Rails and Gallinules, seem to nest most abundantly about the edges of the marsh or about the open water-holes farther out. The dense beds of cat-tails and rushes in the North, and the disheartening saw-grass of the southern swamps are rarely penetrated deeply by nesting birds, so that one has best success in skirting these areas rather than in attempting to plow through them. The nests of marsh birds are usually not difficult to find (if one does not try to keep his feet dry), by simply walking back and forth through the marsh, avoiding or skirting the extensive patches of flags and following more or less the borders of streams or pond-holes. The Rails and Gallinules regularly bend the reeds together over the nest so as to conceal the eggs, but this habit makes the nesting-site even more conspicuous to one who knows what he is looking for.

One more short-cut to finding certain birds' nests is worth mentioning: that is the placing of nesting material such as cotton and short pieces of yarn or string in a convenient place to watch. The Warblers and Goldfinches and Orioles that come for it are easily traced to their abodes.

Birds that nest in colonies, like most of the Herons and Ibises, and which often fly long distances to feed can usually be traced to their rookeries by lining them up when the conspicuous flocks are leaving in the morning or returning in the evening. It frequently requires miles and miles of wearisome travel to get to the rookeries, however, and the author's advice, after a season spent in their quest, is to get somebody else to do it.

Birds' Nests in Winter:

COLLECTING AND IDENTIFYING

When the November winds clear the leaves from the trees and bushes, many of Nature's secrets stand revealed. Along the highways the nests of the Orioles and the Goldfinches, that were so artfully concealed during the summer, now flaunt themselves in our faces. In the shrubbery about the garden the nests of the Song Sparrow and the Catbird and the Yellow Warbler suddenly jump into view as though they were scornfully asking "Where were your eyes last summer?" Now, if ever, we realize how adept at the art of concealing their nests the birds really are. Some of the nests we readily identify, for even though the birds have flown, we remember how frequently we saw them about the particular tree the previous summer. Other nests that we meet with on our walks afield or that are brought to us we fail to recognize.

There is something fascinating about a bird's nest when we stop to examine it, or even if we pass it by with a cursory glance, we cannot help feeling the little romance that surrounds it. We marvel at the skill with which the strings or fibers are woven together, and at the patience required to gather the innumerable tiny grasses and hairs that make up the nest. Until we know the bird that built the nest, however, we are discontented, and it is always with great satisfaction that we finally make up our minds as to just what bird built it.

There is scarcely a schoolroom in the country that does not at some time or other come into possession of a bird's nest or a small collection of nests. Sometimes the children seem to develop a mania for collecting nests and the school is flooded with them. Ordinarily these nests lie around without much care until the teacher gets disgusted with the meaningless litter and throws them into the waste-basket. If, however, the nests are given a little attention; if there is a place to keep the collection; and, particularly, if the teacher can identify the nests, the collection can be made one of the valuable accessions to the schoolroom. It is the intention of these paragraphs to encourage the making of these collections and to show how the nests may be identified.

The best time to start such collections is in November or December after the leaves have fallen. The nests are then easy to find, and no harm is done by collecting them, for the birds have left them and, in very few cases, is the same nest used a second time. Of course, the nest which has been watched through the summer and about which one knows the entire history is the most interesting, but much can be learned from nests that are discovered in winter for the first time. In collecting a nest it is always best to cut off the branch upon which it rests and preserve them together. The position of the nest upon the branch and its method of attachment are often as interesting and as necessary for identification as the materials from which the nest is made. It likewise provides the best means for preserving the nest for, with a few strands of fine copper wire or strong thread, it can be 'sewed' to the branch so that it will not fall off when it dries out. Wire loops or screw eyes can then be fastened to the branch so that it can be hung on the wall or in the cabinet. If for any reason it is not feasible to cut off the branch, the nest should be placed in a cardboard box, such as the old-fashioned collar-box, so that it will hold its shape and not drop litter. If collar-boxes are not available, one can encircle the nest with a strip of heavy paper or light cardboard, fasten it with Scotch tape, and then fasten to a heavy cardboard base in a similar manner. When nests are properly cared for, it is remarkable how many can be kept in a small space. Each nest should bear a neat label giving its name, where it was found, and the name of the person who discovered it. This makes the collection more useful, gives it a neater and more businesslike appearance, and usually gives all the stimulus that is needed to keep up interest. Only such nests as are in a good state of preservation should be kept.

The most satisfactory and most accurate way of identifying a bird's nest is to discover it while it is still occupied and to identify the builder. Then after the young have flown, it can be taken and it will mean much more in the collection. In case it is not found until winter, it still can be identified by means of the appended key. There is a great deal of variation in birds' nests of the same species, particularly when found in winter in different states of preservation. The general type of nest built by each species, however, is farily constant and, in writing the key, the attempt has been made to select the characters which seem most constant. The specific materials of which a nest is constructed often vary according to what is most available, and unusual nests are frequently found that defy identification by anyone but a specialist. Thus, House Wrens ordinarily build the outside of their nests of small twigs, but one was sent to the author which was made chiefly of wire clippings and hair-pins. The size and particularly the depth of a nest vary with the state of preservation in which it is found, and the key will prove practicable only for such nests as are fairly well preserved.

Ninety per cent of the nests found by children in northeastern United States belong to one of the following nine birds that are common, and whose nests are conspicuous when the leaves fall: Catbird, Chipping Sparrow, Goldfinch, Baltimore Oriole, Redstart, Robin, Song Sparrow, Red-eyed Vireo, and Yellow Warbler. The nests of birds that build on the ground are not ordinarily found except when they are occupied, and these can be identified by seeing the birds themselves. In this key, therefore, they are grouped together to save space.

For the benefit of those who are not familiar with the use of keys, the following brief explanation is given: The first section of the key divides the nests into eleven divisions. First determine in which of these a nest belongs, and then turn at once to that division and trace it through. Whenever a letter is doubled or trebled, it indicates alternative conditions, and after determining under which one the nest falls, the others are ignored and the tracing continued under the correct heading.

KEY TO THE NESTS OF THE COMMON SUMMER RESIDENT BIRDS
OF NORTHEASTERN NORTH AMERICA

A. On the ground or in tussocks of grass I
AA. In the ground (in burrows) II
AAA. Above ground, in bushes or trees, on cliffs, or about buildings

  B. Hanging or semi-pensile nests III
BB. Not hanging
    C. In holes in trees or in bird-boxes IV
    CC. Not in holes
      D. Containing sticks or large twigs V
      DD. With no sticks
        E. Felted nests of cottony materials, not lichen covered VI
        EE. Not felted or lichen covered
          F. Containing an inner layer of mud . VII
          FF. With no mud
            G. Covered with lichens VIII
            GG. With no lichens
              H. Mostly of bark, fibers, and rootlets, with or without horsehair lining IX
              HH. Mostly of grasses, rootlets, straws and leaves, usually with horsehair in the lining
                J. Not spherical X
                JJ. Spherical nests XI

I. ON THE GROUND OR IN TUSSOCKS OF GRASS: These nests are seldom found except when occupied, and then can be identified by the birds. Only a list will be given. See also spherical nests.

In Fields: Bobolink, Bob-white, Field Sparrow, Grasshopper Sparrow, Horned Lark, Killdeer, Meadowlark, Nighthawk, Pheasant, Savannah Sparrow, Song Sparrow, Spotted Sandpiper, Vesper Sparrow.

In Woods: Black and White Warbler, Brown Thrasher, Canada Warbler, Hermit Thrush, Junco, Louisiana Waterthrush, Mourning Warbler, Ovenbird, Ruffed Grouse, Song Sparrow, Towhee, Veery, Northern Waterthrush, Whip-poor-will, Woodcock.

In Marshes: Bittern, Black Duck, Black Tern, Coot, Florida Gallinule, King Rail, Loon, Marsh Hawk, Yellowthroat, Pied-billed Grebe, Short-eared Owl, Sora Rail, Swamp Sparrow, Virginia Rail, Wilson's Snipe.

II. IN BURROWS IN THE GROUND:

    A. Nesting in colonies in sand-banks . . . . BANK SWALLOW

  AA. Nesting Singly

        B. Drilling its own burrow, no nest at end . . KINGFISHER

      BB. Utilizing some other burow, nest of straws and feathers . . . . ROUGH-WINGED SWALLOW

III. HANGING OR SEMI-PENSILE NESTS:

    A. In reeds or swamp bushes

        B. Open above

            1. A platform only slightly hollowed

                    LEAST BITTERN

            2. Deeply hollowed . . . . . . RED-WINGED BLACKBIRD

      BB. Spherical nests—opening on side

            LONG- AND SHORT-BILLED MARSH WRENS

  AA. In upland bushes and trees

        B. Small, less than 2 inches deep inside, fully suspended*

            1. In berry bushes . . . . WHITE-EYED VIREO

            2. In low branches or saplings . . . RED-EYED VIREO

            3. In evergreens (usually) . . . . BLUE-HEADED VIREO

            4. In middle of tree . . . . . YELLOW-THROATED VIREO

            5. In tree top or outer branches . . WARBLING VIREO

      BB. Small, semi-pensile, partially supported

                  ACADIAN FLYCATCHER

     BBB. Larger, over 2 inches deep inside

            1. Of dried grasses, sometimes partially supported

                  ORCHARD ORIOLE

            2. Of fibers, strings and the like

                  BALTIMORE ORIOLE

IV. IN HOLES IN TREES OR IN BIRD-BOXES:

    A. Nesting in colonies . . . . PURPLE MARTIN

  AA. Nesting singly

        B. Drillng holes, no nest at bottom

            1. Opening about $1\frac{1}{2}$ inches

                  DOWNY WOODPECKER

            2. Opening about $1\frac{3}{4}$ inches . HAIRY WOODPECKER

* Fastened only at the rim, no support underneath.

3. Opening about 2 inches
> RED-HEADED WOODPECKER

4. Opening over 2 inches............FLICKER

BB. Using old Woodpecker holes or natural cavities of the same size or bird-houses with similar openings, building a nest at bottom of cavity

1. Nest of twigs lined with feathers...HOUSE WREN
2. Nest entirely of grasses............BLUEBIRD
3. Nest of straws and feathers
    a. Nest cuplike, open above....TREE SWALLOW
    b. Nest spherical or partially arched
    > HOUSE (ENGLISH) SPARROW
4. Nest of fibers, moss, wool, and many feathers
    > CHICKADEE AND NUTHATCH
5. Nest usually containing a cast snake-skin and many feathers......CRESTED FLYCATCHER

BBB. Using Flicker holes or natural cavities of similar size, no nest built
> SPARROW HAWK, SCREECH OWL, AND SAW-WHET OWL

BBBB. Using larger natural cavities
> BARRED OWL, GREAT-HORNED OWL, AND WOOD DUCK

V. CONTAINING STICKS OR LARGE TWIGS:
A. Bulky nests in trees, 15 to 60 inches outside diameter

1. Very large, 30 to 60 inches
    > OSPREY AND BALD EAGLE
2. Smaller, no lining, flat...............HERONS
3. Hollowed, lining of bark

CROW AND OWLS { GREAT-HORNED
              { LONG-EARED

4. Hollowed, lining of fresh leaves or evergreens..HAWKS { RED-SHOULDERED
                                                          { RED-TAILED
                                                          { COOPER'S
                                                          { SHARP-SHINNED

5. Spherical nests....................SQUIRRELS

AA. Smaller nests, less than 15 inches outside
B. Cuplike, in chimneys, hollow trees, or silos twigs glued together...........CHIMNEY SWIFT

  BB. Otherwise
    C. Platform, very shallow

      1. No lining . . . . MOURNING DOVE
      2. A little lining . . . . CUCKOOS

    CC. Deeply hollowed, 1 to 3 inches deep
      D. In thickets or scrubby trees, under 3½ inches inside diameter

        1. Lining of leaves and rootlets
         a. Over 3 inches inside
           BROWN THRASHER
         b. 3 inches or less inside . . . . CATBIRD
        2. Lining of bark and wool
          MIGRANT SHRIKE

    DD. In trees often evergreen, over 3½ inches inside diameter . . . . BLUE JAY

VI. FELTED NESTS OF COTTONY MATERIALS:
  A. Nests wider than high, containing thistledown . . GOLDFINCH
  AA. Nests higher than wide, no thistledown
    B. Thick walled, usually in vertical fork of bush or tree
      YELLOW WARBLER
    BB. Thick walled, usually on horizontal branch of apple or similar tree usually decorated with bits of paper
      LEAST FLYCATCHER
    BBB. Thin walled, usually close to trunk of small sapling
      REDSTART

VII. CONTAINING A LAYER OF MUD:
  A. Built in trees
    B. Of grasses and mud, usually no moss, or dead leaves

      1. Under 4 inches inside diameter . . . . ROBIN
      2. Over 4 inches inside diameter . . . . . . GRACKLE

    BB. Containing dead leaves and usually moss
      WOOD THRUSH
  AA. Built on buildings, bridges, or cliffs
    B. Outer layer of grasses, mud within

      1. Under 4 inches inside diameter . . . . ROBIN
      2. Over 4 inches inside diameter . . . . . . GRACKLE

BB. Outer layer of mud, some grasses

      1. Open at top, cup-shaped . . . . BARN SWALLOW
      2. Open at side, gourd-shaped . . . . CLIFF SWALLOW

BBB. Outer layer of moss and mud . . . . PHOEBE

VIII. WITH AN OUTER COVERING OF LICHENS, SADDLED ON BRANCH
   A. Very small, less than 1½ inches outside diameter
                     RUBY-THROATED HUMMINGBIRD
  AA. Larger, over 1½ inches outside diameter

      1. Very deep, over 1½ inches . . BLUE-GRAY GNATCATCHER
      2. Shallow, under 1½ inches . . . . WOOD PEWEE

IX. MOSTLY OF BARK, FIBERS, AND ROOTLETS, WITH OR WITHOUT
    HORSEHAIR LINING
   A. Small woodland nests, usually in evergreens, less than 2
      inches in diameter (seldom found) . . PINE WARBLER, MAG-
      NOLIA WARBLER, BLACK-THROATED GREEN WARBLER, PURPLE
      FINCH, BLACK-BURNIAN WARBLER
  AA. Small woodland nests, less than 2 inches in diameter usually
      in bushes or sprouts

      1. No dead wood in bottom . . . . CHESTNUT-SIDED WARBLER
      2. Bits of dead wood in bottom
                  BLACK-THROATED BLUE WARBLER

  AAA. Orchard or woodland nests, over 2 inches inside diameter
    B. Usually thin, flimsy structures

      1. Little or no lining, usually in high bushes
                 ROSE-BREASTED GROSBEAK
      2. Considerable lining, usually in trees
                 SCARLET TANAGER

    BB. Thick, well-formed structures with some cotton or
      wool

      1. Shallow, about 1 inch deep . . . . KINGBIRD
      2. Deeper, about 1½ inches deep, usually with
        streamers of grass tops . . . . . . CEDAR WAXWING

X. MOSTLY OF GRASSES, ROOTLETS, STRAWS, AND LEAVES, USUALLY
    WITH HORSEHAIR IN THE LINING AND NOT SPHERICAL
   A. With many leaves, placed in weeds, ferns, or low bushes

      1. Under 2 inches inside diameter . . . . . . INDIGO BUNTING

2. Over 2 inches inside diameter

    a. Nest placed on mat of leaves............Veery

    b. Leaves woven into nest....Yellow-breasted Chat

AA. With few or no leaves

    B. Less than 1¾ inches inside diameter

        1. With thick horsehair lining

                Chipping Sparrow

        2. With few hairs, or none.......Field Sparrow

BB. Over 2 inches inside diameter

        1. With many or few hairs in lining

                Song Sparrow

        2. No hairs, a few leaves..Yellow-breasted Chat

Fig. 182. Types of nests of common birds, conspicuous in winter. 1. Robin 2. Redstart and Yellow Warbler 3. Baltimore Oriole 4. Goldfinch 5. Red-eyed Vireo 6. Catbird.

XI. SPHERICAL NESTS OF GRASSES, BARK, OR FIBERS:

    A. On the ground very thickly lined with soft grasses

                                                                MEADOW MOUSE

    AA. In bushes or vines, usually on some old bird's nest and lined with cotton or wool . . . . DEER MOUSE

  AAA. In trees or about buildings

        1. Of bark and fibers, no lining, usually some leaves or sticks, often on an old Crow's nest . . . . SQUIRREL

        2. Of grasses lined with feathers . . . . . HOUSE SPARROW

17

Observation Blinds and Bird Photography

Nearly thirty years have passed since the first edition of this book was published and while the birds themselves are just the same and the problems connected with their photography have changed but little, there have been many changes in cameras, lenses, and films that have simplified the problem of getting pictures of birds. Longer focus lenses permit working at greater distances. Faster films permit shorter exposures even in full color and speed flash units making exposures of from 1/1000 to 1/30,000 of a second permit action pictures, even in color, that were not then possible. The photoelectric cell has replaced the thread for remote control for those who prefer sitting in the open to life in a blind—but the birds still present the same challenge. Larger cameras have been replaced by 35 mm cameras especially for color work, with many makes to choose from. In this chapter we will assume that the reader knows the rudiments of photography and approach the problem from the specialized angle of its application to securing satisfactory pictures of birds.

The simplest kind of bird photography is that through a window of birds coming to feeding stations. If the window glass is good so that the window does not have to be open, the problem is still more simplified. If further, one is equipped with a satisfactory speedlight so that he is not dependent on the sun, his photographic difficulties will be reduced to a minimum and he can concentrate entirely on the birds and the composition of the picture he wishes to secure and devising ways of making the birds perform just as he wishes. The accessories and the type of picture—flight or quiet—are limited only by the ingenuity of the photographer in getting the bird to perform properly on his stage.

One should conceive as completely as possible, from actual observation of the birds, the picture which will be most satisfying and then attempt to reproduce it. Perhaps you want a Cardinal on a branch of flowering dogwood, or Myrtle Warblers on a branch of Camellias. (See color plate of Pine & Myrtle Warblers). One first makes the arrangement that is just what he wants as seen through the camera at the proper distance, etc., imagining that the bird is in the picture. Then he moves the food around on the shelf, arranges obstructions, etc. so that the spot where he wants the bird is the most convenient for the bird to alight before going to the food. If one is working with natural light, one should give thought to a distant light colored background. If speed-lights are being used, an artificial background within 18 inches of the subject which will reflect the proper tone of light to the film is essential unless one is satisfied with the black background that would otherwise result. Light blue or green cloth stretched over heavy cardboard or plywood with no wrinkles usually gives better results than colored or painted cards which often give undesirable reflections. Leafy branches or palmetto fans are less artificial but often have undesirable shadows or patterns.

In setting the flash apparatus, two or three lights are much better than one and they should be set at such angles that they do not produce shadows on the background but still give an even illumination on the subject. (See fig. 190).

June is the month of all months to get really acquainted with birds and to work with a camera. In the southern states the height of the nesting season is in May, but in the northern states it is in June. Some birds begin nesting as early as February or March, but in June practically all of the birds have either eggs or young, and it is at this time that one can get really intimately acquainted with them by observing them at close range. I can still remember the thrill of my first look at a bird through a pair of field-glasses. It was by mere chance that I leveled them at a Robin on the lawn and noticed for the first time its clear yellow bill, the white spots above and in front of its bright eye, and especially did I note the individual feathers of its wings. A whole new world seemed suddenly disclosed to me. But even greater was my delight the first time I seated myself in a blind near a bird's nest and watched the bird come back and settle on its eggs, oblivious to me only arm's length away. It so happened that it was the nest of a Virginia Rail, a bird that we do not get well acquainted with by ordinary means, so that when she came mincing up to her nest, jerking her diminutive henlike tail, casting sidelong glances at the blind, yet showing no fear of it, stopping to probe for some larva under a floating bit of drift, or making a sudden dart at a Donacia beetle, I would not have exchanged my seat on a half-sunken soap-box for the President's chair. I felt that, at last, I had seen a bird as God sees it and as man was intended to see it before he caused all living things to fear him. Years have passed since that first experience in an umbrella blind,

Fig. 183. Umbrella blind at Redwing's nest.

and I have watched hundreds of birds come back to their nest at arm's length in every conceivable situation, but the experience never tires me and never fails to bring me pleasure. At times I feel almost guilty when family secrets are bared before me, but so deep an insight does it give one into the life and character of a bird, that I now feel unfamiliar with the species until I have placed a blind near its nest and watched it for several hours.

There would not be space in this book to tell all of the interesting observations that can be made from a blind near a bird's nest, so rather will I devote a few pages to describing some of the simpler forms of observation blinds and how they are best used. The first suggestion of an observation blind came to me from Prof. F. H. Herrick, when he published, in 1905, his "Home Life of Wild Birds," describing the use of an ordinary tent as a means for studying and photographing birds. This was modified and improved by Dr. F. M. Chapman when he invented the umbrella blind described in "Camps and Cruises of an Ornithologist," in 1907; and then came G. A. Bailey, in 1922, and told us in *Bird-Lore* for November-December about his '*Blind de Luxe.*' So I claim no originality in the blinds described unless it be in the ways I have simplified them to suit my methods of working. Each type of blind has its special virtues and no one is suited to every situation, although the umbrella blind is the most generally useful.

The Umbrella Blind: As originally described by Dr. Chapman, this blind consisted of a 'sign' umbrella, leaf-green in color, with the sides or bag of denim dyed green at the top and brown at the bottom. The umbrella was supported by a jointed brass rod, adjustable like a music-stand, that could be driven into the ground. This makes a rather expensive outfit that one hates to lose in a windstorm or have carried off by mischievous boys. In my experience I have found it just as satisfactory to use an old umbrella that can be picked up for a few cents and in which you can cut slits for ventilation if such are not already present. In place of the adjustable brass rod I cut a 6-foot pole which is easily forced into the ground and to which the umbrella is tied. In place of the parti-colored denim I use cheap dark green cambric, sewed into a big sheet 7 feet long, and of a width slightly greater than the circumference of the opened umbrella. A fold is sewed in the top for a draw string, but the edges of the sheet are pinned with safety pins rather than sewed. The cambric is thin enough so that when one sits inside the closed blind he can see out in any direction, but one on the outside cannot see in.

This type of blind is best suited for observing nests that are built within 6 feet of the ground, but I have used it in the tree tops with Hawks and Herons as well, by building a platform on which to stand, or even without the platform. The chief difficulty in the use of this blind is its tendency to blow and shake in the wind, even when securely guyed, and this often alarms birds like

Marsh Hawks and Cranes, that are naturally wary. In open fields and on beaches where the winds are often strong and where the birds are nesting on the ground, I often substitute a 'pup-tent' that can be so securely fastened that it will not shake in the wind, or some form of box blind if it can be conveniently transported.

Mr. H. H. Cleaves, a very ingenious photographer of wild life, has conceived a much more comfortable and more satisfactory blind for windy situations in which a jointed framework of rattan is covered with artificial grass mats such as are used by undertakers, or merchants for store windows. The author has used with some success a modification of this idea in which the rattan frame is replaced by an umbrella and a rod with an offset. The rod of the umbrella is cut off to about a foot in length so that it will not extend

FIG. 184. Blind set near Emperor Goose nest.

through the middle of the blind. This slips into a T screwed onto the end of a rod shaped like an inverted L made of gas piping. This blind is not as steady as Mr. Cleaves' in a windstorm, but it is much simpler to build and to erect. The grass matting has to be cut to conform to the shape of the umbrella as it is too heavy for a drawstring. The mats come three feet wide and six feet long and it takes three mats for a blind. Used or even discarded mats serve very well for a blind and can be purchased for a nominal sum from florists or cemeteries.

In later years I have used four six-foot lengths of gas piping bent two feet from one end in curves that will produce an arched roof when screwed into a four-way union. Still better is the lighter electric conduit that can be flattened at the curved end and drilled with a quarter-inch hole through which an eye-bolt fits to hold the four legs in place. The covering can be made of grass mats or tough denim, green, gray or brown, with slits or zippered openings for the lens and peepholes. The legs can be cut into shorter lengths for convenience in carrying and screwed together with unions when in use.

Dummy blinds of burlap or any inexpensive material will help the photographer who wants to prepare several nests for photography at the same time. I have sometimes used as many as seven at a time—substituting the real blind when ready to photograph. The pup-tent is most serviceable as an observation blind in open

FIG. 185. Box blind set on Grasshopper Sparrow's nest.

fields, on bare beaches, and on rocky islands where the umbrella blind would flap in the wind and be unnecessarily conspicuous. The closed end should be directed towards the nest so that no guy rope will interfere with the view or with the camera if one is to be used. The open end can be closed with pins, after the observer is safely ensconced, and observations can be made through a small opening from the darkened interior. Owing to the lowness of this form of blind, it is suitable only for birds nesting on or near the ground.

'*The Blind de Luxe*,' invented by G. A. Bailey to soothe his frozen limbs, and described by him in *Bird Lore* for November-

COLORATION

Scarlet Tanager — Male and Young

Scarlet Tanager — Juvenile

Scarlet Tanager — Male in Winter

Scarlet Tanager (male) Spring Molt

COLORATION

Evening Grosbeaks

Evening Grosbeaks (Juvenile)

Male Goldfinch and Juveniles
(Summer Plumage)

Goldfinches (male, female) and Young
with Cardinal in Winter

COLORATION

Purple Finches—Male in Worn Bright Red Plumage; Male in Fresh Pink Plumage

Rusty Blackbirds—Winter Plumage with Brown Edges to Feathers

Shoveller — Breeding Plumage

Shoveller — Eclipse Plumage

COLORATION

Blue Jay and Similarly Colored Young

Male Indigo Bunting with Brown Young Resembling Female

Young Kingfishers Resembling their Respective Parents

Chipping Sparrows — Young Streaked different from either Parent

December, 1922, as "a small house on wheels so constructed that it can be drawn as a trailer behind a car or wagon," has great possibilities for one who demands comfort during his observations. Owing to its weight and bulk it cannot be taken far into rough country, but whenever it can be placed near a nest or near a feeding-station for birds, it insures the comfort of the observer. For my own use I simplified the Bailey blind by reducing its dimensions to about four feet square, so that it would just fit the rear of a light Ford truck and so that it could easily be lifted out and carried short distances, over fences, etc., where the car could not go. It certainly has many advantages over a 'pup-tent' or an umbrella blind, wherever it can be used, but has the great disadvantage of requiring special transportation.

Another substitute for the 'Blind de Luxe' is an ordinary packing-box of sufficient size to permit one to sit inside with a slight

Fig. 186. Tree blind set on Sharp-shinned Hawk's nest (above and lower left). The following year it was used by a Long-eared Owl (lower right).

degree of comfort. An opening is made in one side of the box at the level of a shelf on the inside which will hold a camera. A burlap bag serves as a door and a soap-box as a chair.

Of course, many nests are placed so far above ground and in such inaccessible places that none of the blinds described is exactly suited for the purpose without modification, but a little ingenuity in hanging a platform or foot-rest in an adjacent tree will often permit the use of an umbrella blind or modified tent. When this is impossible, and it still seems desirable to secure photographs at close range, even though the observer himself has to be further removed, it is

FIG. 187. Camera box set near Mourning Dove's nest, and resulting picture.

possible to use a small box that will merely cover the camera. Placed near the nest for a few days as a dummy, the birds will become accustomed to it and thus to the camera. Cleats can be nailed to branches adjacent to the nest, to which the camera can be clamped and covered with the dummy box. The shutter will have to be operated by a thread or other device. If the nest is not too high, a tall tripod can be improvised from saplings, as in the illustration of the Mourning Dove's nest (Fig. 187). The box can be made of wood or of galvanized iron with a hole in one end, through which the lens points, and should be painted dull gray or brown or some unobtrusive color.

The use of the blind is even more important than the details of the making. Birds soon become accustomed to any inaminate object, no matter how large or conspicuous, but they do not tolerate sudden changes of any kind. The blind should not be suddenly dropped down at arm's length from the bird's nest, therefore, but should be left a dozen paces away for a few hours until the birds become accustomed to it and then it can be moved gradually nearer. It is best to leave it in place over night before commencing observations or photography and before bending aside any small branches that obstruct the view. The object of the blind is to observe birds in their natural behavior, not alarmed or disturbed, and they

FIG. 188. Blind, speedlights, and photographer at drumming log of Grouse. A stuffed female grouse has been added to stimulate the male when he returns.

should have entirely accepted it before work is begun. Caution should likewise be used to admit no light into the blind through an excess of peep-holes, etc., because the darker it is within, the less conspicuous will be any motion of the observer.

A confederate, whom we call the "go-awayster" and who will walk away from the blind when one is settled within, is a great time-saver, for no matter how accustomed the bird may be to the blind, if he sees you enter it he will wait a long time for you to come out again before forgetting about you and proceeding to his nest in a natural, undisturbed fashion. If two persons enter a blind and one goes away, however, he is perfectly satisfied, and loses his fear as soon as the confederate has retired to a proper distance. The slightest motion from within the blind will greatly alarm some birds, so that one must be careful to make all the necessary adjustments before his accomplice leaves. If one is using a camera it should be equipped with a lens hood so that any adjustments of the shutter or diaphragm that are necessary will not expose the fingers. The lens hood need be merely a square of cardboard the size of the opening in the blind, with a hole cut in it, into which the lens fits snugly, but it is better if a circlet of cardboard one inch wide be

FIG. 189. Male Ruffed Grouse in display (before the stuffed female.) Photo by D. G. Allen.

glued around the hole so that when the lens fits into this circlet it will set back from the cardboard. This makes the lens less conspicuous and gives more room for the fingers when manipulating the shutter. A small mirror will enable one to see the dial on his shutter and diaphragm from behind and enable him to make any changes desired without turning the camera.

In addition to getting intimately acquainted with the bird under observation from a blind, one can usually learn something about the bird that has never been observed before and add something worth-while to our ornithological knowledge. From the observation blind one can see accurately how the bird uses the implements with which nature has endowed it, and the curious bill of the Crossbill or the Skimmer, the long legs of the Stilt, and the various ornamental feathers of many birds will no longer seem anomalous. One soon learns the relationship that exists between the bird under observation and others that intrude upon its territory. The relations of the sexes, courtship performances, methods of feeding each other, and methods of feeding the young, all take on a new meaning when observed at arm's length. In fact, I know of no better way of gaining an understanding of the various traits and habits of birds and the meaning underlying all bird activities than by spending one's spare time in observation blinds.

BIRD PHOTOGRAPHY

The illustrations in this volume, without which the text would seem lengthy and obscure, are chiefly photographs of wild free birds engaged in some characteristic occupation or standing in some characteristic pose. They have been secured mainly by the use of

FIG. 190. Speedlights, background and Myrtle Warblers make an outdoor studio for photographing birds in flight, at Herbert Stoddard's feeding station in Georgia.

observation blinds set up near feeding stations or near the birds' nests in the manner just described. Having made an interesting observation upon any bird, one can convey that observation to others more accurately and more interestingly by a good photograph than in any other way. Of course one is not able to photograph everything that he sees, owing to the limitations of photography, but if one does his bird study from blinds, photography is less difficult and more successful.

Let us first decide what photographs are desirable, what the requisites of a good bird photograph are, and then see how the observation blind is going to help us secure what is wanted. That perfect photographic representations of birds are highly desirable, no one will deny. They have their place in the science of ornithology in that they portray accurately many points which long descriptions, no matter how carefully drawn, fail to convey. They have their place in art when they bring to us a bit of nature in its most appealing form. They have their place in business when, by their attractiveness, they add to the actual value of a book or a magazine. So, from the standpoint of science, art or business, good bird photographs are desirable.

But to approach perfection, a bird photograph has a difficult road to travel for it must satisfy not only the cruel test of the photographer as to lighting, exposure, and development, but it must satisfy the analysis of the ornithologist, and it must have some artistic merit as well. A photograph of a Wood Pewee, no matter how technically perfect it may be, is of no use to an ornithologist if it looks more like a Phœbe. The photographer must know his birds, not only their plumage and distinctive markings, but their characteristic traits, their personality, their very moods. And in making his exposures he must strive to catch only such attitudes as are characteristic of the species; otherwise his Pewees will turn out Phœbes, his Field Sparrows, Chippies and his Sandpipers will all be 'peeps.' A good black and white bird photograph should be as easy to identify by one familiar with birds as a museum specimen held in the hand, for what it lacks in color it should make up in distinctive pose and character. Needless to say, few photographs are perfect, and many that do not come up to this standard have been reproduced in books and magazines.

There is no longer any need of photographing mounted birds or of publishing photographs of birds in anything but natural and characteristic attitudes. With the birds coming to feed or coming to their nests at arm's length and oblivious to one's presence, all that is needed is a little experience in photography and a little patience to secure photographs that truly represent the species. Bird-feeders and bird-banders can become bird-photographers with little more effort than the purchase of a packing-box, for they already have the birds coming to their food. Of course, it is necessary to establish the feeding-station where the light will be good at the time at one's disposal for photography unless one is equipped with a speed light. The spot should not be on the north side of a house nor where near

Fig. 191. A Waxwing returns to a handful of youngsters. A speedlight photograph.

by branches of trees or shrubbery will throw distressing shadows across the subject. One should use equal care in the selection of the background against which the birds are to be seen, for dark backgrounds are unsatisfactory for most subjects, and strong contrasts of lights and shadows are even worse. A uniform light gray is best, such as obtains when the background is several yards away and well lighted. It is likewise often desirable to include the background or a part of it as the setting for the bird, and if it is made appropriate to the bird and the season, the resulting photograph should be much more attractive than the mere portrait of the bird. During the winter, snow- or ice-covered branches of pine or hemlock, during the early spring, pussy-willows, and, a little later, the wild flowers in their season, can all be used very effectively, but one must be very careful to avoid exaggeration and artificiality in the arrangements. It is possible to reproduce at a feeding-station almost any picture which one sees on his walks afield if he will but arrange his setting in front of the packing-box and then bait the bird to the proper place. A Woodpecker drilling for borers, a Chickadee among the pussy-willows, a Whitethroat or a Towhee among the hepaticas, Cedar Waxwings on the mountain-ash berries, all can be photographed in front of the blind if one has a successful feeding-station. Indeed there is no end to the possibilities of pose and attractive setting for a single species, such as the Chickadee.

Fɪɢ. 192. White-throated and Song Sparrows at a feeding station "arrangement."

And, then, there is always the chance of some new bird visiting the feeding-station and, if the packing-box is already there, it is a simple matter to secure his portrait. A photographic record of all the species that visit a feeding-log during the season is a wonderfully interesting study and provides a fascinating sport.

A few words about the use of a bird blind at a feeding-station may not be amiss. Inasmuch as it is to be left outside in all kinds of weather, it is well to cover the top with roofing paper so as to keep the inside dry and prevent the box from warping. One can hinge the rear boards to serve as a door, or remove them entirely and hang a burlap curtain in their place. The openings for the camera should be about 4 inches square, one about a foot from the roof and another about a foot from the floor, and one perhaps half way up, depending on the nature of the feeding-station and the various settings to be used. Instead of using a tripod, which is very much in the way in a box, shelves can be fastened just below each opening, to which the camera can be clamped with old-fashioned curtain clamps. If desired, these shelves can be hinged and given an adjustable support so that the angle of the camera can be changed at will. It is nearly as satisfactory, however, to have them permanent in position and wedge up the rear or front of the camera as desired.

A device of much importance is the lens-hood, already mentioned, for it will save a great deal of time by allowing one to change the speed of the shutter or the aperture of the lens without showing his fingers to the birds. It will likewise conceal the motion of any of the working parts of the shutter, which is very necessary with slow exposures. The card of the lens-hood should be about the size of the aperture in the box, except for a slit at the top through which one can watch operations. The ring which fits around the lens should be wide enough to permit the fingers to manipulate the shutter, but not so wide as to cut off any light. With a short focus lens it must be narrower, but its maximum width can easily be determined for each lens by experiment.

NEST PHOTOGRAPHY

Even more interesting than photographing birds at feeding-stations, however, is studying and photographing their home-life at the nest. Much more ingenuity will be required in the selection of the most suitable blind and its proper placement than in feeding-station photography because nests are placed in such diverse situations. What is perfectly suitable in gardens, pastures or marshes might be entirely unsuccessful in wind-swept fields or on rocky islands. It is always a satisfaction merely to have found a bird's nest. How much more elation then does one feel when he has secured a good photograph of the nest and eggs, then successfully outwitted the parent birds with his blind, and finally secured a permanent record of the bird's appearance and actions when oblivious to human presence.

It would be obviously impracticable and without the scope of this book to devote many pages to the elements and technique of photography itself. We must assume that one knows how to manipulate his camera and knows the principles of exposure and development as applied to ordinary photography. We can here merely call attention to some of the essentials as applied to the photography of birds.

1. *Focusing the camera.*

As in most types of photography one should be careful in placing his blind and camera in such a position, relative to the feeding log or nest, that the sun will be more or less at his back during the

Fig. 193. Nest and eggs of Redwinged Blackbird—a good arrangement and angle of view.

hours he wishes to photograph. This is especially important in color photography. A blind, therefore, as previously stated should *never* be placed on the north side of the nest or feeding-station. If the camera is pointed down at approximately a 45° angle the resulting picture will be the least distorted and the nest most pleasing. If one is photographing any deep nest such as that of a Redwing or Song Sparrow it may be necessary, even with the camera at that angle, to move the eggs to the back of the nest to have them show properly. If one knows in advance just where the bird will alight, the camera should be focused on that point, but in the case of nesting birds one cannot always know whether it will come from the front, side, or back, and he may want all parts in focus. If such is the case he should focus near the front of the nest and then shut down the lens diaphragm until both the back and front are sharp. This will necessitate greatly lengthening the exposure, which owing to the activity of the bird may not always be possible. In photographing nest and eggs on a bright day it is usually most satisfactory to close the diaphragm to a small aperture, throw a shadow over the entire nest to get uniform light, and give a long exposure. This is sometimes possible with incubating birds also, but more often one has to content himself with short exposures and use the lens more or less wide open with resulting loss of 'depth of focus.' One should always give twice as long an exposure for 'close-ups' as for landscapes. The best way to learn the correct exposure for different subjects and different light conditions is to purchase a good exposure meter and study it. One must not expect the best results from his bird photographs until he has so mastered his camera that its manipulation and the computing of the proper exposure are instinctive. Then he can concentrate on the bird and the picture that he desires, rather than on the operation of the camera. One can learn a great deal about exposures and composition of the picture by studying the photographs in Allan Cruickshank's book *Birds in the Wilderness* or his more recent book *Hunting with a Camera.*

18

Learning Bird-Songs

Imagine me sitting in a New York City railroad station trying to assemble my thoughts on the songs of birds. All about me is the murmur of strange voices, interrupted occasionally by the blare of a passing motor car or the stentorian calls of an attendant announcing a train. There are hundreds of voices, all strange to me, and they mingle in one great hubbub from which I can derive neither pleasure nor interest. Still, voices are interesting to me, and I enjoy listening to people talk.

I think how different it would be if I could recognize a few of the voices about me as those of friends, how much more enjoyable and how much more profitable would be my wait for the train. It brings to my mind my first experiences in the woods, when all of the wood-folk were strangers to me, when I scarcely knew the call of the cicada from that of the tree-toad, and when all birds seemed to call and sing alike. There was a hubbub in the woods in those days; the morning chorus of songsters was a disturbing noise; my ears brought me little pleasure.

And now I think over how, one by one, I learned the different calls of the wild folk until the hubbub changed to music, and the morning chorus, instead of being a disturbance, became a joy to be looked forward to and long remembered. As I sit in the lonely station full of people, I know how I would feel if I should suddenly hear the voice of a friend talking near me, and I realize that it would be the feeling that came to me when I first recognized the bell-like notes of the Wood Thrush rising above the clamor of the lesser birds. It is the feeling that still comes to me when I listen to the chorus of voices on a May morning and pick out one friend after another as he announces his presence, his 'good morning,' if you will, to all his brothers and to me. For now my ears bring to me even

342

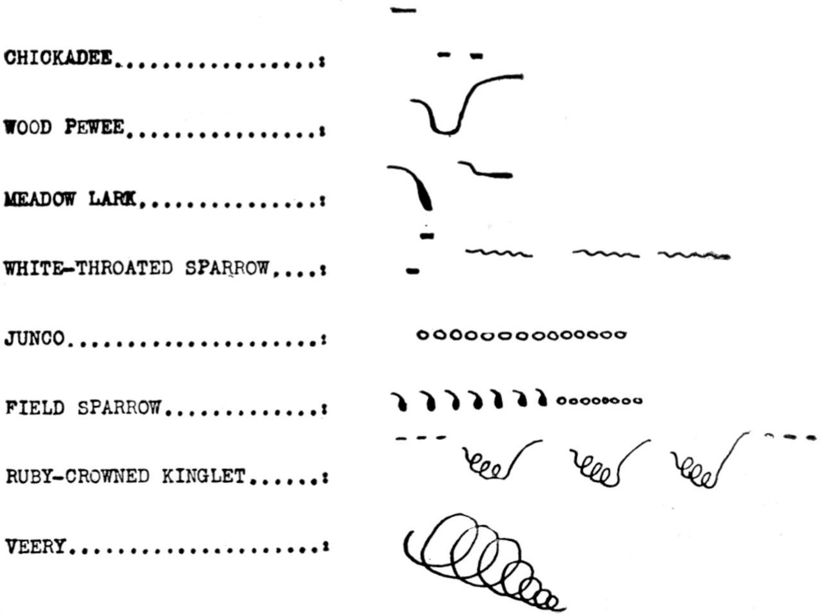

CHICKADEE..................:

WOOD PEWEE................:

MEADOW LARK...............:

WHITE—THROATED SPARROW....:

JUNCO.....................:

FIELD SPARROW.............:

RUBY—CROWNED KINGLET......:

VEERY.....................:

SYMBOLS FOR BIRDS' SONGS

CHICKADEE ....Phe-be-be
WOOD PEWEE ....Pee-a-wee
MEADOWLARK ....Spring-is-here
WHITE-THROATED
  SPARROW ....Poor-Sam-Peabody, Peabody, Peabody
JUNCO ....Sweet, Sweet, Sweet, Sweet, Sweet, Sweet
                         Sweet
FIELD SPARROW ......Here, Here, Here, Here, Sweet, Sweet, Sweet,
                         Sweet
RUBY-CROWNED   See-see-see,
  KINGLET ....Just look at me, just look at me,
                 Just look at me, see-see-see
VEERY ....Turee, aree, aree, aree, aree

Fig. 194. Symbols and catch phrases simplify the learning of bird songs.

as much pleasure as my eyes, and I am sorry for those who do not hear.

Many persons have come to me with the query as to how they can learn the songs of birds, or how I learned them, until I am forced to try to arrange my thoughts and experiences into these few paragraphs, hoping that they may stimulate others to enter a field

Fig. 195. The author in one corner of the Cornell Library of Natural Sounds: tapes of bird songs recorded in the field and phonograph records prepared from them.

that is as elusive as it is enjoyable, as intangible as it is profitable.

The greatest difficulty in discussing the subject of bird-song is in the shortcomings of the English language, for words fail to convey the impressions made by the voices of birds, just as our artificial musical scale fails to adapt itself to their music. There are, however, a few principles which, if borne in mind, facilitate the learning of birds' songs. In the first place, one must not expect to learn them all at once, for the learning of birds' voices is even more time-consuming than learning the birds themselves. One must follow up every strange call that he hears and identify the musician, and perhaps repeat this several times for each bird before one can hope to recognize every bird that he hears. Most persons have difficulty in memorizing a complex sound so that they will recognize it when heard again. Or, after it has been heard many times and has become a familiar sound, many have difficulty in linking up the name of the bird with the song unless the sound can be associated with some visual impression that can be remembered and tied to the name of the bird. If the song of the bird brings to mind a certain picture or image, it is comparatively easy to associate the name of the bird with that picture. The pictures may be of very different types, according to the complexity or quality of the song. Some match up readily with spoken words or phrases, while others, and perhaps the majority, have a quality difficult to express in language and are best represented by symbols. Thus, the syllables *PHE-BE* admirably fit the song of the Chickadee, the word *PEE-A-WEE,* that of the Wood Pewee, and the phrase *POOR-SAM-PEABODY-PEABODY-PEA-BODY,* that of the White-throated Sparrow. Other songs, however, like those of the Chipping Sparrow, Ruby-crowned Kinglet, and Veery are best represented by symbols. Some songs may be represented by both.

In using symbols to represent bird-notes, the writer avoids the customary musical notation because, to his mind, the arbitrary notes of the man-made scale are adapted to relatively few birds' songs. The symbols which have proved most satisfactory to him are series of lines, dashes, dots, circles, etc., placed in such relation to one another that their vertical position, as in musical notation, indicates their pitch, the length of the line or dash, the duration of the note, and

FIG. 196. A Chestnut-collared Longspur sings into the microphone.

the shape of the symbol, the quality. The last is the most difficult to explain and is doubtless a personal matter of reminiscence or association. They have, however, proved useful to hundreds of students, and are given for what they are worth. Thus, a very fine hissing note, like that of the Golden-crowned Kinglet or Cedar Waxwing, is represented by a thin line, a somewhat fuller whistle like that of the Chickade or Pewee, by a broader line, and a still fuller mellow note, like that of a Junco, by small circles. A clear note is represented by a straight line or dash, a tremulous note by a wavy line, and a warble, by a more or less coiled or spiral line. If a bird's song is continuous, the lines are all connected, if discontinuous, they are spaced according to the phrases of the bird's song. A glance at the accompanying table (Fig. 194) should indicate the

FIG. 197. A Lesser Prairie Chicken booms into the mike. Photo by James Tanner.

writer's meaning. Those unfamiliar with any of the songs listed can compare the foregoing table of phrases, which fit some of the songs nearly as well as the symbols, and the curious shapes may take on some meaning.

As in many other subjects, when one has mastered one song completely, the whole subject becomes much more lucid. If anyone interested will attempt to symbolize some common song with which he is familiar, the simple little diagrams here shown will become much clearer, and he will soon be taking down unfamiliar songs in a strange shorthand script that will cause him to remember the songs.

A number of birds have songs which have the exact quality of

a high-pitched, human whistle and can be closely imitated by anyone willing to practice. So accurately can these songs be imitated that
it will often deceive the birds themselves, and they will approach
very closely in their search for the other bird. Particularly is this
true of Chickadees, Wood Pewees, Field Sparrows, White-throats,
and Baltimore Orioles. Upon several occasions the writer has had

FIG. 198. The author records more distant calls of seabirds with the aid of a
parabolic reflector and microphone set at the focal point (an electric ear). Photo
by P. P. Kellogg.

birds of various species approach within a few feet, and he has had
Chickadees perch on his cap and hover before his face peering into
the little round hole in search of the other bird. Sometimes even
while surrounded by a class of fifteen or twenty students, the little
Chickadee has performed thus in search of his whistling fellow.

Since this was written the learning of bird songs has been much
simplified by the publication of phonograph records of birds' songs,
and especially by the recent "Field Guide to Bird Songs" matching

Peterson's "Field Guide to the Birds," both published by Houghton Mifflin Company.*

It is now possible to hear the song of any eastern bird whenever desired. "Don't wait until spring for the birds to sing" is the slogan of the Cornell ornithologists, who have pioneered in the sound recording. The matter of using symbols or phrases to remember the songs, however, still retains its importance, though now by playing the records over and over again, it will be easier to invent one's own memory aids.

* Further information about all the records of bird songs can be secured from the Cornell Laboratory of Ornithology, 33 Sapsucker Woods Road, Ithaca, New York.

19

Birds as Pets

The natural interest in birds with which children are endowed expresses itself in many ways. To some the bright feathers are most appealing, to others the cheerful songs. Some enjoy most their companionship in the woods and fields; others are not satisfied until by sling-shot or gun or trap, the birds have been reduced to actual possession. Kindlier children, whose primitive instincts to kill have been supplanted by more humane thoughts, still find enjoyment in actual possession, expression itself in the care for crippled birds or young which seem to have lost their parents. Nor are we adults so different from children in our bird interests, except as our experience and education permits us to express ourselves in somewhat broader fields. Some of us are quite satisfied to spend the time at our disposal in walks afield, identifying and studying and photographing the birds in their natural habitats. Others of us, either in the name of science or in the name of sport, still enjoy reducing the birds to actual possession where they can be handled and the details of their plumage or structure studied at leisure. Still others of us enjoy the close companionship of birds that is afforded by keeping them as pets, dependent upon us for food and for shelter.

Fig. 199. "Leave it alone" is the best advice to those who find "lost" or apparently deserted young birds.

At times these different interests have seemed quite intolerant of one another. The ardent field naturalist has disparaged the 'closet ornithologist' or laboratory scientist, and neither of them has placed any value on the observations of the aviculturist until the keeping of native birds in captivity has been entirely suppressed.

349

As time goes on, however, we are becoming more tolerant of each other's interests and coming to a realization that the observations of all groups are necessary to an intelligent and rational understanding of bird-life. The field ornithologist, the laboratory scientist, the sportsman, and the aviculturist must meet on a common ground, or, better still, meet in the same individual, and give him breadth of interest and understanding in all matters pertaining to bird-life.

It is not intended that this chapter be a treatise on aviculture, but rather a few suggestions as to how more pleasure can be had from captive birds, and mistakes avoided which might otherwise destroy one's faith in this type of bird-study. So many kind persons attempt the impossible in trying to act as foster parents for certain types of young birds that it is little wonder that they lose interest in all birds as pets.

Mr. John M. Phillips, former Conservation Commissioner of Pennsylvania, tells the story of how his family attempted to care for a family of House Wrens whose parents had been killed by a neighbor's cat. Wrens are entirely insectivorous, and Mr. Phillips, knowing this, got up at daybreak and began gathering caterpillars and spiders and beetles to fill their gaping mouths. By working hard until breakfast-time he managed to keep them quiet, but long before breakfast was over they were again clamoring for food. The combined efforts of the entire family, including the maid and the butler were insufficient to supply the insects that the young birds demanded, so that when business engagements required Mr. Phillips at his office, he detailed two men from the factory to go to the woods with axes and split open dead logs for ant-eggs and grubs, but all to no avail. The young birds grew hungrier and hungrier, and finally in spite of the labors of six persons, died of starvation. Here was a lesson in the amount of food required by young birds and the futility of trying to raise insectivorous birds on a natural diet. Had Mr. Phillips had an unlimited supply of meal-worms or "ant eggs," and been able to devote his entire time from daylight until dark to merely feeding the family of young birds, he would probably have succeeded in raising them. Or had he been familiar with the avicultural methods so well developed in England, he might have been able to raise them on artificial foods. But being a great-hearted American in a country that has given scant attention to the rearing of birds in captivity, he worked nobly but in vain and was rewarded with the keen disappointment that has met hundreds of others under similar circumstances.

FIG. 200. Feeding Jimmie. Young Crows make interesting pets.

The rearing of insectivorous birds is always difficult, and even the keeping of mature birds of many species in captivity is impossible except by aviculturists of considerable experience. They are, therefore, unsatisfactory as pets, except for those persons who glory in the accomplishment of difficult tasks. Unless one wishes to go deeply into the science of aviculture, he would do better to confine his attention to seed-eating species like the Canary and its relatives, to omnivorous species like the Crow, to carnivorous birds like the Hawks and Owls, or to game-birds and water fowl. A good introduction to the whole subject of the care of birds in captivity will be found in a book by Lee S. Crandall, former Curator of Birds at the New York Zoölogical Park, entitled 'Pets and How to Care for Them.'

"But what am I to do when I find a young bird that has lost its mother?" you naturally ask. "What should Mr. Phillips have done?"

Fortunately, it is not often that both parents are killed and a young bird left entirely an orphan. If only one parent is killed, the survivor will ordinarily do double duty until the young are reared. Recall the published record of a House Wren, whose mate had been killed, feeding its young 1,217 times in the 15 hours and 45 minutes of daylight. Most 'orphan birds' that are brought home because they have lost their parents are really not orphans at all, but members of families that have become somewhat scattered upon leaving the nest, and the parents are busily feeding the other members of the family. The distressing cries which may have attracted one's attention are, in reality, given reflexly by the young bird so that the parent birds can more easily find it when its turn to be fed comes. The best thing to do in such a case, therefore, is to put the young bird on a branch out of harm's way and let it continue to call for its mother. If it is growing dark and you are fearful that a cat may find it before its mother does, it may be better to take it home for the night, but it should be returned to its perch very early the next morning, in time for an early breakfast. If one has time to wait, he will be rewarded by a sight of the family reunion and, perhaps, with the experience of finding a bird apparently devoid of the fear of man. He may even be able to hold the young bird in his hand and have the parent bird come and feed it as though he were nowhere around. Particularly is this true with Warblers, Vireos, and many Sparrows, the males of which, though timid at other times, seem to lose entirely their fear of man when the young first leave the nest and demand constant feeding. Such a wild free bird makes the ideal pet while the experience lasts, and, of course, no idea of caging it should be entertained. Rather, every effort should be made to bring other people and particularly children to it that they may share your experience.

But to return to captive birds, the pages of nature magazines are replete with stories of Crows and Robins that have been successfully reared in captivity, and one reading them is certainly impressed with the fact that their foster-parents not only derived great pleasure from their companionship but also that they were enabled to make observations on those species that should be very enlightening to students knowing the bird only in the field. Similarly, Magpies and Blue Jays make interesting pets, and Starlings, Blackbirds, various Sparrows, Waxwings, Catbirds, Thrashers, Bluebirds, and

Thrushes are nearly as easily reared as are young Robins on a mixed diet of meal-worms, yolk of hard-boiled egg (finely grated), bread and milk, and berries in season. Canker-worms, while they last, and maggots that have been reared on clean liver, or that have been allowed to 'scour' in bran, or that have pupated, make an ideal addition to the menu. Earthworms and canned dogfood are perfectly acceptable to the larger species.

It is contrary to our present laws to retain most of these birds in captivity without a permit, except the Crows, Magpies, Grackles, and Starlings, but any and all of them can be given their liberty when able to shift for themselves and many will cherish your companionship for some time, coming back to be fed or to roost in the cage. Some species will gradually revert to the wild and will migrate with their kind, but others, like the Crows and Magpies, become entirely domesticated, shunning their wild brothers and enjoying human companionship like a dog or a cat. Such birds make the best pets, although when given their liberty they often become quite mischievous.

Some of the most ideal bird pets are numbered among the gamebirds and the water-fowl, and the bird-lover who has a small stream that can be dammed to form a water-fowl pond, or part of an acre that can be fenced for rearing Pheasants or Grouse or Quail, has an unlimited store of pleasure ahead of him. The State Conservation Department, from whom a permit for keeping birds in captivity should be secured, can likewise supply information on how to raise them. With a little experience one will soon have a host of pets that will be profitable as well as companionable to him.

For a number of years it was my good fortune to have a small pond on my grounds which I kept stocked with as great a variety of native water-fowl as it was possible to obtain, and I learned more about ducks in those few years of intimacy with them and took more real pleasure in them than in all the years of duck-hunting and duck-watching preceding its acquisition. The pond was enclosed by a low fence to keep out dogs and to keep the ducks from wandering. The birds I could not replace were always pinioned, the others clipped so that after molting they could once more fly. After a few days on the pond they all lost their fear and some soon learned to eat from my hand. So far as I could tell, they behaved in a perfectly normal manner, feeding and fighting and courting in the way characteristic of each species. On this little pond, by mere casual observation I was able to watch at close range the courtship performances of at least fifteen species of our native ducks, and acquired a volume of notes on their calls and their plumage changes that would have taken years of close application in the field and the collection of innumerable specimens. One never tired of watching them, and friends and neighbors, not particularly interested in birds, passing the pond, delayed their journeys, fascinated by them. The Pintails and Widgeon standing on their heads in shallow water to nose out a bit of grain from between the pebbles on the bottom, the Canvasbacks and Scaups diving in the deeper parts of the pond, their great feet churning the water into a vortex behind them and their bodies encased in a silver plating of air-bubbles, caused no end of amusement. And when the nesting season arrived there was the joy of discovering the nests of the Wood Ducks, and the Pintails and the Mallards. Wild trapped birds seldom nest, but those which have been hatched and raised in captivity regularly do so, and the most pleasure of all was raising the young. This is ordinarily done in a separate enclosure with domestic hens as foster mothers, for the old ducks are often quite cannibalistic to each others' young. One summer a whole brood of young Teal, which hatched near the pond, were gobbled up by the Wood Ducks as soon as they got on the water.

One who is fond of brightly colored pets can do no better than to enclose part of his grounds and keep some of the hardier Pheasants, like the Golden, the Silver, the Lady Amherst, or the Reeves, not to mention the Ring-necked which has become acclimatized and feral in most of the northern states. An enclosure 15 feet square will make several birds happy, but care must be exercised not to crowd males together during the breeding season, for if any females are present they will invariably kill each other. There is a great deal of individuality among Pheasants, and some become very tame and companionable, while others of the same species remain wild and intractable. One who develops an interest in raising Pheasants not only creates a source of pleasure to himself but also may establish quite a lucrative business. One should not start such a business, however, without first getting a permit from his State Conservation Department.

Equally interesting are the Grouse and the Quail, particularly the beautiful California Quail with its curious plume and soft coloring. When raised by hand and properly tamed, it makes a most lovable pet.

Hawks and Owls are rather easily kept in captivity, but the majority of species do not make good pets, even if taken when very young and raised by hand. They learn to recognize their keepers, and if kept in large cages will learn to come when called, but they are usually rather sullen. It is possible to train Duck Hawks and Goshawks and, possibly, others to hunt, but these birds are usually kept tethered and hooded when not in use and, fascinating as the sport of falconry may be, the Hawks do not seem like pets. I have raised Sparrow Hawks, Duck Hawks, Sharp-shinned Hawks, Cooper's Hawks, Marsh Hawks, and Red-shouldered Hawks, and, without exception, when they were mature and given their liberty they left without as much as a 'thank-you,' nor have I ever seen one of them since to recognize it. Nor are the Owls much better, though they are somewhat more amusing. One little Florida Burrowing Owl that we raised from babyhood was a great pet of the family for over a year, and was perfectly hardy in an outdoor cage, even in severe winter weather. He had many quaint little ways that endeared him to every one, but one spring night he dug out of his cage and never came back.

Neither Hawks nor Owls should be given too much plain meat without any waste material, like fur, bones, or feathers. They should be fed once a day, but not more than they will eat, and food should not be left standing before them, except in the case of those Owls that will feed only at night. Mice, House Sparrows, or heads of poultry should constitute the main food, with scraps of beef or hamburg steak when the others are not available.

One of the most interesting bird pets we have ever had was a young Black Tern which was brought to us when scarcely more than out of the shell. Its main items of diet were mealworms, earthworms, bits of beef, and small minnows. When it was able to fly, we gave it its liberty, and it was quite delightful to see it flit from its cage like a large butterfly, glide down to Cayuga Lake a mile away, and then, after an hour or so, to watch it come back, gracefully circling over the trees and droping ever so lightly to the roof of its cage on the lawn. There it would sun itself for a while, but finally it would jump down inside with all the confidence of a person returning to his own fireside.

Pets are not real pets unless they are happy, and no bird should ever be kept in confinement unless its plumage and appearance and actions bespeak contentment. A contented captive bird behaves in a manner perfectly normal to that species, and many valuable observations can be made on it that will supplement those made in nature.

20

Suggestions for the Intensive Study of a Species

To any reader of this book who feels that he would like to enter upon the scientific study of birds, the following outline is offered to direct his efforts. With the aid of the initial chapters of the book he should try to determine for some one common bird that interests him, the facts called for in the outline.

He should first consult every source of information available in some good library: the files of all the ornithological journals, the Zoölogical Record, and the various books dealing with birds. After consulting all these he will undoubtedly find that on many of the subjects, no information is available. If the fact that something in the life of a common bird is unknown to science does not inspire him to go ahead and seek the truth himself, then perhaps he is on the wrong track and his interests in ornithology lie along other lines. The highways and by-ways of ornithology are many and varied and what appeals to one person may make no impression on another. Indeed it is to be expected that scientific ornithology would appeal to relatively few. It is to these few who have a consuming love of birds, yet who find the mere identifying of them insufficient to their ardor or interest, that the following outline is suggested as a guide to the scientific study of birds in their haunts.

OUTLINE FOR THE STUDY OF A BIRD

I. *Identification and Classification.*

In what ways does a bird differ from all other animals? How does the species in question differ from other birds and what does it have in common with closely related species? This gives its classification

357

and reasons therefor. Give a complete description of all plumages and of the feather arrangement.

II. *Distribution.*

On a map of the world block out the distribution of the species in summer and winter, indicating the route used in going from one range to the other. Indicate the distribution of the various races or subspecies.

III. *Habits.*

A. The bird in winter.

Food and method of securing it; daily feeding range; seasonal range; social relations, (flocks or solitary); sexual relations, (sexes associated or apart); evidences of song, fighting or display of plumage; method of roosting; any behavioral patterns.

B. Migration.

(1) Migration period: Time required for all to leave winter quarters, and to arrive on nesting grounds.

(2) Method of migrating: Flocks or solitary; day or night; formation of the flock (one sex or mixed).

(3) Route of migration between winter and summer homes.

(4) Order of arrival on nesting grounds: Of males, females; adults and immatures; residents and transients.

(5) Conditions governing migration: Temperature, wind, humidity, etc.

(6) Speed of migration and rate of daily advance. Length of fattening delays.

(7) Food habits during migration and habitats frequented.

(8) Structural changes during migration: Plumage, secondary sexual characters, reproductive organs.

(9) Evidences of sexual activity during migration: Song, fighting, display of plumage, etc.

(10) Hazards and losses.

C. Nesting.

(1) Breeding range: Geographical, ecological. Determine reasons for restrictions.

(2) Selection of the 'territory' or nesting area: Sex selecting same; controlling factors, extent, methods of defending, etc.

(3) Courtship methods: Song, fighting, display of plumage, dances, aerial evolutions, or antics of any kind; list of call notes and variation in songs.

      (4) Selection of nesting site: Conditions governing; sex selecting site; method, variations.

      (5) The nest: Location, size, and materials; sex building it; time required, variations with season and with locality.

      (6) The eggs: Number, color, size, weight, range of variation.

      (7) Incubation: Period, sex performing, activities during.

      (8) Hatching: Method, time required, egg tooth.

      (9) Food during the nesting season.

D. The young.

      (1) Description at hatching: Color of skin, bill, legs, lining of mouth; color and arrangement of down; weight of young.

      (2) Growth changes from day to day.

      (3) Food and method of feeding.

      (4) Parental care, brooding, nest sanitation.

      (5) Time spent in nest and method of leaving; exercises.

      (6) Development of fear and other instincts.

      (7) Care and training after leaving nest; duration of parental care.

E. Second broods: Frequency of; rematings, change of mates and explanation for.

F. Post-nesting activities of young and adults: Food, flocking, roosting, wandering. Prenuptial fighting, displays etc.

G. Molting: Method and time required for the various molts of young and old; habits during molting period.

H. Fall migration: To be treated like spring migration.

IV. *Enemies and Diseases.*

Factors controlling the increase of the species. Carnivorous birds and animals, ecto- and endoparasites, bacterial diseases and factors augmenting each.

V. *Conclusions. Adaptations and Maladaptations to Its Life.*

Origin of the species, reasons for present distribution; reasons for present dominance or scarcity; economic status and best methods for controlling or increasing the species.

Suggested Reading

A partial list of the significant books and articles covering the field of this book and useful for those who would continue their studies beyond the contents of this *Book of Bird Life*.

GENERAL

Allen, A. A., *Ornithology Laboratory Notebook*. Ithaca, N. Y.: Comstock Publishing Co., Inc., 1947.

———— *Stalking Birds with Color Camera*. Washington, D. C.: National Geographic Society, 1951.

Allen, Glover M., *Birds and Their Attributes*. Boston: Marshall Jones Co., 1925.

American Ornithologists' Union, *Check-list of North American Birds*. 5th ed., Baltimore, Md.: Lord Baltimore Press, 1957.

Beebe, C. W., *The Bird, Its Form and Function*. New York: Henry Holt and Co., 1906.

Chapman, Frank M., *Camps and Cruises of an Ornithologist*. New York: D. Appleton & Co., 1908.

———— *My Tropical Air-Castle*. New York: D. Appleton & Co., 1929.

———— *Handbook of Birds of Eastern North America*. New York: D. Appleton Century, 1940.

Coues, Elliott, *Key to North American Birds*. 5th ed., Boston: The Page Co., 1903.

Eaton, E. H., *Birds of New York*. 2 vols., Albany, N. Y.: New York State Museum, 1909 and 1912.

Forbush, E. H., *Birds of Massachusetts and other New England States*. Mass. Dept. of Agriculture, 1925, 1927, 1929.

Gilliard, E. Thomas, *Living Birds of the World*. Garden City, N. Y.: Doubleday and Co., 1958.

Hann, Harry W., *The Biology of Birds*. Ann Arbor, Mich.: Edwards Brothers, Inc., 1953.

Hess, Gertrud, *The Bird: Its Life and Structure*. Translated from the German by Phyllis Barclay-Smith. Philadelphia: Chilton Co., 1951.

Peterson, Roger T., *Birds over America*. New York: Dodd, Mead & Co., 1948.

——— and James Fisher, *Wild America*. Boston: Houghton Mifflin Co., 1955.

Pettingill, Olin S., Jr., *A Laboratory and Field Manual of Ornithology*. Minneapolis, Minn.: Burgess Publishing Co., 1956.

Pycraft, W. P., *A History of Birds*. London: Methuen and Co., 1910.

Roberts, T. S., *Birds of Minnesota*, 2 vols., Minneapolis, Minn.: University of Minnesota Press, 1932.

Taverner, P. A., *Birds of Canada*. Ottawa, Canada: National Museum of, Bulletin No. 72. Biological Series N. 19, 1934.

Van Tyne, Josselyn and Andrew J. Berger, *Fundamentals of Ornithology*. New York: John Wiley & Sons, Inc., 1959.

Wallace, George J., *An Introduction to Ornithology*. New York: The Macmillan Co., 1955.

Wing, Leonard W., *Natural History of Birds. A Guide to Ornithology*. New York: Ronald Press Co., 1956.

Woods, Robert S., *The Naturalists' Lexicon*. Pasadena, Calif.: Abbey Garden Press, 1944.

ANATOMY

Chamberlain, Frank W., *Atlas of Avian Anatomy: Osteology, Arthrology, Myology*. East Lansing, Mich.: Michigan State College Agriculture Experimental Station Memoir Bulletin 5, 1943.

Coues, Elliott, *Key to North American Birds*. 5th ed., Boston: The Page Co., 1903. (Introductory chapters.)

Fisher, Harvey I., "Avian Anatomy, 1925-1950, and Some Suggested Problems," *Recent Studies in Avian Biology*. Urbana: University of Illinois Press, 1955, pp. 57-104.

Galigher, A. E., *The Essentials of Practical Microtechnique in Animal Biology*. Berkeley, Calif.: Laboratory of Microtechnique, 1934.

Hardy, E., "The Microscope in Ornithology," *Watson's Microscope Record* 28: 18-19; 29: 20 (1933).

Hyman, Libbie, *Comparative Vertebrate Anatomy*. Chicago: University of Chicago Press, 1942.

Pumphrey, R. J., "The Sense Organs of Birds," *Ibis* 90: 171-199 (1948).

ATTRACTING BIRDS

Baker, John H. (ed.), *The Audubon Guide to Attracting Birds*. New York: Doubleday, Doran & Co., Inc., 1941.

Baynes, E. H., *Wild Bird Guests: How to Entertain Them*. New York: E. P. Dutton & Co., 1915.

McAtee, W. L., *Wildlife Food Plants: Their Value, Propagation and Management*. Ames, Iowa: Collegiate Press, 1939.

————— *Attracting Birds.* Conservation Bulletin No. 1, U.S. Department of the Interior, Fish and Wildlife Service, 1947.

————— *Homes for Birds.* Conservation Bulletin No. 14, U.S. Department of the Interior, Fish and Wildlife Service, 1957.

————— *Plants Useful in Wildlife Management.* Conservation Bulletin No. 7, U.S. Department of the Interior, Fish and Wildlife Service, 1957.

McElroy, Thomas P., Jr., *The New Handbook of Attracting Birds.* New York: Alfred A. Knopf, 1960.

McKenny, Margaret, *Birds in the Garden.* New York: Reynal and Hitchcock, 1939.

Mason, Edwin A., *Massachusetts Audubon Society. List of Shrubs and Trees for Attracting Birds.* South Lincoln, Mass.: Massachusetts Audubon Society, Drumlin Farm, 1959.

Pickens, Andrew L., "Attracting Birds in the Southeastern States," *Bird-Lore* 28: 102-107 (1926).

Sherwood, Mary P. and Eva L. Gordon, *Inviting Bird Neighbors.* Ithaca, N. Y.: Cornell 4-H Club Bulletin, 1960.

Terres, John K., *Songbirds in Your Garden.* New York: Thomas Y. Crowell Co., 1953.

BANDING

Baird, James, Chandler S. Robbins, Aaron M. Bagg, and John V. Dennis, "Operation Recovery," The Atlantic Coastal Netting Project, *Bird-Banding* 29: 137-168 (1958).

Baldwin, S. Prentiss, "Bird-Banding by Means of Systematic Trapping," *Proceedings Linnaean Society of New York* 31: 23-56 (1919).

Baumgartner, A. Marguerite, "Experiments in Feather Marking Eastern Tree Sparrows for Territory Studies," *Bird Banding* 9: 124-135 (1938).

Butts, Wilbur K., "A Study of the Chickadee and White-breasted Nuthatch by Means of Marked Individuals: Part I. Methods of Marking Birds," *Bird-Banding* I: 149-168 (1930).

Grinnell, Joseph, "Bird-netting as a method in Ornithology," *Auk* 42: 245-251 (1925).

Cole, L. J., "The Early History of Bird-banding in America," *Wilson Bulletin* 34: 108-115 (1922).

Lincoln, F. C., "The History and Purposes of Bird-Banding," *Auk* 38: 217-228 (1921).

————— "Calculating Waterfowl Abundance on Basis of Banding Returns," Circular U.S. Department of Agriculture No. 118: 1-4 (1930).

————— "Bird-Banding," *50 Years' Progress of American Ornithology.* Lancaster, Pa.: American Ornithologists' Union, 1933, pp. 65-87.

——— *Manual for Bird Banders.* Washington, D. C.: Fish and Wildlife Service, 1947.

Low, Seth H., "Banding with Mist Nets," *Bird-Banding* 28: 115-128 (1957).

Wood, Harold B., "The History of Bird-Banding," *Auk* 62: 256-265 (1935).

BIRD BEHAVIOR

Allen, A. A., "The Red-winged Blackbird: A Study in the Ecology of a Cat-tail Marsh," *Proceedings Linnaean Society of New York 1912-13.* No. 24-25, 1914.

——— "Sex Rhythm in the Ruffed Grouse and other Birds," *Auk* 51: 180-199 (1934).

Armstrong, Edward A., *Bird Display and Behaviour.* New York: Oxford University Press, 1947.

——— "The Ecology of Distraction Display," *British Journal Animal Behavior* 2: 121-135 (1954).

Baker, E. C. Stuart, *Cuckoo Problems.* London: H. F. & G. Witherby, 1942.

Bissonnette, Thomas Hume, "Studies on the Sexual Cycle in Birds. I, II, & III," *American Journal of Anatomy* 45: 289-305; 46: 307-343; 46: 477-497 (1930).

——— "Studies on the Sexual Cycle in Birds IV," *Journal Experimental Zoology* 58: 281-319 (1931).

——— "Studies on the Sexual Cycle in Birds V," *Physiological Zoology* 4: 542-574 (1931-1932).

——— "Photoperiodicity in Birds," *Wilson Bulletin* 49: 241-270 (1937).

Burger, J. Wendell, "A Review of Experimental Investigation on Seasonal Reproduction in Birds," *Wilson Bulletin* 61: 211-230 (1949).

Chance, Edgar P., *The Truth about the Cuckoo.* London, 1940.

Davis, David E., "The Phylogeny of Social Nesting Habits in the Croto-phaginae," *Quarterly Review of Biology* 17: 115-134 (1942).

——— "Recent Emigrations of Northern Shrikes," *Auk* 66: 293 (1949).

——— "Breeding Biology of Birds," *Recent Studies in Avian Biology.* Urbana, Ill.: University of Illinois Press, 1955, pp. 264-308.

Dilger, William C., "Hostile Behavior and Reproductive Isolating Mechanisms in the Avian Genera Catharus and Hylocichla," *Auk* 73: 313-353 (1956a).

——— "Adaptive Modifications and Ecological Isolating Mechanisms in the Thrush Genera Catharus and Hylocichla," *Wilson Bulletin* 68: 171-199 (1956b).

――― "Relationships of the Thrush Genera Catharus and Hylocichla," *Systematic Zoology* 5: 174-182 (1956c).

Dilger, William C. and Paul A. Johnsgard, "Comments on Species Recognition with Special Reference to the Wood Duck and the Mandarin Duck," *Wilson Bulletin* 71: 46-53 (1959).

Domm, L. V., "Recent Advances in Knowledge Concerning the Role of Hormones in the Sex Differentiation of Birds," *Recent Studies in Avian Biology*. Urbana: University of Illinois Press, 1955, pp. 309-325.

Eibl-Eibesfeldt, I. and Sol Kramer, "Ethology, the Comparative Study of Animal Behavior," *Quarterly Review of Biology* 33: 181-211 (1958).

Emlen, John T., "Techniques for Observing Bird Behavior under Natural Conditions," *Annals of the New York Academy of Science* 51: 1103-1112 (1950).

――― "Territory, Nest Building and Pair Formation in the Cliff Swallow," *Auk* 71: 16-35 (1954).

――― "The Study of Behavior in Birds," *Recent Studies in Avian Biology*. Urbana: University of Illinois Press, 1955, pp. 105-153.

Ewer, R. F., "Ethological Concepts," *Science* 126: 599-603 (1957).

Friedmann, Herbert, *The Cowbirds, A Study in the Biology of Social Parasitism*. Springfield, Ill.: Charles C. Thomas, 1929.

――― "The New Study of Bird Behavior," *Bird-Banding* 1: 61-66 (1930).

――― "The Breeding Habits of the Weaverbirds: A Study in the Biology of Behavior Patterns," *Smithsonian Report for 1949, 1950*, 293-316, 1950.

――― *The Honey Guides*. United States National Museum Bulletin 208, 1955.

Herrick, C. Judson, *Neurological Foundations of Animal Behavior*. New York: Henry Holt & Co., 1924.

Herrick, F. H., "Nests and Nest Building in Birds," *Journal of Animal Behavior* 1: 159-192; 244-277; 336-373 (1911).

――― *Wild Birds at Home*. New York: D. Appleton-Century Co., 1935.

Hinde, R. A., "The Biological Significance of the Territories of Birds," *Ibis* 98: 340-369 (1956).

Koch, S. (ed.), *Some Recent Trends in Ethology: Psychology, A Study of a Science*. New York: McGraw-Hill, 1959, Study I, Vol. II, 561-610.

Howard, H. Eliot, *Territory in Bird Life*. London: John Murray, 1920.

Hoyt, J. Southgate Y., "Observations on Nesting Associates," *Auk* 65: 188-196 (1948).

Kendeigh, S. Charles, "Territorial and Mating Behavior of the House Wren," *Illinois Biological Monographs* 18, No. 3, 1-120 (1941).

――― "Measurement of Bird Populations," *Ecological Monographs* 14: 67-106 (1944).

———— "Parental Care and Its Evolution in Birds," *Illinois Biological Monographs 22*. Urbana: University of Illinois Press, 1952.

Lack, David, "The Psychological Factor in Bird Distribution," *British Birds* 31: 130-136 (1937).

———— "Pair-Formation in Birds," *Condor* 42: 269-286 (1940).

———— "Some Aspects of Instinctive Behaviour and Display in Birds," *Ibis* 83: 407-441 (1941).

Lorenz, Konrad A., "The Companion in the Bird's World," *Auk* 54: 245-273 (1937).

———— *The Comparative Method in Studying Innate Behaviour Patterns.* Symposia of the Society for Experimental Biology, No. 4 (1950). *Physiological Mechanisms in Animal Behaviour*. New York: Academic Press, 1950.

———— *King Solomon's Ring.* New York: Thomas Y. Crowell Co., 1952.

———— "The Objectivistic Theory of Instinct," *L'Instinct dans le comportement des animaux et de l'homme.* Paris: Masson et Cie., 1956.

Marshall, A. J., "Non-breeding among Arctic Birds," *Ibis* 94: 310-333 (1952).

Mayr, Ernst, "Bernard Altum and the Territory Theory," *Proceedings Linnaean Society of New York*. Nos. 45, 46: 24-38 (1935).

———— "The Sex Ratio in Wild Birds," *American Nat.* 73: 156-179 (1939).

Morris, Desmond, "The Function and Causation of Courtship Ceremonies," *L'Instinct dans le comportement des animaux et de l'homme.* Paris: Masson et Cie, 1956.

Richdale, L. E., *Sexual Behavior in Penguins.* Lawrence, Kansas: University of Kansas Press, 1951.

Schiller, C. H. (ed.), Instinctive Behavior. New York: *International University Press*, 1957.

Schorger, A. W., "The Deep Diving of the Loon and Old-squaw and Its Mechanism," *Wilson Bulletin* 59: 151-159 (1947).

Scott, John W., "Mating Behavior of the Sage Grouse," *Auk* 59: 477-498 (1942).

Thomson, A. L., "Factors Determining the Breeding Seasons of Birds: An Introductory Review," *Ibis* 92: 173-184 (1950).

Thorpe, W. H., "The Learning Abilities of Birds," *Ibis* 93: 1-52; 252-296 (1951a).

———— "The Definition of Terms used in Animal Behaviour Studies," *Bulletin on Animal Behaviour* 9: 34-40 (1951b).

———— "The Process of Song-learning in the Chaffinch as Studied by Means of the Sound Spectrograph," *Nature* 173: 465-469 (1954).

———— *Learning and Instinct in Animals.* Cambridge, Massachusetts: Harvard University Press, 1956.

Tinbergen, N. "The Behavior of the Snow Bunting in Spring," Trans. *Linnaean Society of New York* 5: 1-95 (1939).

———— "An Objectivistic Study of the Innate Behavior of Animals," Series D. Bibliotheca Biotheoretica. Leiden: C. J. Brill, 1942.

———— "Social Releasers and the Experimental Method Required for Their Study," *Wilson Bulletin* 60: 6-51.

———— *The Study of Instinct.* Oxford: Clarendon Press, 1951.

———— "'Derived' Activities: Their Causation, Biological Significance, Origin and Emancipation During Evolution," *Quarterly Review of Biology* 27: 1-32 (1952).

Whitaker, Lovie M. "A Resumé of Anting, with Particular Reference to a Captive Orchard Oriole," *Wilson Bulletin* 69: 195-262 (1957).

BIRD WATCHING

Beidleman, Richard G., "Bird-Watching—Hobby of the Half Century," *Audubon Magazine* 53: 316-323; 368-373 (1951).

Fischer, Richard B., "That Big Day," *Audubon Magazine* 55: 114-117, 142 (1953).

Hickey, J. J., *A Guide to Bird Watching.* New York: Oxford University Press, 1943.

Job, H. K., *The Sport of Bird Study.* New York: Macmillan Co., 1908.

———— *How to Study Birds.* New York: Outing Co., 1910.

Kirkman, F. B., "The Bird-watcher's Guide," *British Birds* 4: 8-13 (1910).

Nicholson, E. M., *The Art of Bird-Watching.* Chas. Scribner's Sons, New York: 1932.

———— *How Birds Live. 2nd ed.* London: Williams and Norgate, 1929.

Pettingill, Olin Sewall, Jr., *A Guide to Bird Finding East of the Mississippi.* New York: Oxford University Press, 1951.

———— *A Guide to Bird Finding West of the Mississippi.* New York: Oxford University Press, 1953.

Scheider, Fritz, "Methods in Bird Watching," *Kingbird* 8: 2-4 (1958).

CENSUS

Cooke, May T., *The Purpose of Bird Censuses and How to Make Them.* United States Department of Agriculture, Circ. 261 (1927).

Crissey, W. F., Counting Ducks. *Atlantic Naturalist* 8: 77-82 (1952).

Lack, David, "A Review of Bird Census Work and Bird Population Problems," *Ibis,* 1937: 369-395.

Pough, Richard H., "How to Take a Breeding Bird Census," *Audubon Magazine* 40: 288-297 (1947).

CLASSIFICATION

Beddard, Frank E., *The Structure and Classification of Birds*. London: Longmans, Green and Co., 1898.

Delacour, Jean and Ernst Mayr, "The Family Anatidae," *Wilson Bulletin,* 57: 3-55 (1945).

———— "A Classification of the Oscines (Aves)," *Contributions in Science, No. 16.* Los Angeles County Museum, 1957.

Friedmann, Herbert, "Recent Revisions in Classification and Their Biological Significance," *Recent Studies in Avian Biology.* Urbana: University of Illinois Press, 1955, pp. 23-43.

Mayr, Ernst, *Systematics and the Origin of Species.* New York: Columbia University Press, 1942.

———— Criteria of Subspecies, Species and Genera in Ornithology. *Annals N. Y. Academy of Science,* 44: 133-140 (1943).

———— "The Number of Species of Birds," *Auk,* 63: 64-69 (1946).

———— "Speciation in Birds. Progress Report on the Years 1938-1950." *Proceedings of the Tenth International Ornithological Congress* 1950. 91-131 (1951).

———— "The Sequence of the Songbird Families," *Condor,* 60: 194-195 (1958).

Mayr, Ernst and Dean Amadon, "A Classification of Recent Birds," *American Museum Novitates.* No. 1496 (1951).

Mayr, Ernst, E. Gorton Linsley, and Robert L. Usinger, *Methods and Principles of Systematic Zoology.* New York: McGraw-Hill Book Co., 1953.

Miller, Alden H., Systematic Revision and Natural History of the American Shrikes (Lanius). *Univ. Calif. Publ. Zool.,* 38: 11-242 (1931).

———— "Concepts and Problems of Avian Systematics in Relation to Evolutionary Processes." *Recent Studies in Avian Biology.* Urbana: University of Illinois Press, 1955, pp. 1-22.

Moreau, R. E., "Some Recent Terms and Tendencies in Bird Taxonomy," *Ibis* 90: 102-111 (1948).

Neave, Sheffield Airey. *Nomenclator Zoologicus.* A List of the Names of Genera and Subgenera in Zoology from the Tenth Edition of Linnaeus, 1758 to the End of 1935. Zoological Society of London, 1939-1940.

Peters, J. L., *Checklist of Birds of the World.* (9 vol.) Cambridge, Mass.: Harvard Univ. Press, 1931-1960.

Schenk, Edward T., and John H. McMasters, *Procedure in Taxonomy.* 3rd ed. Stanford, Calif.: Stanford Univ. Press, 1956.

Stresemann, Erwin, "Aves." Vol. 7, part 2, of *Handbuch der Zoologie,*

W. Kukenthal and T. Krumbach. Berlin: Walter de Gruyter, 1927-1934.
——— "Scientific Nomenclature," *Auk,* 41: 507-512 (1924).
——— "The Formenkreis—Theory," *Auk,* 53: 150-158 (1936).
Wetmore, Alex, *A Revised Classification for the Birds of the World.*
  Smithsonian Miscellaneous Collection, Vol. 117, No. 4: 1-22 (1951).
——— "The Classification of the Oscine Passeriformes," *Condor,* 59:
  207-209 (1957).

COLORATION

Allen, J. A., "Alleged Changes of Color in the Feathers of Birds Without
  Moulting," *Bulletin Amer. Museum of Natural History.* 8: 13-44 (1896).
Cott, Hugh B., *Adaptive Coloration in Animals.* London: Methuen and
  Co., 1940.
Fox, Denis L., *Animal Biochromes and Structural Colors.* England: Cam-
  bridge University Press, 1953.
Gower, Carl. "The Cause of Blue Color as Found in the Bluebird
  (*Sialia sialis*) and the Blue Jay (*Cyanocitta cristata*)" *Auk* 53: 178-185
  (1936).
Greenewalt, Crawford H., Werner Brandt, and Daniel D. Friel, "Iri-
  descent Colors of Hummingbird Feathers," *Journal of the Optical
  Society of America,* vol. 50, no. 10: 1005-1013 (1960).
Ridgway, Robert, *Color Standards and Color Nomenclature.* Washington,
  D.C.: Pub. by author, 1913.
Stresemann, Erwin, "The Development of Theories Which Affected the
  Taxonomy of Birds," *Ibis,* 92: 126-131 (1950).
Swynnerton, C. F. M., "On the Coloration of the Mouths and Eggs of
  Birds-1. The Mouths of Birds," *Ibis,* 1916: 264-294.
Thayer, Gerald H., *Concealing-coloration in the Animal Kingdom.* New
  York: The Macmillan Co., 1909.

CONSERVATION

Gabrielson, Ira N., *Wildlife Conservation.* New York: The Macmillan
  Co., 1941.
——— *Wildlife Refuges.* New York: The Macmillan Co., 1943.
Greenway, James C., Jr., *Extinct and Vanishing Birds of the World.*
  Special Pub. No. 13. New York: Am. Comm. for International Wild
  Life Protection, 1958.
Gustafson, A. F., H. Ries, C. H. Guise, and W. J. Hamilton, Jr., *Con-
  servation in the United States.* 2nd ed. Ithaca, N.Y.: Comstock Pub-
  lishing Co., Inc., 1944.
Hornaday, Wm. T., *Our Vanishing Wildlife: its Extermination and
  Preservation.* New York: Chas. Scribner's Sons, 1931.

—— *Thirty Years' War for Wild Life.* New York: Chas. Scribner's Sons, 1931.

DISTRIBUTION

Allen, J. A., "The Geographical Origin and Distribution of North American Birds, Considered in Relation to Faunal Areas of North America," *Auk* 10: 97-150 (1893).

Barden, Albert A., Jr., "Distribution of the Families of Birds," *Auk,* 58: 543-557 (1941).

Darlington, Philip J., Jr., *Zoogeography: The Geographical Distribution of Animals.* New York: John Wiley and Sons, 1957.

Daubenmire, Rexford F., "Merriam's Life Zones of North America," *Quarterly Review of Biology* 13: 327-332 (1938).

Dementiev, G. P. and V. F. Larionov, The Development of Geographical Variations, with Special Reference to Birds. *Proceedings of the Zoological Society of London* 115: 85-96 (1945).

Dice, Lee R., *Biotic Provinces of North America.* Ann Arbor, Mich.: University of Michigan Press, 1943.

Grinnell, Joseph, "Field Tests of Theories Concerning Distributional Control," *Amer. Nat.* 51: 115-128 (1917).

Griscom, Ludlow, "Distribution and Origin of the Birds of Mexico," *Bull. Mus. Comp. Zool.* 103: 341-382 (1950).

Gulick, Addison, "Biological Peculiarities of Oceanic Islands," *Quarterly Review of Biology* 7: 405-427 (1932).

Kendeigh, S. Charles, "History and Evaluation of Various Concepts of Plant and Animal Communities in North America," *Ecology* 35: 152-171 (1954).

—— "A Study of Merriam's Temperature Laws," *Wilson Bulletin* 44: 129-143 (1932).

Merriam, C. Hart, "Results of a Biological Survey of the San Francisco Mountain Region and Desert of the Little Colorado, Arizona," *North American Fauna* No. 3. (1890).

—— "Laws of Temperature Control of the Geographic Distribution of Terrestrial Animals and Plants," *National Geographic Magazine* 6: 229-238 (1894).

—— Life Zones and Crop Zones of the United States. *United States Department of Agriculture Bulletin No. 10* (1898).

Miller, A. H., "A Review of Centers of Differentiation for Birds in the Western Great Basin Region," *Condor* 43: 257-267 (1941).

Newton, Alfred, "Geographical Distribution," *A Dictionary of Birds.* London: Adam and Charles Black, pp. 311-363 (1893-96).

Peterson, Roger T., "Life Zones, Biomes, or Life Forms?," *Audubon Magazine* 44: 21-30 (1942).

Shelford, Victor E., "Life Zones, Modern Ecology and the Failure of Temperature Summing," *Wilson Bulletin* 44: 144-157 (1932).

——— (ed.), "Bird Distribution and Ecological Concepts. A Symposium," *Wilson Bulletin* 57: 191-201; 243-252 (1945).

Wallace, Alfred Russell, *The Geographical Distribution of Animals*. 2 vols. London: Macmillan and Co., 1876.

EGGS

Amadon, Dean, "Bird Weights and Egg Weights," *Auk* 60: 221-234 (1943).

Davie, Oliver, *Nests and Eggs of North American Birds*. Philadelphia: David McKay, 1898.

Jourdain, F. C. R., "The Bearing of Oology on Classification." *Bulletin of British Ornithologists' Club* 36: 11-28 (1915).

Newton, Alfred, "Eggs," *A Dictionary of Birds*. London: Adam and Charles Black, 1893-96, pp. 182-192.

Reed, Chester A., *North American Birds Eggs*. New York: Doubleday, Page and Company, 1904.

Romanoff, Alexis and Anastasia Romanoff, *The Avian Egg*. New York: John Wiley and Sons, 1949

ECOLOGY

Allen, A. A., "The Red-winged Blackbird: A Study in the Ecology of a Cat-tail Marsh," *Proc. Linn. Soc. New York 1912-13*. No. 24-25 (1914).

Clements, Frederick E. and Victor E. Shelford, *Bio-ecology*. New York: John Wiley and Sons, 1939.

Colquhoun, M. K., "The Density of Woodland Birds Determined by the Sample Count Method," *Journal of Animal Ecology* 9: 53-67 (1940).

Lack, David, "Ecological Aspects of Species-formation in Passerine Birds," *Ibis* 86: 260-286 (1944).

——— *The Natural Regulation of Animal Numbers*. London: Oxford University Press, 1954.

McAtee, W. L., "The Relation of Birds to the Woodlots in New York State," *Roosevelt Wild Life Bulletin*. Vol. LV, No. 1 (1926).

Pitelka, Frank A., "Distribution of Birds in Relation to Major Biotic Communities," *Amer. Midl. Nat.* 25: 113-137 (1941).

Sclater, Philip Lutley, "On the General Geographical Distribution of the Members of the Class Aves," *Jour. Linn. Soc. London* 2: 130-145 (1858).

——— "On Recent Advances in our Knowledge of the Geographical Distribution of Birds," *Ibis* 1891: 514-577.

Silloway, Perley M., "Relation of Summer Birds to the Western Adirondack Forest," *Roosevelt Wild Life Bulletin,* Vol. I, no. 4. (1923).

ECONOMIC IMPORTANCE

Forbush, E. H., *Useful Birds and Their Protection.* Boston: Mass. State Board of Agriculture, 1907.

Henderson, Junius, *The Practical Value of Birds.* New York: The Macmillan Co., 1927.

McAtee, W. L., "The Local Suppression of Agr. Pests by Birds," *Annual Report Smithsonian Institute,* 1920; 411-438.

———— Economic Ornithology. *Fifty Years' Progress of American Ornithology.* 1883-1933, pp. 111-129. Lancaster, Pa.: American Ornithologists' Union, 1933.

— ————*Wildlife Food Plants: Their Value, Propagation, and Management.* Ames, Iowa: Collegiate Press, Inc., 1939.

Weed, Clarence M. and Ned Dearborn, *Birds in Their Relation to Man.* Philadelphia, Pa.: J. P. Lippincott Co., 1903.

FEATHERS

Brodkorb, Pierce, 1949 (1951) The Number of Feathers in Some Birds. *Quart. Jour. Fla. Acad. Sci.,* 12(4): 1-5.

Hutt, F. B. and Lelah Ball, "Number of Feathers and Body Size in Passerine Birds," *Auk* 55: 651-657 (1938).

Wetmore, Alexander, "The Number of Contour Feathers in Passeriform and Related Birds," *Auk* 53: 159-169 (1936).

Wray, Richard S., "On the Structure of the Barbs, Barbules, and Barbicels of a Typical Pennaceous Feather," *Ibis,* 1887: 420-423.

FOSSIL BIRDS

Heilmann, Gerhard, *The Origin of Birds.* New York: D. Appleton & Co., 1927.

Gregory, William K., "Theories of the Origin of Birds," *Annals of the New York Academy of Science* 27: 31-38 (1916).

Howard, Hildegarde, "A Preliminary Survey of Trends in Avian Evolution from Pleistocene to Recent Time," *Condor,* 49: 10-13 (1947).

Lydekker, Richard, "Fossil Birds" in A. Newton and H. Gadow, *A Dictionary of Birds.* London: Adam and Charles Black, 1893-96, pp. 277-289.

Marsh, O. Charles, *Odontornithes: A Monograph on the Extinct Toothed Birds of North America.* Washington, D.C.: Government Printing Office, 1880.

Miller, Loye, and Ida DeMay, "The Fossil Birds of California," *University of California Publications in Zoology* 47: 47-142 (1942).

Wetmore, Alexander, "Recent Additions to our Knowledge of Prehistoric Birds, 1933-1949," *Proceedings of the Tenth International Ornithological Congress, June 1950.* Uppsala, Sweden, pp. 51-74 (1951)

———— A Check-list of the Fossil and Prehistoric Birds of North America and the West Indies. *Smithsonian Miscellaneous Collection* 131, No. 5 (1956).

FIELD GUIDES

Alexander, W. B., *Birds of the Ocean.* New York: G. P. Putnam's Sons, 1954.

Blake, Emmet R., *Birds of Mexico.* Chicago: The University of Chicago Press, 1953.

Bond, James, *Birds of the West Indies.* Boston: Houghton Mifflin Co., 1961.

Hausman, Leon A., *Field Book of Eastern Birds.* New York: G. P. Putnam's Sons, 1946.

Hoffman, Ralph, *Birds of the Pacific States.* Boston: Houghton Mifflin Co., 1927.

Kortright, Francis H., *The Ducks, Geese and Swans of North America.* Washington, D.C.: American Wildlife Institute, 1942. (8th printing, 1957.)

Peterson, Roger Tory, *A Field Guide to the Birds,* 2nd ed. Boston: Houghton Mifflin Co., 1947.

———— *A Field Guide to the Birds of Texas.* Boston: Houghton Mifflin Co., 1960.

———— *A Field Guide to Western Birds,* 2nd ed. Boston· Houghton Mifflin Co., 1961.

Peterson, Roger Tory, Guy Montfort and P. A. D. Hollom, *A Field Guide to Birds of Britain and Europe.* Boston: Houghton Mifflin Co., 1954.

Pough, Richard H., *Audubon Guides. All the Birds of Eastern and Central North America.* Garden City, N. Y.: Doubleday and Co., Inc., 1953.

———— *Audubon Western Bird Guide.* Garden City, N. Y.: Doubleday and Co., Inc., 1957.

Reed, Chester A., *Bird Guide: Land Birds East of the Rockies.* Garden City, N.Y.: Doubleday and Co., Inc., 1951.

Saunders, Aretas A., "The Summer Birds of the Alleghany State Park," *Roosevelt Wild Life Bulletin,* Vol. 1, No. 3. Syracuse, N. Y.: 1923.

Palmer, E. Laurence, *Fieldbook of Natural History.* New York: McGraw-Hill Book Company, Inc., 1949.

FLIGHT

Aymar, Gordon C., *Bird Flight.* New York: Dodd, Mead Co., 1936.

Brown, R. H. L., "The Flight of Birds. II. Wing Function in Relation to Flight Speed," *Journal of Experimental Biology* 30: 90-103 (1953).

Cooke, May Thatcher, *Flight Speed of Birds.* United States Department of Agriculture Circular No. 428 (1937).

Daneel, A. B., "The Speed and Height of Bird Flight," *Ostrich* 14: 61-64 (1943).

Engels, William Louis, "Wing Skeleton and Flight of Hawks," *Auk* 58: 61-69 (1941).

Graham, R. R., "The Part Played by Emarginated Feathers and the Alula in the Flight of Birds," *Bulletin of British Ornithologists' Club* 52: 68-79 (1932).

Gray, James, "The Flight of Animals," *Smithsonian Institute Publication 4200*, 1955 (1951). (Smithsonian Report for 1954: 285-303.)

Harrisson, T. H., "On the Normal Flight Speed of Birds," *British Birds* 25(4): 86-96 (1931).

Horton-Smith, C., *The Flight of Birds.* London: H. F. and G. Witherby, 1938.

Minertzhagen, R., "Some Preliminary Remarks on the Velocity of Migratory Flight among Birds with Special Reference to the Palearctic Region," *Ibis* (1921) 228-238.

———— "The Speed and Altitude of Bird Flight (with notes on Other Animals)," *Ibis* 97: 81-117 (1955).

Nair, K. R., "A Comparison of the Muscles in the Forearm of a Flapping and a Soaring Bird," *Journal of Animal Morphology and Physiology* 1: 71-76 (1954).

Poole, Earl L., "Weights and Wing Areas in North American Birds," *Auk* 55: 511-517 (1938).

Savile, D. B. O., "The Flight Mechanism of Swifts and Hummingbirds," *Auk* 67: 499-504 (1950).

———— "Adaptive Evolution in the Avian Wing," *Evolution* 11: 212-224 (1957).

Warner, Lucien H., "Facts and Theories of Bird Flight," *Quarterly Review of Biology* 6: 84-98 (1931).

Wetmore, Alexander, "The Speed of Flight in Certain Birds," *Condor* 18: 112-113 (1916).

GENETICS

Dobzhansky, Theodosius, *Genetics and the Origin of Species.* New York: Columbia University Press, 1937.

HIBERNATION

Bartholomew, George A., Thomas R. Howell and Tom J. Cade, "Torpidity in the White-throated Swift, Anna Hummingbird, and Poor Will," *Condor* 59: 145-155 (1957).

HISTORY

Allen, Elsa G., "The History of American Ornithology before Audubon." Philadelphia: *Transactions of the American Philosophic Society* 41(3): 387-591 (1951).

Coues, Elliott, *Key to North American Birds,* Vol. I (Historical Preface). 5th ed. Boston: The Page Co., 1903.

Mayr, Ernst, "History of the North American Bird Fauna," *Wilson Bulletin* 58: 3-41 (1946).

HYBRIDISM

Berger, Andrew J., "The Golden-winged-Blue-winged Warbler Complex in Michigan and the Great Lakes Area," *Jack-Pine Warbler* 36: 37-73 (1958).

Cockrum, E. Lendell, "A Check-list and Bibliography of Hybrid Birds in North America North of Mexico," *Wilson Bulletin* 64: 140-159 (1952).

Parkes, Kenneth C., "The Genetics of the Golden-winged X Blue-winged Warbler Complex," *Wilson Bulletin* 63: 5-15 (1951).

Sibley, Charles G., "The Evolutionary and Taxonomic Significance of Sexual Dimorphism and Hybridization in Birds," *Condor* 59: 166-191 (1957).

LIFE HISTORIES

Allen, A. A., "The Red-winged Blackbird: A Study in the Ecology of a Cat-tail Marsh," *Proceedings Linnaean Society of New York* No. 24-25: 43-128 (1914).

———— *American Bird Biographies*. Ithaca, N.Y.: Comstock Publishing Co., 1934.

———— *The Golden Plover and Other Birds*. Ithaca, N.Y.: Comstock Publishing Co., 1939.

Bent, Arthur C., "Life Histories of North American Birds," *United States National Museum Bulletins,* Nos. 107, 113, 121, 126, 130, 135, 142, 146, 162, 167, 170, 174, 176, 179, 191, 195, 196, 197, 203, 211 (1919-58).

Bump, G., R. W. Darrow, F. C. Edminster, and W. F. Crissey, *The Ruffed Grouse, Life History, Propagation, and Management*. Albany: New York State Conservation Department, 1947.

Edminster, Frank C., *The Ruffed Grouse, Its Life Story, Ecology and Management*. New York: The Macmillan Co., 1947.

Hann, Harry W., "Life History of the Oven-bird in Southern Michigan," *Wilson Bulletin* 49: 145-237 (1937).

Herrick, F. H., *The Home Life of Wild Birds.* New York: G. P. Putnam's Sons, 1902.

―――― *The American Eagle.* New York: D. Appleton-Century Company, 1934.

Howell, Joseph C., Notes on the Nesting Habits of the American Robin (*Turdus migratorius L.*) *American Midland Naturalist* 28: 529-603 (1942).

Lack, David, *The Life of the Robin.* London: H. F. and G. Witherby Ltd., 1943.

Linsdale, Jean M., "The Natural History of the Magpies," *Pacific Coast Avifauna,* No. 25. Berkeley, Calif.: Cooper Ornithological Club, 1937.

Nice, Margaret Morse, "*Studies in the Life History of the Song Sparrow,* I and II," *Transactions of Linnaean Society of New York,* Vols. 4 & 6 (1937, 1943).

Palmer, Ralph S., "A Behavior Study of the Common Tern," (*Sterna hirundo hirundo L.*) *Proceedings Boston Society of Natural History,* 42: 1-119 (1941).

Pettingill, Olin S., Jr., *The American Woodcock, Philohela minor* (Gmelin). *Memoirs* Boston Society of Natural History 9: 167-391 (1936).

Pickwell, Gayle B., "*The Prairie Horned Lark,*" *Transactions of Academy of Science of St. Louis,* 27: 1-153 (1931).

Schwartz, Charles W., "The Ecology of the Prairie Chicken in Missouri," *University of Missouri Study* 20(1): 1-99 (1945).

Skutch, Alexander F., "Incubation and Nestling Periods of Central American Birds," *Auk* 62: 8-37 (1945).

―――― "Outline for an Ecological Life History of a Bird, Based upon the Song Tanager *Ramphocelus passerinii costaricensis,*" *Ecology,* 31: 464-469 (1950).

―――― "Life Histories of Central American Birds," *Pacific Coast Avifauna,* No. 31 (1954).

Soper, J. Dewey, "Life History of the Blue Goose, *Chen caerulescens* (Linnaeus)," *Proceedings Boston Society of Natural History* 42: 121-225 (1942).

Stoddard, H. L., *The Bob White Quail: Its Habits, Preservation and Increase.* New York: Charles Scribner's Sons, 1931.

Stokes, Allen W., "Breeding Behavior of the Goldfinch," *Wilson Bulletin* 62: 107-127 (1950).

Stoner, Dayton, "Studies on the Bank Swallow, *Riparia riparia riparia* (Linnaeus) in the Oneida Lake Region," *Roosevelt Wild Life Annals,* 4(2): 122-233 (1936).

Van Someren, V. G. L., "*Days with Birds: Studies of Habits of Some East*

African Birds," *Fieldiana: Zoology,* 38. Chicago Nat. History Museum, 1956.

Walkinshaw, L. H., "The Sandhill Cranes." *Cranbrook Institute of Science, Bulletin No. 29,* Bloomfield Hills, Mich.: 1949.

———— "Life History of the Prothonotary Warbler," *Wilson Bulletin* 65: 152-168 (1953).

Wallace, George J., "Bicknell's Thrush, Its Taxonomy, Distribution and Life History," *Proceedings Boston Society of Natural History* 41: 211-402 (1939).

MANAGEMENT

Leopold, Aldo, *Game Management.* New York: Charles Scribner's Sons, 1937.

Trippensee, R. E., *Wildlife Management.* New York: McGraw-Hill Book Co., Inc., 1948, 1953 (2 vols.).

Wing, Leonard W., *Practice of Wildlife Conservation.* New York: John Wiley & Sons, Inc., 1951.

MIGRATION

Amadon, Dean, "Continental Drift and Bird Migration," *Science* 108: 705-707 (1948).

Beecher, William J., "The Unexplained Direction Sense of Vertebrates," *Scientific Monthly* 75: 19-25 (1952).

Brewster, William, "Bird Migration," *Memoirs Nuttall Ornithology Club, No. 1,* 1886.

Clarke, William Eagle, *Studies in Bird Migration.* (2 vols.) London: Gurney and Jackson, 1912.

Cooke, Wells W., "Bird Migration," *U.S. Department of Agriculture Bulletin* 185: 1-47 (1915).

———— "Our Greatest Travellers," *National Geographic Magazine Vol. XXII,* pp. 346-365.

Gadow, Hans, *The Wanderings of Animals.* London: Cambridge University Press, 1913.

Griffin, Donald R., "The Sensory Basis of Bird Migration," *Quarterly Review of Biology* 19: 15-31 (1944).

———— "Homing Experiments with Leach's Petrels," *Auk* 57: 61-74 (1940).

———— "Homing Experiments with Herring Gulls and Common Terns," *Bird-Banding* 14: 7-33 (1943).

———— and R. J. Hock, "Experiments on Bird Navigation," *Science* 107; 347-349 (1948).

———— "Bird Navigation," *Biol. Reviews* 27: 259-400 (1952).

Ingram, Collingwood, "Notes on the Height at which Birds Migrate," *Ibis* 1919: 321-325 (1919).

Kramer, Gustav, "Experiments on Bird Orientation," *Ibis* 94: 265-285 (1952).

Lack, David, "The Problem of Partial Migration," *British Birds* 37: 122-130, 143-150 (1943-44).

———— and Elizabeth Lack. "Passerine Migration through England," *British Birds* 42: 320-326 (1949).

———— and R. M. Lockley, "Stockholm Bird Observatory Homing Experiments, 1.", 1936-37; "Puffins, Storm-Petrels and Manx Shearwaters," *British Birds* 31: 242-248 (1938).

Lincoln, F. C., *The Migration of American Birds.* New York: Doubleday Doran & Co., Inc., 1939.

———— *Migration of Birds.* Washington, D. C.: U.S. Fish and Wildlife Service, Circular 16: 1-102 (1950).

Lowery, George H., Jr., "Trans-Gulf Spring Migration of Birds and the Coastal Hiatus," *Wilson Bulletin* 57: 92-121 (1945).

———— "A Quantitative Study of the Nocturnal Migration of Birds," *University of Kansas Publications Museum of Natural History* 3: 361-472 (1951).

Matthews, G. V. T., "The Experimental Investigation of Navigation in Homing Pigeons," *Journal of Experimental Biology* 28: 508-536 (1951).

———— *Bird Navigation.* Cambridge, England: Cambridge University Press, 1955.

Moreau, R. E., "The Migration System in Perspective," *Proceedings 10th International Ornithological Congress 1950.* Uppsala, Sweden, pp. 245-248 (1951).

Newman, Robert J., "Wings Across the Moon," *Audubon Magazine* 54: 212-218 (1952).

Rowan, William, "Relation of Light to Bird Migration and Developmental Changes," *Nature* 115: 494-495 (1925).

———— "On Photoperiodism, Reproductive Periodicity and the Annual Migrations of Birds and Certain Fishes," *Proceedings Boston Society of Natural History* 38: 147-189 (1926).

———— "Experiments in Bird Migration. I," *Proceedings Boston Society of Natural History* 39(5): 151-208 (1929).

———— *The Riddle of Migration.* Baltimore, Md.: Williams & Wilkins Co., 1931.

———— "Experiments in Bird Migration III" *Proceedings National Academy of Science* 18: 639-654 (1932).

———— "Experiments in Bird Migration," *Transactions Royal Society of Canada, 40* (ser. 3, sect. 5): 123-135 (1946).

Thomson, A. L., *Bird Migration*. London: H. F. & G. Witherby Ltd., 1949.

———— "The Study of the Visible Migration of Birds: An Introductory Review," *Ibis* 95: 165-180 (1953).

Thorpe, W. H., "A Discussion of the Orientation of Birds on Migratory and Homing Flights: Recent Biological Evidence for the Methods of Bird Orientation," *Proceedings Linnaean Society of London* 160: 85-94 (1949).

Wetmore, Alex, *The Migrations of Birds*. Cambridge, Mass.: Harvard University Press, 1926.

Wolfson, Albert, "A Preliminary Report on Some Experiments on Bird Migration," *Condor* 42: 93-99 (1940).

———— "Light Versus Activity in the Regulation of the Sexual Cycles of Birds: The Role of the Hypothalamus," *Condor* 43: 125-136 (1941).

———— "Regulation of Spring Migration in Juncos," *Condor* 44: 237-263 (1942).

———— "The Role of the Pituitary, Fat Deposition, and Body Weight in Bird Migration," *Condor* 47: 95-127 (1945).

———— "Bird Migration and the Concept of Continental Drift," *Science*, 108: 23-30 (1948).

———— "Day Length, Migration and Breeding Cycles in Birds," *Scientific Monthly*, 74: 191-200 (1952).

Wynne-Edwards, V. C., "Yeagley's Theory of Bird Navigation," *Ibis*, 90: 606-611 (1948).

Yeagley, Henry L., "A Preliminary Study of a Physical Basis of Bird Navigation," *Journal of Applied Physics* 18: 1035-1063 (1947).

———— "A Preliminary Study of a Physical Basis of Bird Navigation. Part II, *Journal of Applied Physics* 22: 746-760 (1951).

Zimmer, John T., "Notes on Migrations of South American Birds," *Auk* 55: 405-410 (1938).

MUSEUM METHODS

Anderson, R. M., "Methods of Collecting and Preserving Vertebrate Animals," *Bulletin of National Museum of Canada, No. 69* (1949).

Baldwin, S. P., H. C. Oberholser, and L. G. Worley, *Measurements of Birds*. Cleveland: Scientific Publication of the Cleveland Museum of Natural History 2, 1931.

Chapin, James P., "The Preparation of Birds for Study," *Guide Leaflet No. 58*. New York: American Museum of Natural History, 1940.

Chapman, Frank M., "Collections of Birds in the United States and Canada. Exhibition Collections," *Fifty Years' Progress of American*

Ornithology. Lancaster, Pa.: American Ornithologists' Union, 1933, pp. 143-157.

Davie, Oliver, *Methods in the Art of Taxidermy*. Columbus: Hann and Adair, 1894.

Hornaday, William T., *Taxidermy and Zoological Collecting: A Complete Handbook for the Amateur Taxidermist, Collector, Osteologist, Museum-builder, Sportsman, and Traveller*. New York: Scribners, 1897.

Maynard, C. J., *Manual of Taxidermy*. S. E. Cassino and Co., 1883.

Moyer, John W., *Practical Taxidermy*. New York: The Ronald Press Co., 1953.

Rowley, John, *The Art of Taxidermy*. New York: D. Appleton and Co., 1898.

Van Tyne, Josselyn, "Principles and Practices in Collecting and Taxonomic Work," *Auk* 69: 27-33 (1952).

NESTS

Allen, Arthur A., *Key to the Nests of the Common Summer Resident Birds of Northeast North America*. Ithaca, N. Y.: Slingerland-Comstock Co., 1922.

Headstrom, Richard, *Birds' Nests*. New York: Ives Washburn, Inc., 1949.

PETS

Comstock, Anna B., *The Pet Book*. Ithaca, N. Y.: Comstock Publishing Co., 1914.

Crandall, Lee S., *Pets and How to Care for Them*. New York: New York Zoological Park, 1921.

Ficken, R. W. and W. C. Dilger, "Insects and food mixtures for insectivorous birds," *Avicultural Magazine* 67: (2) (1961).

BIRD PHOTOGRAPHY

Brownell, L. W., *Photography for the Sportsman Naturalist*. New York: Macmillan, 1904.

Chapman, Frank M., *Bird Studies with a Camera*. New York: D. Appleton & Co., 1900.

———— "The Use of a Blind in the Study of Bird Life," *Bird-Lore* 10: 250-252 (1908).

Cruickshank, Allan D., *Hunting with a Camera*. New York: Harper and Bros., 1957.

Dugmore, A. R., *Nature and the Camera*. New York: Doubleday Page & Co., 1902.

Fischer, Richard B., "Bird Photography for Bird-Banders," *Bird-Banding* 23: 63-72 (1952).

Gross, Alfred O., "History and Progress of Bird Photography in America," *50 Years' Progress of American Ornithology*. Lancaster, Pa.: American Ornithologists' Union, pp. 159-180 (1933).

Hosking, Eric and Cyril W. Newberry, *The Art of Bird Photography*. New York: Transatlantic Arts, Inc., 1948.

Morris, P. A., *Nature Photography Around the Year*. New York: D. Appleton Century Co., Inc., 1938.

Nesbit, William, *How to Hunt with the Camera*. New York: E. P. Dutton & Co., 1926.

Shiras, George, *Hunting Wild Life with Camera and Flashlight*. (2 vols.) Washington, D. C.: National Geographic Society, 1936.

PHYSIOLOGY

Baldwin, S. Prentiss and S. Charles Kendeigh, "Physiology of the Temperature of Birds," *Scientific Publications Cleveland Museum of Natural History* 3: 1-196 (1932).

———— "The Mechanical Recording of the Nesting Activities of Birds," *Auk* 47: 471-480 (1930).

———— "Variations in the Weight of Birds," *Auk* 55: 416-467 (1938).

Kendeigh, S. Charles, "The Role of Environment in the Life of Birds," *Ecological Monographs* 4: 299-41 (1934).

———— "Effect of Air Temperature on the Rate of Energy Metabolism in the English Sparrow," *Journal of Experimental Zoology* 96: 1-16 (1944).

———— "Resistance to Hunger in Birds," *Journal of Wildlife Management* 9: 217-226 (1945).

Sutter, Ernst, "Growth and Differentiation of the Brain in Nidifugous and Nidicolous Birds," *Proceedings 10th International Ornithological Congress 1950*. Pp. 636-644 (1951).

Wetmore, Alexander, "A Study of the Body Temperature of Birds," *Smithsonian Miscellaneous Collection* 72: 1-52 (1921).

PLUMAGE CHANGE

Dwight, Jonathan, Jr., "The Sequence of Plumages and Moults of the Passerine Birds of New York," *Annals New York Academy of Science* 13: 73-360 (1900).

Humphrey, Philip S. and Kenneth C. Parkes, "An Approach to the Study of Molts and Plumages," *Auk* 76: 1-31 (1959).

Lesher, S. W. and S. Charles Kendeigh, "Effect of Photoperiod on Molting of Feathers," *Wilson Bulletin* 53: 169-180 (1941).

Stone, Witmer, "The Molting of Birds with Special Reference to the Plumages of the Smaller Land Birds of Eastern North America," *Proceedings Academy of Natural Science of Philadelphia* 1896: 108-167 (1896).

REFUGES

Gabrielson, Ira, *Wild Life Refuges*. New York: The Macmillan Co., 1943.

Kendeigh, S. Charles, "Nature Sanctuaries in the United States and Canada," *The Living Wilderness* Vol. 15, No. 35: 1-46 (1950-51).

Massingham, H. J., *Sanctuaries for Birds and How to Make Them*. London: G. Bell and Sons Ltd., 1924.

RESEARCH

Bagg, Aaron M. and Gustav Swanson, "Graduate Research in Ornithology," *Wilson Bulletin* 64: 60-63 (1952).

BIRD SONG AND RECORDING

Allen, Arthur A., "Hunting with a Microphone the Voices of Vanishing Birds," *National Geographic Magazine* 71: 696-723 (1937).

Allen, Francis H., "The Evolution of Bird Song," *Auk* 36: 528-536 (1919).

Brand, Albert A., "Recording Sounds of Wild Birds," *Auk* 49: 436-439 (1932).

———— "Hunting with a Sound Camera," *Natural History* 33: 381-394 (1933).

———— "A Method for the Intensive Study of Bird Song," *Auk* 52: 40-52 (1935).

———— "Vibration Frequencies of Passerine Bird Song," *Auk* 55: 263-268 (1938).

Brand, Albert R. and P. Paul Kellogg, "Auditory Responses of Starlings, English Sparrows and Domestic Pigeons," *Wilson Bulletin* 51: 38-41 (1939).

Craig, Wallace, "The Song of the Wood Pewee, *Myiochanes virens* Linn.: A Study of Bird Music," *N. Y. State Museum Bulletin* 334: 1-186 (1943).

Fuertes, Louis Agassiz, "Impressions of the Voices of Tropical Birds," *Bird Lore* 15: 341-344 (1913).

Kellogg, P. P., "Hunting the Songs of Vanishing Birds with a Microphone," *J. of the Society of Motion Picture Engineers* 30: 201-207 (1938).

Mathews, F. Schuyler, *Field Book of Wild Birds and Their Music*. New York: G. P. Putnam's Sons, 1921.

Sanborn, Herbert C., "The Inheritance of Song in Birds," *Journal of Comparative Psychology* 13: 345-364 (1932).

Saunders, Aretas A., *Bird Song*. Albany, N. Y.: New York State Museum Handbook 7, 1929.

———— *A Guide to Bird Songs*. Garden City, N. Y.: Doubleday and Co. Inc., 1951.

Scott, William E. D., "The Inheritance of Song in Passerine Birds," *Science* 19: 154 (1904a).

———— "The Inheritance of Song in Passerine Birds," *Science* 20: 282-283 (1904b).

Witchell, Charles A., *The Evolution of Bird-Song, with Observations on the Influence of Heredity and Imitation*. London: Adam and Charles Black, 1896.

SMELL

Lewis, John B., "Sight and Scent in the Turkey Vulture," *Auk,* 45: 467-470 (1928).

Strong, R. M., "On the Olfactory Organs and the Sense of Smell in Birds," *Journal of Morphology* 22: 619-661 (1911).

Walter, W. G., "Some Experiments on the Sense of Smell in Birds," *Arch. Néerland Physiol.,* 27: 1-72 (1943).

VANISHING BIRDS

Allen, A. A., "Hunting with a Microphone the Voices of Vanishing Birds," *National Geographic Magazine* 71: 696-723 (1937).

Allen, A. A. and P. P. Kellogg, "Recent Observations on the Ivory-billed Woodpecker," *Auk* 54: 164-184 (1937).

Allen, Robert P., "The Roseate Spoonbill," *Research Report No. 2*. New York: National Audubon Society, 1942.

———— "The Whooping Crane," *Research Report No. 3*. New York: National Audubon Society, 1952.

———— "The Flamingoes: Their Life History and Survival," *Research Report No. 5*. New York: National Audubon Society, 1956.

———— *On the Trail of Vanishing Birds*. New York: McGraw-Hill, 1957.

Banko, Winston E., "The Trumpeter Swan. Its History, Habits and Population in the United States," *North American Fauna No. 63*. U.S. Fish and Wildlife Service, 1960.

Greenway, James C., Jr., "Extinct and Vanishing Birds of the World." *Special Publication No. 13*. New York: American Committee for International Wild Life Protection, 1958.

Hornaday, W. T., *Our Vanishing Wildlife*. N. Y. Zoological Society, 1913.

Koford, Carl B., "The California Condor," *Research Report No. 4*. New York: National Audubon Society, 1953.

Tanner, James T., "The Ivory-billed Woodpecker," *Research Report No. 1*. New York: National Audubon Society, 1942.

WATERFOWL

Allen, A. A., "Duck Hunting with a Color Camera," *National Geographic Magazine* 100: 514-539 (1951).

Hochbaum, H. Albert, *The Canvasback on a Prairie Marsh*. Washington, D. C.: American Wildlife Institute, 1944.

——— *Travels and Traditions of Waterfowl*. Minneapolis, Minn.: University of Minnesota Press, 1955.

Kortright, F. H., *Ducks, Geese and Swans of North America*. Washington, D. C.: American Wildlife Institute, 1943.

Phillipps, John, *A Natural History of the Ducks*. (4 vols.) Boston: Houghton Mifflin Co., 1922-26.

Scott, Peter, *A Coloured Key to the Wildfowl of the World*. Slimbridge, England: The Wildfowl Trust, 1957.

Index

385